PARTICLES
and their interactions

J. G. POWLES

Professor of Physics, University of Kent

ADDISON-WESLEY PUBLISHING COMPANY

London · Reading, Massachusetts · Menlo Park, California
Don Mills, Ontario · Sydney · Manila

To JILL

It seems probable to me, that God in the beginning formed Matter in solid, hard, massy, impenetrable, moveable Particles—ISSAC NEWTON

Preface

The present book has developed from a course of lectures given to first-year undergraduates at the University of Kent at Canterbury. Students intending to specialize in physics, electronics, chemical physics, chemistry, and chemical engineering all take a largely common course. This part of the course is also taken by some mathematics students. An attempt has been made to have an integrated rather than an additive set of courses. Consequently, the traditional boundaries have been considerably eroded in the interests of presenting a unified view of certain aspects of physical science. The other principal integrated course is one on waves.

The above context has largely determined the content of the book. It seemed, nevertheless, to form a natural unity and so is likely to be useful to a much wider audience than that to which it was originally addressed. It would, for instance, make good background material and reading for those taking a more traditional course in physics, chemistry, or engineering. It is thought that the book may also be acceptable to the more adventurous physics teachers to enable them to keep the necessary one jump ahead of their better students. The book should be a useful supplement to the official handbooks for those intending to implement the American PSSC courses or the British Nuffield A-level syllabuses in physics, chemistry, and physical science.

As far as possible, the treatment is logical and deductive. When this is not so, the fact is pointed out and the procedure is usually justified by the assumption that the reader is already familiar with the concepts at a more elementary level. Thus we use the idea of energy in Chapter 3 before it is properly discussed in Chapter 5. There are some more serious claims on the credulity of the reader, for example, that the mean energy of a particle at temperature T is kT in Chapter 3 which is not explained until Chapter 11. However, these few cases are justified by their extreme utility.

For the reasons given above, the book does not include an adequate treatment of many important matters essential to a proper knowledge of the principles of physical science, such as interference and diffraction, wave mechanics, optics, electricity and magnetism, and molecular structure and reactivity. Nevertheless, a liberal interpretation of the word particle does bring in a surprisingly wide range of physical principles. It is in harmony with current trend to particalize everything. Wave mechanics is out and quantum mechanics is in and second quantization reduces everything to quasi-independent quasi-particles—at least, if this cannot be done, the problems are not soluble.

The mathematical tools used correspond to the usual level of instruction in a first-year science course in a British university with the possible exception of vector fields which are, however, used only sparingly.

Both cgs and MKS units are used as appeared convenient in the belief that physical scientists must be able to use both systems or indeed any convenient system of units.

It is recommended that there should be an accompanying practical physics course containing a large coherent component on the determination of the fundamental constants. This represents a valid course of measurements which has a clear unity even to the worst educated first-year student, while at the same time introducing him to a wide variety of experimental techniques. The actual experiments suggested are listed at the end of the book. They are frequently referred to in the text and form a very useful link between theory and experiment.

Considerable emphasis is laid in the book on getting actual numerical results even if only in order of magnitude. The problems are mostly of a similar nature. These often illustrate matters discussed in the text, particularly where explicit reference is made to a problem in the text. In other cases, the problems carry matters discussed in the text to a slightly higher level. The reader is urged to do the problems. Answers are provided in note form where necessary.

It is hoped that this book will help to convince others that there is a real advantage in breaking down the old barriers, not only between chemistry and physics, but also between 'heat', 'light', and 'sound' and such relics of nineteenth century science.

In an elementary book of this sort, it is impossible to acknowledge all the many sources of information. However, the author is bound to record the influence on him of the remarkable *Feynman Lectures on Physics* which represent an ideal in elementary textbooks which few can emulate. Feynman's book is, however, in many ways more acceptable to lecturers than to students, and not all students are as robust as those of "Cal. Tech.". It is hoped that this book retains the enthusiasm and provocativeness of Feynman but makes less severe demands on lecturer and student alike.

It is a pleasure to record my thanks to Miss Gillian Watson who typed the many versions of this book and who can read my handwriting better than I can. I am grateful to Dr. A. D. C. Grassie of the University of Sussex, to Dr. E. F. W. Seymour of the University of Warwick, to Mr. R. M. Sillitto of the University of Edinburgh, and to Dr. J. H. Pain of Imperial College, London, for reading the manuscript. Dr. D. H. Niblett of the University of Kent at Canterbury has made many valuable comments on the book which have removed numerous obscurities and notably improved the presentation. As to the errors which remain, I can only quote the well known maxim, "a book is never finished, it is abandoned".

Canterbury, June 1968   J. G. POWLES

Contents

Glossary of symbols

SYMBOLS FOR PHYSICAL QUANTITIES

A (atomic) mass number; area; scattering cross-section per unit volume

$\mathscr{A}$ collision cross-section

a acceleration; side length of unit cell; parameter of the Morse potential; constant in the van der Waals equation

B magnetic field strength

$B_n(T)$ nth virial coefficient

b constant in the van der Waals equation; impact parameter

C_v molar specific heat at constant volume

c velocity of light

c_v specific heat per molecule

D self-diffusion coefficient

d distance between molecules

d_0 atomic or molecular diameter; equilibrium distance for an isolated pair of atoms

d_m distance between atomic nuclei in a molecule

d_n nuclear diameter

E energy; Young's modulus: electric field strength

ΔE interaction energy; activation energy

E_b nuclear binding energy

E_F Fermi energy

E_{ph} energy of a photon

e elementary charge

F a faraday; force; Helmholtz free energy $(U - TS)$; electric field strength (in cases where the usual symbol E could be confused with energy)

G universal gravitational constant; Gibbs free energy $(H - TS)$

g acceleration due to gravity

H enthalpy $(U + PV)$

h Planck's constant; height

$\hbar$ $h/2\pi$

I moment of inertia; luminous intensity

i electric current

J angular momentum

K equilibrium constant; thermal conductivity

k Boltzmann constant; rate constant of a chemical reaction

L latent heat

l length; mean free path

M magnetization; axial modulus of elasticity; mass (of e.g. the Sun); molecular weight

m mass (of a particle)

m_0 rest mass

m_e mass of an electron

m_p mass of a proton

m_{ph} mass of a photon

N number of molecules in a gas; number of particles; number of events (in probability); number of target particles per unit volume

N_0 Avogadro number

$\mathcal{N}$ number of complexions

$\mathcal{N}^*$ number of complexions of the most probable arrangement

$\mathcal{N}_a$ number of complexions of a given arrangement

n refractive index; number of moles; number of units of energy

n number of particles per unit area or per unit volume

P pressure; probability

p momentum; probability density

Q charge on the nucleus

q quantity of heat; electric charge; some coordinate

R molar gas constant; radius (of e.g. the Earth)

R_∞ Rydberg constant

r radius

r_0 first Bohr radius of an atom; mean radius of electron orbit

r_e classical radius of the electron

S entropy; surface energy

s separation distance

T kinetic energy; temperature (absolute); torque

T_B Boyle temperature

T_m melting temperature

$\mathscr{T}$ period of oscillation

t time

U internal energy

u velocity

V potential difference; potential energy; volume

V_m volume of the molecules in a gas

v velocity of a particle

W weight

w work done

Δx a small but finite interval

Z partition function; nuclear charge

α Hubble constant; molecular polarizability; coefficient of linear expansion; fine structure constant

ε energy of a particle

$\varepsilon(x)$ energy associated with x

ε dielectric constant

ε_0 permittivity of free space

ϵ unit of discrete energy (energy interval)

ϵ_s energy of the sth level

η viscosity

κ force constant; susceptibility

λ wavelength

μ electric dipole moment; viscous retarding force coefficient

μ_p magnetic moment of a proton

ν frequency; speed of rotation

ρ density

σ distance of closest approach; Poisson ratio

τ half-life; average reorientation time; time for significant change to occur; relaxation time

φ work function

Ω solid angle

ω angular velocity

UNIT SYMBOLS

Å   ångström unit (10^{-8} cm, 10^{-10} m)

cal   calorie

deg   degree

dyn   dyne

ev   electronvolt

g   gramme

h   hour

Hz   hertz (cycle per second)

J   joule

kwh   kilowatt hour

l   litre

m   metre

mol   mole (gramme-molecule)

P   poise

r_{no} fermi

rad   radian

s   second

   v   volt
   w   watt
 wb   weber
 μ_B the Bohr magneton

ABBREVIATIONS

a.m.u.	atomic mass unit
cgs	centimetre–gramme–second
CRO	cathode ray oscilloscope
d	a deuteron
e	an electron
e.s.u.	electrostatic unit
H	heads (of a coin)
K.E.	kinetic energy
MKS	metre–kilogramme–second
n	a neutron
n.t.p.	normal temperature and pressure
p	a proton
P.E.	potential energy
r.m.s.	root mean square
T	tails (of a coin)
u.v.	ultraviolet
vol.	volume
wt.	weight

CHAPTER 1

Introduction

What art was to the ancient world, science is to the modern.   DISRAELI

The particles with which this book is concerned are physical particles, such as atoms, electrons, nuclei, protons, mesons, photons, gravitons, etc., rather than the point masses used in mathematics. The examples of particles just given are all small in relation to macroscopic objects but it will sometimes be convenient to treat quite a large body such as the Earth or even a galaxy as a particle.

If we take a sample of water, we can divide it up until we have molecules of water and then if we put the molecules together again we shall again get water. However, if we break up the water molecules into hydrogen and oxygen atoms and then put them together again we shall probably get mostly hydrogen and oxygen gas—which is not water. It is therefore usually clear when we are taking an important step. Having divided a water molecule into atoms of hydrogen and oxygen, which are particles, we could proceed to break up a hydrogen atom into an electron and a proton which again are particles. At the moment, the electron and proton are called "fundamental particles" because no-one has succeeded in breaking them up into further constituent particles or in finding any internal structure. The steps in our break-up process are usually ones of increasing energy, as illustrated in Table 1.1.

All these particles are permanent, as far as we know, e.g. a water molecule will always remain a water molecule if we leave it alone—we shall assume we have a means of testing whether it is still a water molecule after a certain time. We can, in fact, do this experiment—for a short time interval—by, say, measuring a few physical properties of the substance water at intervals. We naturally assume that if the water molecules changed, the properties of the water substance would change.

However, there are many things which spontaneously change in time, e.g. a $^{238}_{92}$U nucleus spontaneously splits *on the average* in 4.5×10^9 years* into a $^{234}_{90}$Th nucleus and an α particle. A neutron splits into a proton and an electron, n $\rightarrow$ p + e$^-$, in 23 minutes, on the average.*

Similarly, molecules can be inherently unstable, e.g. a molecule of ozone may decompose spontaneously into an oxygen molecule and an oxygen atom according

---

* This is actually the "half-life".

Table 1.1

Approximate energy	ev* per particle	kcal mol^{-1}†	erg per particle
To separate argon molecules from one another	0.065	1.5	10^{-13}
To separate water molecules from one another	0.47	10.8	7×10^{-13}
To separate H_2O into $H_2 + \frac{1}{2} O_2$‡	2.5	57.8	4×10^{-12}
To give $H_2 \rightarrow H + H$	4.5	103.4	7×10^{-12}
To give $H \rightarrow p + e^-$	13.6 (1 rydberg)	313	2×10^{-11}
To give $d \rightarrow n + p$	$\sim 10 \times 10^6$ (10 Mev)	2.3×10^8	1.6×10^{-5}
To give $^{16}O \rightarrow 8p + 8n$	127.5×10^6	3×10^9	2×10^{-4}

* One electronvolt is the energy acquired by one electronic charge falling through a potential difference of one volt; that is "1 ev" $= eV$ where $e = 1.6 \times 10^{-19}$ coulomb and $V = 1$ volt, therefore "1 ev" $= 1.6 \times 10^{-19}$ joule (in MKS units) or (4.8 $\times 10^{-10}$ e.s.u. of charge)(1/300 e.s.u. of p.d.) $= 1.6 \times 10^{-12}$ erg (in cgs units).

One kcal mol^{-1} is the corresponding energy (in kilocalories) for one mole of the particles, i.e. for N_0 of them where N_0 is Avogadro's number, 6.0×10^{23} mol^{-1}.

$$\therefore \quad 1 \text{ ev per particle} \equiv \frac{1.6 \times 10^{-19}}{4.2 \times 10^3} \times 6.0 \times 10^{23} \text{ kcal mol}^{-1} = 23 \text{ kcal mol}^{-1}$$

Thus 1 ev per particle $\equiv 1.6 \times 10^{-12}$ erg per particle $\equiv 23$ kcal mol^{-1}. The values of the fundamental constants are given in the section "Laboratory Experiments" at the end of the book.

† k here means 10^3 and is not Boltzmann's constant.

‡ We mean half the energy to split 2 H_2O into 2 $H_2 + O_2$.

to the relation $O_3 \rightarrow O_2 + O + 17$ kcal mol^{-1} (or 1.2×10^{-12} erg molecule^{-1}). This is true only of what a chemist would call exothermic reactions or what a physicist would call an excited state. Fundamental particles can only disintegrate into particles whose masses add up to less than that of the original particle. The question of what is a distinct particle is a subtle one. Is an excited hydrogen atom still to be regarded as a hydrogen atom, since its properties, especially the chemical ones, are different in important respects? In dealing with "particles", we shall have sometimes to take account of this possibility of spontaneous change. In fact, the study of the time dependence of phenomena is an important part of physical science. Another possibility is that when two or more particles come together in suitable circumstances they may change into other particles. For example, an electron and a positron can disappear and yield two γ rays or photons (particles of electromagnetic radiation), $e^+ + e^- \rightarrow 2\gamma$.

The sort of particles which interest us often serves to define our field of interest in the physical sciences. Thus the nuclear physicist is interested in how and why nucleons (neutrons and protons) form nuclei and what happens when things are done to nuclei such as banging them together in accelerating machines, exciting them with electromagnetic energy (photons), and so on. In this case, he is using high energies, millions of electronvolts (Mev), and so the electrons do not matter much.

Chemists are most often interested in how atoms form into molecules and the properties of those molecules. This depends on the nuclei involved mainly through only one important property of the nucleus, its electric charge (Ze). This determines the number of electrons and the arrangement of those Z electrons about the nucleus (particularly the outer ones which determine most of the chemical properties of the molecules).

The interactions between the atoms or the molecules determine the physical properties of a pure substance. Some people are interested, say, in the structure of the crystals of substances or if they are not crystalline why they are not crystalline. Some people are interested in the surface properties such as how the atoms are arranged there or how they move over the surface. Some people are interested in how atoms or molecules react with each other on a surface, which may be quite different from how they react in the form of a gas or in solution. Some people find out about atoms and molecules by studying the interaction of electromagnetic radiation with them—atomic spectroscopists, who are usually physicists, and molecular spectroscopists, who are usually chemists. Some people are interested in how molecules move in solids and liquids. If there are more or less free electrons present, as in a metal, people will be interested in how these behave in a variety of circumstances, for instance how the electrons contribute to the specific heat or the thermal conductivity of the metal or how the electrons get or can be got from the inside to the outside of a piece of metal. Some people like to work on the properties of nuclei or atoms or molecules themselves as individual entities. Others work on the properties of large agglomerations of particles, as many as 10^{23} particles at a time. In fact, the distinction between different fields of study is often not very sharp and that is why we all need to know the basic facts and ideas in order to go into any one of these fields—but of course we will tend to learn more about certain parts which interest us particularly. However, part of the fascination is that we never really know what is going to be needed next. For example, in nuclear magnetic resonance, we use the magnetic moment of *nuclei* to study *molecular* motion in *substances* by using *electromagnetic* interactions. Some chemists study the *chemical* reactions which result from *neutron* irradiation. The fundamental particle physicists have to know about liquid hydrogen because it is used in bubble chambers and about single crystals of anthracene and about semiconductors and about magnets because they are used in manipulating and detecting the fundamental particles. The electronicians are particularly interested in electrons, in beams as in valves, in solids as in transistors, or in space because of propagation of electromagnetic waves. The fastest way to transmit information is by electromagnetic waves and the easiest way to interact with these is by using electrons.

In the first part of this book, we deal with particles as individuals, although we deduce many of their properties from the behaviour of large numbers of particles. Strictly speaking, of course, we have *always* to deal with large numbers of particles, since our senses only react to macroscopic amounts of matter. Thus we may say colloquially that we can "observe" one photon in a photomultiplier but what we in fact observe is the effect on an instrument of the pulse of some 10^8 electrons initiated by the photon. In the Millikan oil drop experiment, we say we observe one electronic charge but we actually observe the motion of one charged drop of liquid interacting with a lot of air. Nevertheless, it is correct to assume not only that such particles exist, but also that they have certain properties, and that many of these properties can be deduced from the study of agglomerations of large numbers of them. In the later chapters, we consider explicitly the properties of bodies composed of large numbers of particles. We are then interested in the bodies themselves and only in the particles to the extent that the properties of the particles determine the properties of the macroscopic bodies.

Again, when a large number of particles form a macroscopic body, they are often interacting quite strongly together and it becomes less sensible and convenient to think of the individual particles as separate entities. It is then often convenient to think in terms of pseudo- or quasi-particles. Thus, if we take a piece of a solid in the form of a rod and strike one end sharply, a pulse of sound travels down the rod at a fairly definite velocity and is reflected at the far end. This is quite reminiscent of the behaviour of a ball bouncing against a wall and we are led to think in particle terms for the behaviour of the pulse of sound. The pulse of sound, in rather more refined terms, indeed behaves in many respects as a particle and is called a phonon. It is quite different from the atomic particles but is due to the presence and the interactions of large numbers of them. Such quasi-particles are often a convenient and useful concept when a complex and complicated system of real particles is slightly disturbed from a quiescent state. The pulse of sound did not disturb the actual atoms in the rod very much but it was a readily observed change from the quiescent state of the rod before it was struck.

CHAPTER 2

Atoms, the first particles

Ce n'est jamais par les routes les plus simples et les plus directes que
l'ésprit humain parvient aux verités ... LAGRANGE

2.1 EVIDENCE FOR THE EXISTENCE OF ATOMS

The idea that matter is composed of discrete particles rather than continuous
substance is a very old one. In the days of Democritus, this concept of atoms (or
molecules) was just a philosophical speculation. It was not put on an experimental
basis until the work of Dalton at the beginning of the nineteenth century. Even
until about 1900, the atomic theory of matter was not universally accepted. In
this chapter, we shall use the term atom to mean either atom or molecule, in
order to avoid continual repetition. However, we must be careful to make the
proper distinction between atoms and molecules at the appropriate time, since
a great deal of confusion was caused in the early days by not clearly recognizing
the difference.

Since atoms were the first physical particles and a lot of physical theory is
based on ideas from the atomic theory, let us look at the evidence for the existence
of atoms. We shall find that the atomic theory explains a vast number of experimental results in a simple and elegant manner.

The initial evidence for the existence of atoms came from the empirical laws
of chemical combination:

The law of constant composition (or definite proportions): A chemical
compound, no matter how it is prepared, always contains its constituent
elements combined together in fixed proportions by weight, e.g. 9 g of water
always contain 8 g of oxygen and 1 g of hydrogen.

The law of multiple proportions: If two elements combine together to form
two or more compounds, then the weights of one of these elements which
combine with a fixed weight of the other element bear a simple numerical
relation to one another.

The law of constant composition can be most easily explained if it is assumed
that each element is composed of atoms of a definite weight and that chemical
combination takes place between individual atoms in a definite ratio. This con-
trasts with the mixing of two liquids, which can combine in any proportions.

The atomic theory is also able to explain the law of multiple proportions. Consider the reaction of carbon and oxygen which can produce two quite different substances: carbon monoxide which is poisonous, and carbon dioxide which is not. Carbon monoxide (which we will call CO_n) consists of 43% carbon and 57% oxygen by weight, while carbon dioxide (CO_m) contains 27% carbon and 73% oxygen.

$$\therefore \quad \frac{\text{wt. of C}}{n \times (\text{wt. of O})} = \frac{43}{57} \text{ for carbon monoxide,}$$

and

$$\frac{\text{wt. of C}}{m \times (\text{wt. of O})} = \frac{27}{73} \text{ for carbon dioxide.}$$

$$\therefore \quad \frac{m}{n} = \frac{73}{27} \cdot \frac{43}{57} \approx 2.$$

This simple *integral* result suggests that discrete atoms or particles form discrete molecules. We would provisionally make the simplest assumption, that $n = 1$, and therefore that $m = 2$, so that carbon monoxide is CO and carbon dioxide is CO_2. Note, however, that this result is not unique, as we could, for example, have CO_2 and CO_4 but the ambiguity can be removed by the requirements of consistency and simplicity for a range of examples.

Further evidence for the existence of atoms is provided by the fact that the *volumes* of gases which react bear simple numerical relations to each other. It is found, for instance, that 1 volume of oxygen reacts with 2 volumes of hydrogen to give 2 volumes of water vapour. Note that the relation is only true for gases and for the same pressure throughout. Thus, in the example given, the pressure and temperature must be such that the water remains in the gaseous form; for example, if the pressure is atmospheric, the temperature must be well above 100°c. The simple relations are only true to a good approximation if all the gases involved obey the gas laws, PV/T is constant, to a good approximation. Avogadro interpreted this law of combining volumes to mean that "Under conditions of equal temperature and pressure, equal volumes of all gases contain equal numbers of particles" and we can see that this is a plausible conclusion from the following analysis. The result is illustrated for macroscopic volumes by Fig. 2.1. If we accept Avogadro's hypothesis and we imagine the volumes of gas successively reduced, we could presumably get down eventually to volumes so small that they contain one particle. Then for the chemical reaction in question we would have the various possibilities shown in Fig. 2.2. In this picture, note that we have craftily introduced molecules rather than atoms as the smallest particle of a substance (e.g. ∞ and ∞). This

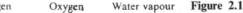

Hydrogen   Oxygen   Water vapour   **Figure 2.1**

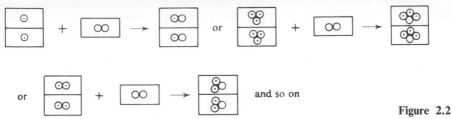

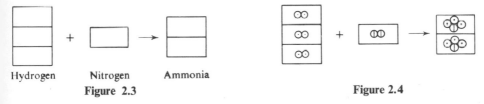

Figure 2.2

proposal, which was also made by Avogadro, was a most controversial and difficult additional complication at the time that this matter was under discussion. (The representations we use for atoms are those used by Dalton in 1807.)

We are unable with the present experimental result to choose between the various alternatives given in Fig. 2.2. Actually, the third alternative is correct, although the first is simpler and therefore *a priori* to be preferred. However, if we try to explain a wider range of gas reactions, we can choose the correct one, since the possibilities which make *all* the results consistent are limited. Consider, therefore, another reaction (Fig. 2.3): 3 vol. of hydrogen + 1 vol. of nitrogen → 2 vol. of ammonia. Hence hydrogen cannot be monatomic, since three atoms cannot give two molecules. The next simplest possibility is that hydrogen is diatomic. Similarly, nitrogen must be at least diatomic and the *simplest* result in this case is given in Fig. 2.4.

Hydrogen   Nitrogen   Ammonia

Figure 2.3   Figure 2.4

It may appear an astounding accident that the simple reactive gases turn out to be diatomic. Actually, in a way, they are simple *because* they are diatomic. The atoms of hydrogen ⊙ are very reactive, including with each other, but the diatomic hydrogen molecule ⊙⊙ is relatively unreactive and so hydrogen is a simple substance. However, if the hydrogen molecules get split up, as in a flame, the atoms are reactive again and can combine with another simple gas (oxygen) to form a third unreactive gas, water vapour. The fact that the smallest particle of an element may be a molecule rather than an atom is a complication; indeed, if the molecules which form gases had been only a little more complex, it would have taken much longer to explain the law of combining volumes.

The laws of electrolysis also indicate the existence of atoms or more precisely of ions. If we pass a given quantity of electricity through a conducting liquid, we always get the same amount (or a *simple* multiple of this amount) of a given substance evolved or deposited. Further, the amounts of the products always bear a simple relation to one another, e.g. in the electrolysis of water we get 2 volumes of hydrogen at the cathode and 1 volume of oxygen at the anode, which clearly must be related to the law of combining volumes. This can be explained by the atomic hypothesis together with an atomic hypothesis for electricity.

The simplicity of some of the physical properties of substances and the simple relations between them are an indication of the atomic nature of matter, although it is not easy to deduce precise facts about the properties of the atoms from them. It is well known, for instance, that crystals grow with plane faces and that many crystals can be cleaved to give faces which are extremely flat. The angles between the flat faces are found to be quite accurately fixed for a given crystal and do not depend on the size of the faces or where they are in the crystal. This would not be expected if matter were continuous. We should expect to get curved faces and any angle, as seen after smashing a block of toffee. The regularity and reproducibility of faces and angles is readily explained in terms of crystals being composed of regular stacks of atoms. We should expect the crystal to grow such that layer upon layer of atoms are added, with the result that flat faces tend to be formed. (Actual growth patterns on crystals on closer inspection are complex but in such a way as to correspond to the addition of atoms to a regular array.) Cleavage planes (Fig. 2.5) are those planes which pass between atoms rather than through them. Thus, for a simple cubic structure, the crystal would cleave more readily in planes parallel to the lines of atoms rather than at any other angle. The planes and the right angles between them therefore reflect directly the cubic array of the atoms. Mineralogists were very early in using the angles of crystal faces to identify minerals. The angles can now be explained in terms of the crystal structure of the arrays of atoms or molecules.

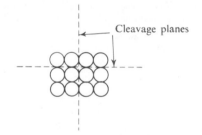

Figure 2.5

Finally, we can note the simplicity and universality of the gas laws. It is found that, for all gases, PV/T is constant, with small deviations, as contrasted with the diverse properties of solids and liquids. These facts are simply explained if we assume that substances are composed of atoms and that the atoms are close together in solids and liquids but are far apart in a gas. A typical gas is mostly space and hence the uniformity of many of the properties of gases.

2.2 AVOGADRO'S NUMBER

Avogadro's hypothesis and the law of combining volumes give us a simple and direct interpretation of atomic and molecular weights. Suppose that n_A volumes of a gas A combine with n_B volumes of a gas B. Since, by Avogadro's hypothesis, a unit of volume of any gas contains the same number (say N) of molecules, the weight of A taking part in the reaction is $W_A = n_A m_A N$ and the weight of B taking part is $W_B = n_B m_B N$, where m_A and m_B are the weights of one molecule of A and B respectively. Therefore

$$\frac{W_A}{W_B} = \frac{n_A m_A N}{n_B m_B N} \quad \text{or} \quad \frac{m_A}{m_B} = \frac{W_A}{W_B} \times \frac{n_B}{n_A}.$$

Thus the weights of the reacting molecules can be compared by comparing volumes and weights of the gases taking part in the reaction. If we arbitrarily introduce a *standard* weight of a given gas A as being M_A, we have arbitrarily fixed a standard number of molecules N_0 where $M_A = m_A N_0$. The standard M_A was at first chosen as one gramme of hydrogen atoms, or two grammes of hydrogen molecules. It has since been changed to correspond first to the ^{16}O atom and then to the ^{12}C atom, which illustrates the arbitrary nature of the choice. Once M_A is fixed, values of M for other gases are obtained by experiment. The choice of M_A fixes the value of N_0, which is called Avogadro's number. It is the number of atoms in a gramme-atom or the number of molecules in a gramme-molecule (mole). Its value was never known by Avogadro. There are various ways in which it may be determined and some of these will now be considered.

Although the idea of Avogadro's number arose first in connexion with gases, it is of course true that a given mass of gas will still contain the same number of atoms when it has been cooled down to become a liquid or a solid. Thus measurements of Avogadro's number are not restricted to gases, and one of the most direct and accurate methods is to use x rays diffracted from crystals. X rays are electromagnetic radiation with a wavelength of a few ångström units (1 ångström unit $\text{Å} = 10^{-8}$ cm $= 10^{-10}$ m). As the atoms in crystals are arranged in regular planes separated by equal distances of a few ångström units, they will diffract x rays in a similar manner to the diffraction of visible light by a diffraction grating.* By measuring the angle at which the x rays are diffracted, the spacing of the planes of atoms may be determined if the wavelength of the x rays is known. The wavelength of the x rays can be measured by diffraction through a ruled grating, whose spacing can be determined by relating it to the standard metre. When the spacing of the planes of atoms has been measured, it is possible to deduce a value for Avogadro's number. We will take sodium chloride as an example. Sodium chloride consists of Na^+ and Cl^- ions arranged so that the ions of each type form a simple cubic array as shown in Fig. 2.6. Other evidence (see Chapter 4) suggests that a sodium chloride crystal is an array of ions rather than of atoms. It is energetically favourable for a chlorine atom to gain an electron and for a sodium atom to lose one if circumstances permit this. If ions are formed, they will clearly tend to pack together such that each positive ion is surrounded by as many negative ions as possible and each negative ion is surrounded by as many positive

---

* See, for example, R. S. LONGHURST, *Geometrical and Physical Optics,* Longmans Green, London (1957).

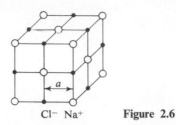

Cl⁻ Na⁺   **Figure 2.6**

ions as possible so that the electrostatic energy is as low as possible. Suppose that x-ray diffraction gives us the distance a between the nuclei of adjacent Na^+ and Cl^- ions. (It is actually more subtle than this because x rays are affected mostly by the electrons which are in clouds round the nuclei.) Then we can divide the crystal up into cubes of side a each of which "contains" one sodium nucleus or one chlorine nucleus, so that each Na^+Cl^- "molecule" can be regarded as occupying a volume $2a^3$. Since one mole of salt contains N_0 molecules, by definition, it occupies a volume $2N_0a^3$. We can also determine the molecular weight M chemically, and we can measure the density ρ. The volume of one mole is then M/ρ. Equating these two volumes, we have

$$2N_0a^3 = \frac{M}{\rho} \quad \text{or} \quad N_0 = \frac{M}{2\rho a^3}.$$

For NaCl, x-ray diffraction gives $a = 2.81$ Å. With $M = 58.5$ and $\rho = 2.16$ g ml^{-1} we get

$$N_0 = \frac{58.5}{2 \times 2.16 \times (2.81 \times 10^{-8})^3} \text{ mol}^{-1} = 6.1 \times 10^{23} \text{ mol}^{-1}.$$

Another direct way of getting Avogadro's number is by radioactivity; the principle is as follows. A radioactive substance, such as radium, produces α particles which are helium nuclei having an atomic mass of four units. The rate of emission of α particles from a given sample of radium can be measured directly by observing the scintillations produced when the particles strike a phosphor. We can also collect the helium resulting in a given time from the emitted particles and measure its volume at a known temperature and pressure. This experiment was performed by Dewar in 1908. The mass of helium produced can then be calculated from the gas law $PV = nRT$ where n is the number of moles of the gas present and R is the gas constant (see below). Alternatively, the mass of helium produced could be measured directly. Since the number of atoms N in a known weight of helium W has been measured, then Avogadro's number may be obtained immediately from the relation

$$N_0 = N \times (4/W).$$

In practice, this is an extremely difficult method of measuring Avogadro's number but it would be very direct if the practical difficulties could be overcome. An alternative to measuring the helium produced is to measure the decrease in weight of the radium itself over a long period. We should then have to be sure that the only massive particles ejected are α particles and to allow for the decrease in emission as the radioactivity decayed. An alternative to counting the scintillations due to the α particles is to measure the electric charge produced over a period of time and to use the fact that each α particle carries a charge $2e$ where e is the electronic charge and is assumed to be known. This also is a difficult experiment.

We can also find Avogadro's number from electrolysis. A given quantity of electricity, known as the faraday, will liberate one gramme atomic weight of any monovalent ion. Thus we determine the value of the faraday by electrolysing salt solution (Fig. 2.7) and measuring the charge required to deposit or collect a gramme atomic weight of sodium and chlorine at the electrodes. Actually, the sodium and chlorine usually react, and it is more convenient to measure, say, the deposition of copper from copper sulphate solution. Although the copper ion is divalent, this makes no essential difference.

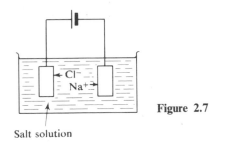

Figure 2.7

Salt solution

It is found that the faraday is 96,500 coulomb mol^{-1} (see Experiment 8). We assume we know about the quantization of electric charge and that the charge on a monovalent ion is exactly equal to that on an electron. We also assume that allowance has been made for multiply charged ions if these arise. Thus, if we use the electrolysis of copper sulphate, the charge required to deposit one gramme-atom (63.5 g) of copper is two faraday, since the ion in question is Cu^{2+}. Hence we have that the faraday is given by

$$F = N_0 e, \quad \text{that is } N_0 = F/e.$$

But from a quite independent experiment, for example the Millikan oil drop experiment (see Experiment 1), we can measure the electronic charge. The result is

$$e = 1.60 \times 10^{-19} \text{ coulomb.}$$

Therefore, using the relation just given, we have

$$N_0 = \frac{9.65 \times 10^4 \text{ coulomb mol}^{-1}}{1.60 \times 10^{-19} \text{ coulomb}} \approx 6 \times 10^{23} \text{ mol}^{-1}, \quad \text{as before.}$$

Historically, this experiment was first used the other way round. In 1830, Faraday suggested that *if* matter was atomic, then electrolysis suggests that electricity is also atomic. The first reasonably reliable estimate of the quantum of electric charge was made in 1874 by use of the relation $e = F/N_0$ many years before the Millikan oil drop experiment. The unit of electric charge can also be obtained from the experiment we described earlier on the radioactive disintegration of radium by measuring the total charge carried by a measured number of α particles; we should expect the result to be $2e$ per α particle.

It is also clear that the atomic theory of matter implies that the unit of negative charge, as on the electron, is very closely equal to the unit of positive charge, as on the proton. This could be shown, for instance, by demonstrating that a hydrogen atom is not deflected by a uniform electric field. It is not very conclusive to observe that materials tend to be electrically neutral since, if the units of positive and negative charge differed slightly, a macroscopic piece of material would soon acquire a slight excess or defect of electrons and would then appear to be neutral. It is now known experimentally that the difference in the electric charge of an electron and a proton, if any, is less than one part in 10^{21}. The consequences of quite a small difference are far-reaching: the expansion of the universe could be explained by a difference of only one part in 10^{19}.

We can get Avogadro's number indirectly by weighing a given volume V of a gas at a known pressure P and temperature T (see Experiment 7). By finding the number n of moles of gas, we can substitute in the perfect gas equation

$$PV = nRT$$

to determine the gas constant R. We shall show in Section 10.2 that $R = N_0 k$, where k is the Boltzmann constant, which we can obtain independently (see Section 2.3) and so $N_0 = R/k$. The measured value of R is 1.98 cal deg^{-1} mol^{-1} or 8.3×10^7 erg deg^{-1} mol^{-1} and $k = 1.38 \times 10^{-16}$ erg deg^{-1}. Hence $N_0 \approx 6 \times 10^{23}$ mol^{-1} once more.

It is difficult to measure fundamental quantities such as N_0 directly and independently to sufficient accuracy. It is usually necessary to measure a number of quantities which involve several fundamental constants.* Among the indirect methods of measuring Avogadro's number is one in which it can be estimated from the fact that the sky is blue (Problem 7.10)!

We have examined the determination of Avogadro's number in some detail because of its importance to the atomic theory of matter. Indeed, the fact that Avogadro's number proves to have the same value for a number of different independent experiments is one of the strongest pieces of evidence for the existence of atoms.

2.3 BOLTZMANN'S CONSTANT

Boltzmann's constant is an important quantity which we shall have occasion to use frequently and so we get familiar with it by learning how to measure it, even though we shall have to assume a bit of theory which is discussed in Chapter 10.

---

* J. H. SANDERS, *The Fundamental Atomic Constants*, Oxford University Press, London (1961).

We can get k from a study of Brownian motion. The theory goes as follows. Consider a particle in a liquid which moves randomly due to collisions with molecules of the liquid. This motion is called the Brownian motion or kinetic motion of the particle. The particle is continually moving in an apparently random manner as it exchanges energy with the continually moving molecules. In the experiment, spherical particles of PVC (polyvinyl chloride) about a micron (10^{-4} cm) in diameter can be used. Consider the force on such a particle due to the surrounding molecules. This force may be divided into two parts. If the particle is moving with velocity dx/dt in the liquid (regarded as a continuous fluid), it will be subject to a viscous retarding force $\mu(dx/dt)$. This is certainly true if the particle is considerably larger than the surrounding molecules, since then the motion of the particle involves the movement of large numbers of the surrounding molecules and the motion of large numbers of molecules must be describable by macroscopic parameters. However, if we look at the situation in detail, as we must, we see that the actual force on the particle is varying rapidly with time because it is actually due to the forces exerted by many individual molecules. We can allow for this by an additional force F whose properties are described below. In actual fact, the division of the force on a particle into two parts, one macroscopic and slowly varying with time and one microscopic and rapidly varying with time, is a rather subtle matter and raises a number of difficulties.* The difficulties are particularly acute when the particle being studied is comparable in size with the surrounding particles. However, we shall be concerned with a large particle surrounded by small ones (Fig. 2.8); our PVC particles have a diameter some ten thousand times greater than that of the water molecules in which they are dissolved. The acceleration of the particle is $m(d^2x/dt^2)$ and so the equation of motion of the particle is

$$F = m\frac{d^2x}{dt^2} + \mu\frac{dx}{dt}.$$

F, d^2x/dt^2, and dx/dt vary with time. Multiplying by x,

$$Fx = mx\frac{d^2x}{dt^2} + \mu x\frac{dx}{dt}.$$

But

$$x\frac{d^2x}{dt^2} = \frac{1}{2}\frac{d^2}{dt^2}(x^2) - \left(\frac{dx}{dt}\right)^2$$

and

$$x\frac{dx}{dt} = \frac{1}{2}\frac{d}{dt}(x^2),$$

$$\therefore \quad Fx = \tfrac{1}{2}m\frac{d^2}{dt^2}(x^2) - m\left(\frac{dx}{dt}\right)^2 + \tfrac{1}{2}\mu\frac{d}{dt}(x^2).$$

---

* F. REIF, *Fundamentals of Statistical and Thermal Physics*, McGraw-Hill, New York (1965), gives a good discussion of Brownian motion.

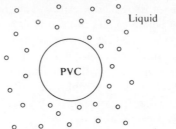

Liquid

PVC

Figure 2.8

We now average all terms in this equation over a large number of collisions
which we cannot see individually. It is shown in Section 13.6 and Problem 13.10
that there are of order 10^{10} collisions per second of a molecule in a gas at n.t.p.
A liquid is about 10^3 times more dense than such a gas and the number of collisions
per molecule (for a gas) is proportional to the density. Because of the finite size of
the molecules the number of "collisions" is somewhat higher than for an ideal gas of
the same density. We may expect roughly therefore that there are some 10^{14}
collisions per second per molecule in a typical liquid. Hence F changes appreciably
in 10^{-14} second but x varies only slowly, as illustrated in Fig. 2.9. In taking the
average of the product of x and F, we can therefore average over F first; in other
words, $\overline{xF} \approx (x\overline{F})$. But $\overline{F} = 0$ and so $\overline{xF} = 0$ (see Problem 2.11). Also

$$\tfrac{1}{2}m \overline{\left(\frac{dx}{dt}\right)^2} = \tfrac{1}{2}m\overline{v_x^2} = \tfrac{1}{2}kT$$

where k is Boltzmann's constant. This result is related to the kinetic theory of
gases and equipartition of energy which is discussed in Chapters 10 and 11. T is
the absolute temperature. Boltzmann's constant k may be regarded as the factor
which tells us the mean thermal energy kT associated with the temperature T.
Substituting these two results in the equation above we get

$$\tfrac{1}{2}m\,\overline{\frac{d^2}{dt^2}(x^2)} - kT + \tfrac{1}{2}\mu\,\overline{\frac{d}{dt}(x^2)} = 0,$$

or

$$\overline{\frac{d^2}{dt^2}(x^2)} + \frac{\mu}{m}\,\overline{\frac{d}{dt}(x^2)} = \frac{2kT}{m}.$$

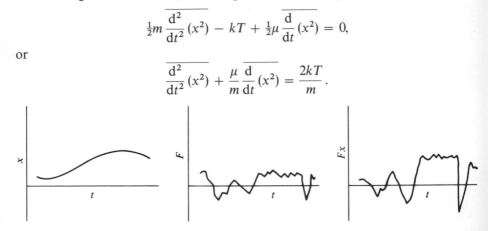

Figure 2.9

Put

$$Z = \frac{d}{dt}(x^2)$$

so that

$$\frac{dZ}{dt} + \frac{\mu}{m}Z = 2kT/m.$$

Multiply each side by $\exp[(\mu/m)t]$, so that

$$\frac{d}{dt}\{Z \exp[(\mu/m)t]\} = (2kT/m)\exp[(\mu/m)t].$$

Integrate to give

$$Z \exp[(\mu/m)t] = (2kT/m)\int \exp[(\mu/m)t]\, dt + C,$$

where C is a constant.
Hence

$$Z \equiv \frac{d\overline{(x^2)}}{dt} = (2kT/\mu) + C\exp[-(\mu/m)t].$$

Although the integration constant turns out not to be important and really involves a more elaborate analysis,* we can determine C from the behaviour of the particle for very short times. For times such that $(\mu/m)t \ll 1$, we can expand the exponential and get

$$\frac{d\overline{(x^2)}}{dt} = (2kT/\mu) + C[1 - (\mu/m)t + \cdots]$$

$$= (2kT/\mu + C) - C(\mu/m)t + \cdots.$$

Hence

$$\overline{x^2} = (2kT/\mu + C)t - \tfrac{1}{2}C(\mu/m)t^2 + \cdots + C',$$

for $t \ll m/\mu$, where C' is another constant of integration. If we measure positions from the position at $t = 0$, then $C' = 0$. But, for very short times, the velocity of the particle must be constant, since any accelerating (or decelerating) forces need time to act. We must therefore have $(\overline{x^2})^{1/2} \propto t$, or $\overline{x^2} \propto t^2$, for very short times, since this corresponds to constant velocity. Hence the term in t in the expression above for $\overline{x^2}$ must disappear and so $C = -(2kT/\mu)$. Hence, inserting in the expression which is valid for any time, we have

$$\frac{d\overline{(x^2)}}{dt} = \frac{2kT}{\mu}\{1 - \exp[-(\mu/m)t]\}.$$

The viscous retarding force coefficient μ is given by Stokes' expression and is $6\pi\eta a$ where η is the viscosity of the fluid and a is the radius of the moving particle (see Problem 5.1). For our PVC particle with diameter $(2a)$ of one micron (10^{-4} cm)

---

* D. K. C. MACDONALD, *Noise and Fluctuations*, Wiley, New York (1962), p. 33.

and with a mass $m \approx 10^{-12}$ g (calculated from the diameter and the density o
PVC, which is about 1 g cm^{-3}) and for water which has a viscosity of about 0.01
we find $\mu \approx 10^{-5} \text{ g s}^{-1}$ and $m/\mu \approx 10^{-7}$ s. Since we shall certainly measur
$\overline{x^2}$ for times much longer than this we can ignore the term $\exp\left[-(\mu/m)t\right]$ in the
equation for $d(\overline{x^2})/dt$. Hence we have

$$\overline{x^2} = \frac{2kT}{\mu} t,$$

where again the constant of integration is zero if we measure x as the distance
moved from the initial time ($t = 0$). But the motion of the particle is the same
on average, in any direction and so $\overline{x^2} = \overline{y^2} = \overline{z^2}$. If the actual distance moved
in any direction is r, we have $\overline{r^2} = \overline{x^2} + \overline{y^2} + \overline{z^2} = 3\overline{x^2}$ so that

$$\overline{r^2} = \frac{6kT}{\mu} t, \qquad \text{that is } \frac{\overline{r^2}}{t} = \frac{kT}{\pi a \eta}.$$

Hence, by measuring $\overline{r^2}/t$, we can find k, Boltzmann's constant. To determine
$\overline{r^2}/t$ experimentally we must measure r very many times for a given value of t (say
30 s) and take the average of r^2/t. For particles of diameter 1 micron suspended
in water at room temperature, $\overline{r^2}/t$ is found to be of order $2 \times 10^{-8} \text{ cm}^2 \text{ s}^{-1}$.

$$\therefore \quad \frac{6kT}{\mu} \sim 2 \times 10^{-8} \quad \text{or} \quad k \sim \frac{10^{-5}}{6 \times 300} \times 2 \times 10^{-8} \sim 10^{-16} \text{ erg deg}^{-1}$$

(more precisely, $k = 1.38 \times 10^{-16} \text{ erg deg}^{-1}$).

Putting $t = 1$ s, we have $(\overline{r^2})^{1/2} \approx 10^{-4}$ cm. Thus our particles move, on the average,
a distance of the order of their own diameter in the first second.

As mentioned in the previous section, we can use our value of k, together with
a measurement of the gas constant R, to obtain a value of Avogadro's number,
since $N_0 = R/k$. We could, of course, equally well use independently measured
values of N_0 and R to deduce a value of k indirectly.

Although we have analysed the Brownian motion of a large particle as a
method of introducing and measuring Boltzmann's constant, it should be realized
that this is an important effect in itself. The motion of the PVC particle is the
response to the random thermal motion of the molecules of water. This random
thermal motion, or thermal energy, which is of order of magnitude kT for a particle
in any body at temperature T, is the origin of many important phenomena. It
means, for instance, that there is an important limit to the accuracy of all measurements carried out at a finite temperature. The Brownian motion causes a fluctuation in all readings if the measuring technique is sensitive enough. It is not
difficult to see the fluctuations in deflexion of a sensitive galvanometer, for instance.
The thermal fluctuations in motion of the electrons in a metal lead to a random
voltage being produced on any conductor which will ultimately be dominant as we
try to observe smaller and smaller signals. In many modern devices, we are in

act limited by thermal "noise" and elaborate measures have to be taken to reduce its effects. The most obvious thing to do is to reduce the temperature, since the thermal energy is kT and is directly proportional to the absolute temperature.

PROBLEMS

.1. Show that one electronvolt of energy per particle corresponds to 23 kilocalories per mole of particles.

.2. Show that a charge of one faraday falling through a potential difference of one volt corresponds to an energy of 23 kcal. Why is this?

.3. The fine structure constant is $\alpha = e^2/4\pi\varepsilon_0 hc$. Show that it is a pure number (Section 5.6) and has the approximate numerical value $1/137$ (in e.s.u. $4\pi\varepsilon_0 = 1$).

.4. The ionization potential of the hydrogen atom is 13.6 v. The energy of a particle of electromagnetic radiation (photon) of wavelength λ is hc/λ. Find $1/\lambda$ for a photon with energy 13.6 ev. Why is this numerically equal to the Rydberg constant?

.5. Calculate the mass of the electron from the experimental values of N_0, e/m, and F.

.6. For a series of substances which are all oxides of nitrogen it is found that the ratio of the mass of oxygen to that of nitrogen has the following values: 0.57, 1.13, 1.71, 2.29, and 2.86. Discuss the significance of this result and a possible deduction from it.

2.7. Is Avogadro's number an integer?

2.8. The density of liquid air is about 800 times that of air at n.t.p. Show that the molecules in air at n.t.p. are, on average, about nine molecular diameters apart.

2.9. Estimate the root mean square distance moved in one minute due to Brownian motion of the following objects immersed in water at room temperature: (a) a submarine, (b) a fish, (c) a dust particle, and (d) a molecule of water (assume they have been in the water a sufficiently long time before the measurement starts).

2.10. Calculate the root mean square velocity of the PVC particles used in the Brownian motion experiment described in Section 2.3.

2.11. As an example of the mean of the product of a slowly and a rapidly varying function of time when the rapidly varying one has zero mean value (cf. $\overline{xF}$, Section 2.3), consider $t \cos \omega t$. Show that the mean of $t \cos \omega t$ is very small compared with the mean of t over the interval 0 to T if $T \gg \omega^{-1}$.

CHAPTER 3

The size of atoms and molecules

When atoms and molecules get too close together they repel; that is what keeps us from falling through the floor! R. P. FEYNMAN

3.1 ATOMIC DIAMETERS

Atoms must be smaller than the wavelength of visible light or we should be able to see them. This means that the diameter d_0 of an atom is less than 4000 Å. The volume of an atom $\frac{4}{3}\pi(d_0/2)^3$ cm^3 is therefore less than $\frac{4}{3}\pi(2000)^3$ Å^3. In other words there can be more than $3/[4\pi(2000)^3]$ atoms per Å^3 or about 10^{13} atoms per cm^3. If we are dealing with a macroscopic amount of matter, we always have a lot of atoms. Actually, in condensed matter (liquids and solids), where the atoms are touching one another, there are usually some 10^{23} atoms per cm^3. In a gas, there are rather fewer atoms per cm^3 since roughly 1 cm^3 of liquid produces about 1000 cm^3 of vapour at n.t.p. Thus, in a gas, the atoms are on average about $(1000)^{1/3} \approx 10$ diameters apart. Some 99.9% of the volume occupied by a gas is space.

We have already seen by direct measurement using x rays that in NaCl the atoms or ions are a few ångströms in diameter. Since we now have N_0 (not necessarily from x-ray measurements in NaCl!), we can see this order of magnitude of atomic size is to be expected in general simply from a consideration of densities of substances (except for very large molecules). For example, the density of solid argon is 1.69 g cm^{-3}. Hence the volume of one mole (40 g) is $40/1.69$ cm^3 and this contains $N_0 = 6 \times 10^{23}$ atoms. Hence the volume per atom of argon is $40/(1.69 \times 6 \times 10^{23})$ cm^3. If we have simple cubic packing and the distance between adjacent atoms is d_0, then the volume per atom is d_0^3 (see also Problem 3.1).

$$\therefore \quad d_0 = \sqrt[3]{\frac{40}{1.39 \times 6 \times 10^{23}}} \text{ cm} = 3.4 \times 10^{-8} \text{ cm} = 3.4 \text{ Å}$$

By measuring a series of ionic crystals using x rays, we can obtain a self-consistent set of diameters of ions. Generally speaking, the size of ions increases, for similar ions, as we go up the periodic table, as is illustrated by Table 3.1. Notice that, although the number of electrons in an ion increases enormously, the diameter does not increase much. On the whole, even the ionic volumes do not increase as fast as the number of electrons, since an increase in nuclear charge goes with the increasing number of electrons and so the electrons are held to the nucleus

Table 3.1

Ion	F^-	Cl^-	Br^-	I^-
Diameter, Å	2.66	3.62	3.92	4.40
Number of electrons	10	18	36	54

more tightly. A similar small change in diameter with atomic number is observed for the rare gas atoms, although the diameters are larger than for ions, since the forces involved are rather weaker. The diameters in Å of the atoms neon, argon, krypton, xenon, and radon are 3.1, 3.9, 4.0, 4.4, and 4.8, respectively. For the transition metals, the atomic diameters actually fall with increasing atomic number. The size of atoms is clearly not a simple matter. On the other hand, as we might expect, the size of an atom can be reduced by stripping electrons off it. The diameters of Cu, Cu^+, and Cu^{2+} are 2.34, 1.92, and 1.44 Å, respectively. The large reduction in size is because the two outer electrons of the copper atom are held rather loosely and therefore have large orbits.

3.2 MOLECULAR DIAMETERS

We can also get an idea of the size, that is d_0, of molecules in many other ways. For example, we can estimate d_0 from deviations from the gas laws and critical data in particular. Thus in the van der Waals correction to the simple gas law $PV = RT$, we have

$$\left(P + \frac{a}{V^2}\right)(V - b) = RT.$$

a and b can be determined by experiment. Roughly speaking, a/V^2 arises because of attraction between the molecules and b is to allow for the repulsion of the molecules (see Section 7.3). As we shall see, the idea of a simple "size" of an atom or a molecule is too naïve. However, it is clear that there must be a sense in which two molecules cannot be in the same volume and, if a molecule is regarded as a hard sphere of diameter d_0, then the centre of another molecule cannot get within a sphere of radius d_0 around the first molecule. There is therefore corresponding to each molecule a volume $\frac{4}{3}\pi d_0^3$ in which the other molecules cannot move. However, this counts the effect of each molecule twice since, if molecule A excludes molecule B, then B excludes A, and so the actual excluded volume per molecule is only $\frac{2}{3}\pi d_0^3$ (but is nevertheless four times the volume of the molecule). Hence, for one mole of gas, the excluded volume is $b = \frac{2}{3}\pi N_0 d_0^3$ and the actual volume available to the molecules is only $(V - b)$. This is clearly important for dense gases and it can be shown from the van der Waals equation (see Problem 3.7) that $b = \frac{1}{3}V_c$ or $RT_c/8P_c$ where V_c is the critical volume, T_c is the critical temperature, and P_c is the critical pressure. The critical point is that at which the liquid and vapour just become indistinguishable. The reason for including the a/V^2 term is quite subtle and is discussed in Chapter 7. For argon, $b = 33$ cm^3 from experiment, so that

$$d_0^3 = \frac{3}{2\pi} \frac{b}{N_0} = \frac{3}{2\pi} \frac{33}{6 \times 10^{23}} = 25 \times 10^{-24} \text{ cm}^3 = 25 \text{ Å}^3$$

$$\therefore \quad d_0 = 2.8 \text{ Å}.$$

We can get a size for molecules from measurement of the viscosity η of a gas and kinetic theory (see Section 7.1). d_0 can also be found from the thermal conductivity of a gas. But both these require more theory than we have at present. Notice that the value of N_0 is needed in the calculation of d_0.

We can also get an estimate of molecular diameters from the dielectric properties of liquids composed of molecules having permanent electric dipoles. If τ is an average time for the reorientation of a polar molecule in a liquid, then the electric polarization, which is due to the partial lining up of the polar molecules in the direction of the field (see Section 11.5), will have decayed appreciably towards zero (in zero field) in a time of order τ and so τ can be measured (see Fig. 3.1). It can be shown that $\tau \approx \pi \eta d_0^3 / 3kT$ where d_0 is the diameter of the molecule, T is the absolute temperature, k is Boltzmann's constant, and η is the viscosity of the liquid. Hence we can estimate d_0 from this experiment. The values found are comparable with those obtained by other methods (see Problem 3.9).

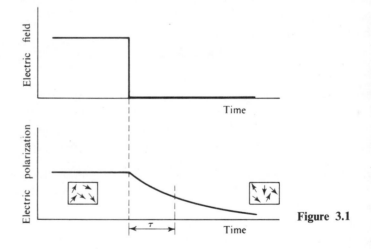

Figure 3.1

A strikingly simple but approximate method of getting the size of a molecule is to take a low molecular weight fatty acid and let a drop of known volume fall gently on a dish of water. The drop spreads out until the acid forms a monolayer on the surface of the water the extent of which can be indicated by allowing it to push aside some dust on the water surface. From the volume of the drop and the area of the layer, we can calculate the thickness. This thickness is the molecular size (actually the length of the molecule). Note that this method of measuring molecular size does not depend on Avogadro's number or on the molecular weight.

Actually, N_0 is a measure of the mass of the proton (more precisely of the hydrogen atom, or even more precisely one twelfth of the mass of a ^{12}C atom). A gramme-atom of hydrogen is 1 g, that is 1 g of hydrogen atoms contains N_0 atoms. Therefore, 1 atom of hydrogen weighs $1/N_0$ g $= 1/(6.02 \times 10^{23}) = 1.66 \times 10^{-24}$ g. This can be estimated independently in the laboratory from the magnetic moment of the proton, $\mu_p \approx e/2\pi m_p c$ e.m.u., where e is the electronic charge in e.s.u., m_p is the mass of the proton in g, and c is the velocity of light in cm s^{-1} (see Experiment 11). Notice that the weighing entered when we determined a density in getting N_0. It is quite easy to weigh an atom if you know how many you have in the sample being weighed!

3.3 NUCLEAR DIAMETERS

Atoms and molecules can only be regarded as stable distinct entities provided we are not too fierce with them. By using sufficient energy (see Table 1.1), the atoms can be broken up into other particles. If we wish to break up atoms, the only really sensible way is to shoot particles at them. Let us look first at the simplest atom, the hydrogen atom (see Fig. 3.2). Assume we know that it consists of a proton and an electron, that its diameter is about 0.5 Å, and that an energy of 13.6 ev or 22×10^{-12} erg is required to separate the two to a large distance.

If we use an electron to split the hydrogen atom, how fast an electron is required? The electron must have an energy of at least 22×10^{-12} erg which it can of course gain by falling through an electric potential difference of 13.6 v.

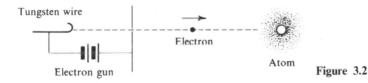

Figure 3.2

Unfortunately, the experiment cannot be done so directly because we cannot get a gas of hydrogen atoms which we require for the target, since they have a strong tendency to recombine in pairs to give hydrogen molecules. However, most atoms or molecules can have their outside electrons knocked off by electrons or other suitable particles which have energies of some tens of ev. Or, of course, we can use electromagnetic radiation of similar energy. The energy of a photon of frequency v is $E_{ph} = hv$, where h is Planck's constant (see Chapter 8). We also have $v\lambda = c$, which is true for all waves, if c is the appropriate velocity. Here c is the velocity of light and λ its wavelength.

Hence

$$E_{ph} = hc/\lambda \quad \text{or} \quad \lambda = \frac{hc}{E_{ph}}$$

For

$$E_{ph} = 13.6\,\text{ev} = 13.6 \times 1.6 \times 10^{-12}\,\text{erg},$$

$$\lambda = \frac{6.6 \times 10^{-27} \times 3 \times 10^{10}}{13.6 \times 1.6 \times 10^{-12}} \approx 0.9 \times 10^{-5}\,\text{cm} = 900\,\text{Å}.$$

This is in the ultraviolet (u.v.) region of the electromagnetic spectrum. Hence u.v. radiation can ionize atoms or molecules. To knock out electrons from the inner shells, we need more energy and hence radiation of shorter wavelength. In fact, this requires x rays or γ rays with wavelengths of order a few ångström units and energies in the kev range.

However, if the projectiles move very fast they do not see the electrons, either because they do not get very close or because they do not spend much time in passing the atom. Such projectiles, for example α particles,* which are fast and much heavier than electrons are not deflected much by them as we show below and so we can use them to look at the nucleus without being bothered by the cloud of electrons.

Consider a collision in which a particle A of mass m_1, travelling with velocity v, strikes a stationary particle B of mass m_2. For convenience let the motion of A be along the line of centres. Then, if the velocities of A and B after the collision are v_1 and v_2, respectively, we have

$$m_1 v = m_1 v_1 + m_2 v_2 \qquad \text{from conservation of momentum (Section 5.2)},$$
$$\tfrac{1}{2} m_1 v^2 = \tfrac{1}{2} m_1 v_1^2 + \tfrac{1}{2} m_2 v_2^2 \qquad \text{from conservation of energy (Section 5.4)}.$$

Then we can eliminate v_2 or v_1 between the two equations and get

$$v_1 = \frac{1 - (m_2/m_1)}{1 + (m_2/m_1)}\,v \quad \text{and} \quad v_2 = \frac{2}{1 + (m_2/m_1)}\,v.$$

If $m_2 \ll m_1$, $v_1 \to v$ and $v_2 \to 2v$, i.e. the heavier body is unaffected. This result is also true if the collision is not head-on and does not require an assumption that the bodies are hard spheres, only that the collision is elastic (see Chapter 7).

This effect is the basis of Rutherford's experiments (1911) which demonstrated the nuclear atom. Rutherford used as projectiles the α particles produced by the spontaneous radioactive disintegration of radium and allowed them to pass through thin films of materials such as mica or gold. The α particles were detected by the scintillation caused when they struck a phosphor screen. A thin film must be used so that the projectile particles are unlikely to suffer more than one collision with a target particle in passing through the film. If multiple collisions occurred, the results would be more difficult to interpret. We can be sure that there are few multiple collisions if there are few single collisions, i.e. if most particles get through without colliding at all. Most of his fast particles went straight through atoms undeflected by an electron, since α particles are some 7500 times more massive

---

* α particles are, as we have already seen, helium nuclei of mass $4m_p$ and charge $+2e$, ^4_2He.

than electrons, that is $m_1/m_2 \sim 7500$. However, a few were deviated by *large* angles (see Fig. 3.3) and this can only be explained by the presence of a small massive nucleus. The angular distribution of the scattered particles depends on the law of force between the projectile and target particles (see Chapter 7).

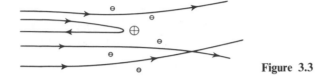

Figure 3.3

One of the most important results of these and other experiments was that the charge on the nucleus is Ze where Z is the atomic number of the element. In fact, Rutherford and collaborators showed that the scattering effect is well explained by purely electrostatic forces and is proportional to Q^2 where Q is the charge on the nucleus (Ze). They found that $Q \approx \frac{1}{2}$ atomic weight $\times$ electronic charge, that is $Q \sim \frac{1}{2}Ae$ or $Z \approx \frac{1}{2}A$ for not too heavy nuclei. A is the mass of the nucleus in units of the mass of the hydrogen atom rounded off to the nearest integer (Section 6.2). The result is now understood because it is now known that nuclei tend to have equal numbers of protons and neutrons. Z is the number of protons each of which carries a charge e and A is the sum of the number of protons and neutrons, since protons and neutrons have practically the same mass. For example, ^{4}He has 2p + 2n, $^6_3$Li has 3p + 3n and $^{12}_6$C has 6p + 6n. The charge Ze on the atomic nucleus was clearly established by Moseley's experiments (1914) on the x-ray emission spectrum of atoms. It is further established by the scattering of x rays by atoms as described in Section 8.7. The minimal separation of an α particle and a nucleus must have been about 6×10^{-13} cm which is the distance at which the kinetic energy of the incident α particles is converted entirely into electrostatic potential energy. Hence the nuclear diameter is less than 6×10^{-13} cm. The nucleus behaved like a point charge and so no explicitly nuclear effect was as yet observed. Actually nuclei are smaller. The α particles could not get nearer because they did not have enough energy to overcome the Coulomb repulsion although they had an energy of about 8 Mev. This is one reason why energetic particles are usually required to study nuclei.

Of course, the Coulomb repulsion prevents us looking for other forces easily. However, we now have neutrons which can be projected at nuclei and there is no Coulomb repulsion and the nuclear forces can be studied more easily. On the other hand, neutrons are not as easy to manipulate as charged particles.

In many cases, the particles begin to be scattered in unexpected ways when the closest approach gets to a few times 10^{-13} cm. For scattering of protons by protons, the results are not explained by the Coulomb "electrostatic" interaction alone when the distance of closest approach is of order 10^{-13} cm. Hence, for distances of this order, other interaction forces become important which are not electrostatic in nature—or alternatively we could say that the laws of Coulomb interaction do not remain valid for such short distances. However, if we consider the scattering of neutrons by protons where there are no Coulomb forces, we again get scattering when the distances of approach become of order 10^{-13} cm. It seems likely therefore that we are dealing with a new force rather than a breakdown of the validity of the Coulomb interaction. A similar effect is observed for scattering of neutrons by neutrons when clearly no electric field at all is involved. For the scattering of neutrons by protons and neutrons by neutrons, the protons and neutrons behave like small spheres of diameter a few times 10^{-13} cm. In the experiment on the scattering of protons by neutrons and vice versa, sometimes a deuterium nucleus is observed to come out! A deuteron is a stable combination of a proton and a neutron, since it has a mass of two atomic mass units and a single positive unit of charge. There must therefore be the possibility of an attractive force between a proton and a neutron. Hence we see that there must be effects corresponding to *both* repulsive and attractive nuclear forces according to the circumstances. This is not as strange as it may seem, since the same situation may arise for atoms (Section 4.5ii); it is a good indication that nuclei are not just simple hard spheres.

The situation for nuclei is entirely dominated by quantum-mechanical effects and so we have to be very careful about what we mean by the diameter of a nucleus and the energy of interaction of two nuclei. Nevertheless, we can say that the diameter is of order 10^{-13} cm and the potential energy of interaction is of order the energy for formation of a nucleus. For a deuterium nucleus, this energy is known to be about 10 Mev or 10^{-5} erg and this sets the order of magnitude of the interaction potential between nuclei as given in Table 1.1. In the classical sense, there is no repulsive force at all! The nuclear potential has a minimum for zero separation of the particles. However, as discussed above, there are also repulsive states in which the potential of interaction of the two particles effectively has a maximum for zero distance between the particles. The situation is very different from the more familiar one for atoms discussed in Chapter 4.

From the scattering of fast neutrons or very fast electrons by nuclei, we can get an estimate of the nuclear diameter d_n. It is more usual to discuss nuclear radii but we shall use diameters so as to be more consistent with the treatment of atoms. It is found that $d_n \approx 2r_{n0}A^{1/3}$ where $r_{n0} = 1.3 \times 10^{-13}$ cm and A is the atomic weight of the nucleus. Notice that this means that the linear dimensions of nuclei, like atoms, do not vary very much; e.g. for ^{238}U, $d_n \approx 16 \times 10^{-13}$ cm, which is only about six times greater than that of a single neutron or proton. The formula for d_n means further that the nucleons in a nucleus are of much the same size as they are when free and so probably retain their identity in much the same way as do the molecules in a liquid. The nuclear forces are of short range and so it is a good approximation to consider the nucleons interacting in pairs. Hence we can get an idea of how nuclei are built up using pairwise forces. Excited states of nuclei correspond to oscillations in the potential well or the whole nucleus rotating like a spinning ball.

For even more energetic collisions we may get particles coming out which certainly were not there in the first place. For example, π mesons may be produced if there is sufficient energy, but to look at this sensibly we must first discuss relativity (Chapter 8). Also in β radioactive emission electrons come out of the nucleus which could not have been in there in the first place (for quantum-mechanical reasons; see Problem 4.21).

3.4 THE DIAMETER OF THE ELECTRON

The electron is a most important particle, so what about its size? This is a question that is difficult to answer. In atomic systems, it is even pretty difficult to say where an electron is. If we do not know where it is, how can we measure its size?

By shooting electrons at each other or at nuclei and studying the way in which the electrons and the nuclei are scattered by each other, it is clear that electrons act as massive point charges at least down to distances of order 10^{-13} cm, since the scattering can be accurately described as resulting only from Coulomb electrostatic interactions between the particles. Hence it is probably sufficient to say for the moment that electrons act like quite small bodies, comparable in size with nuclei. There is a sense in which the "radius" of the electron is of order $e^2/m_e c^2 = 2.8 \times 10^{-13}$ cm. A radius of this order of magnitude is indicated if the mass of the electron is due to its electrostatic self-energy (see Problem 3.6 and Chapter 8). This radius is also correct for the scattering of electromagnetic radiation by electrons (Section 8.7). On the other hand, in connexion with the production and annihilation of electrons, there is a sense in which the electron radius is $\hbar/m_e c$ (see Section 14.3). This is $\hbar c/e^2 \approx 137$ (i.e. the fine structure constant) times the "classical" radius. This again dramitically illustrates that the size of an object depends on how it is measured.

PROBLEMS

3.1. In Section 3.1, it is assumed that in the argon crystal the atoms are arranged on a simple cubic lattice. Find the revised value of d_0 for the actual structure of solid argon, which is face centred cubic.

3.2. The following ionic crystals all have the same structure as NaCl with the lattice constant given in brackets in ångströms. NaF(4.62), NaCl(5.63), NaBr(5.96), and NaI(6.46). Show that these values are consistent with the ionic diameters given in Table 3.1.

3.3. The density of liquid oxygen is 1.14 g cm^{-3}. The van der Waals "b" for oxygen gas is 31.6 cm^3. Show that these two results are roughly consistent.

3.4. Show that the density of the "nuclear fluid" is about 10^{15} times that of water.

3.5. Increasingly large nuclei contain an increasingly large proportion of neutrons; for example $^{16}_{8}O$ has 8p + 8n, $^{56}_{26}Fe$ has 26p + 30n and $^{238}_{92}U$ has 92p + 146n. Explain this by a consideration of the forces between the particles.

3.6. Assume that the electron is a uniformly charged spherical particle of total charge e and radius a. Evaluate the electrostatic self-energy of the particle either (a) by using the fact that the field energy is $E^2/8\pi$ erg per unit volume (for E in e.s.u.)—remember there is also a field inside the sphere—or (b) by finding the energy to "build up" an electron from infinitesimal charges brought from infinity. Assume this electrostatic energy is the energy which gives the electron its rest mass $(m_e c^2)$ and hence show that the "classical radius" of the electron is $\frac{3}{5}(e^2/m_e c^2)$ and that this is of order of magnitude 10^{-13} cm.

3.7. At the critical point, $(dP/dV)_T = 0$ and $(d^2 P/dV^2)_T = 0$. Show that, for the van der Waals equation $(P + a/V^2)(V - b) = RT$, the molar volume at the critical point is given by $V_c = 3b$.

3.8. There are three possible forms for a cubic crystal composed of atoms, simple cubic (s.c.), body centred cubic (b.c.c.), and face centred cubic (f.c.c.). By considering only forces between nearest neighbours, verify the following table.

Structure	Unstable to shear?	Unstable to uniaxial compression?
s.c.	Yes	No
b.c.c.	No	Yes
f.c.c.	No	No

(HINT: The crystal, for this purpose, is a set of sticks joining the atomic positions with universal joints at the atomic nuclei.)

3.9. Estimate the diameter of a water molecule from the information that the viscosity of water at 20°C is about 0.01 P (N.B. cgs units) and that the dielectric relaxation time at this temperature is about 10^{-11} s (see Section 3.2).

CHAPTER 4

Forces between atoms and molecules

Instead of saying that the particles are hard, spherical and elastic, we
may if we please say that the particles are centres of force.   J. C. MAXWELL

What exactly do we mean by the "size" of an atom? We have talked rather glibly
of the diameter of an atom in Chapter 3 but this quantity is actually rather
indefinite—it depends how you measure it! Atoms are not just hard spheres with
definite boundaries, although this is quite often a good first approximation in
suitable circumstances and the approximation was used profitably in Chapter 3.
If we look more closely, we find that the situation is more complex. Suppose we
have two atoms approaching each other in head-on collision. If the atoms are
similar, we might define the diameter of each atom as the distance of closest
approach. However, if the atoms are not hard elastic spheres, this distance will
vary with the velocity of approach of the two atoms. The faster they approach
the closer they get and so, on our definition, the smaller they are. Again the atom
being investigated may behave quite differently with respect to different second
atoms and so the size is not even a property of one atom. We must be very explicit
in talking about atomic or molecular size and say exactly how we propose to
measure the size, since the size can depend enormously on how we measure it. If we
use another atom to measure the size of a given atom, the size is likely to turn out to
be some few times 10^{-8} cm but if we use a neutron to measure the size of the same
atom the size is likely to turn out to be some few times 10^{-13} cm.

4.1 THE INTERACTION ENERGY

The forces between atoms or between molecules must be attractive at large
distances for otherwise atoms would not come close together to form liquids
and solids. The forces must be repulsive at small distances otherwise substances
would collapse. Thus the variation of force with distance is expected from these
elementary observations to have the form shown in Fig. 4.1(a). It is usually more
useful to discuss the interaction energy involved rather than the forces and this is
given in Fig. 4.1(b). It will be seen in Chapter 5 that the potential energy and the
force are related by

$$\text{Force} = -d(\text{potential energy})/d(\text{distance}).$$

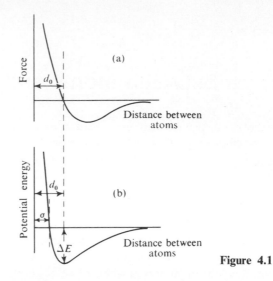

Figure 4.1

Thus the value of the force at any point is given by the negative of the slope (or derivative) of the potential energy curve at that point and conversely the potential energy curve is just the negative of the integral of the force curve. It is convenient, but not essential, to take the potential energy as zero when the atoms are very far apart, when the force between them is zero. The separation d_0 for zero force, or minimum of potential energy, is the separation for static equilibrium of an isolated pair of atoms or molecules. This distance is usually a good measure of the separation of atoms or molecules even when there are more than two particles interacting at once, as in a solid. It can be loosely regarded as the diameter of an atom or molecule and it is for this reason we use the same symbol d_0 as in Chapter 3. The separation σ (see Fig. 4.1b), when the potential energy is zero, is often used as a characteristic distance. It is the distance of closest approach of two atoms which start from rest at a large distance.

The magnitude of ΔE determines to a considerable extent the form of the macroscopic substance which the molecules or atoms produce at a given temperature. Note that this ΔE is for a *pair* of isolated atoms or molecules. It is about $2 \times \frac{1}{12}$ of the energy quoted in Table 1.1 which was obtained from the sublimation energy per atom or molecule of the corresponding liquid or solid assuming about twelve nearest neighbours. The amount of energy available due to thermal agitation at temperature T is about kT per particle. This is closely related to the result already used in Chapter 2 for a liquid, that $\frac{1}{2}mv_x^2 = \frac{1}{2}kT$. We note again the great importance of k, Boltzmann's constant, in any considerations involving a system having a temperature. Now if we have a gas at temperature T, the molecules are not stuck together—we saw they are on average at least 10 diameters apart. Hence they must be attracted together by forces which correspond to an energy much less than kT. Hence we have $kT > \Delta E$ for a substance which is a gas at temperature T. For $300°\text{K}$ (room temperature), $kT = 1.38 \times 10^{-16} \times 300$

Table 4.1

	Neon	Argon	Krypton	Xenon	Radon
$\Delta E/k$, deg	36	120	160	240	280
T_m, °K	25	84	116	161	202
$(\Delta E/k)/T_m$	1.44	1.43	1.38	1.49	1.39

erg = 4×10^{-14} erg (or 2.6×10^{-2} ev). Hence for say argon, which is a gas at room temperature, we expect that the forces between two argon atoms is such that $\Delta E < 4 \times 10^{-14}$ erg. The actual value of ΔE for argon (Table 4.1) is about 2×10^{-14} erg, so this is true.

Nevertheless, all the atoms tend to get together with the distance between them at about d_0 if they can. As we lower the temperature, kT gets smaller and eventually kT becomes comparable with ΔE and we get a solid or liquid. We would expect the solid to start breaking up when the atoms can no longer be held in fixed positions and so we get melting when $kT \approx f\Delta E$, where f is the fraction of "bonds broken" to form a liquid from a solid, say $f \sim \frac{1}{2}$, and so this is the condition for melting. As we see below, the molecules in a liquid are not very far apart and so clearly rather less energy change than ΔE is involved. Nevertheless, relative values of ΔE are significant. If ΔE is small, as in argon, then the melting temperature is low. In fact, it is 84°K for argon. If ΔE is larger (see Table 1.1), we need a higher temperature to melt the solid, for example ice melts at 273°K, and this is no doubt associated with the strong hydrogen bonds (Section 4.5) formed between the water molecules in the ice. It is usually quite difficult in general to get an accurate value of ΔE from the phenomenon of melting. Perhaps the best estimate of ΔE is obtained from the energy of sublimation. However, for similar substances, the value of ΔE can be a good guide to the melting temperature and vice versa, particularly if the solid is an atomic one of simple structure. This is so for instance for the solid rare gases. For this series of atoms, the values of ΔE are well known and are given in Table 4.1 in units of temperature, i.e. the value of $\Delta E/k$, and are compared with the melting temperature T_m (strictly the triple point temperature which is the temperature at which solid, liquid, and vapour coexist). The constancy of the ratio $(\Delta E/k)/T_m$ shows that there is a simple relation between ΔE and T_m for this series of similar substances.

We can estimate ΔE for an ionic crystal, since we think we know the forces of attraction involved—they are electrostatic. ΔE roughly corresponds to the energy released in bringing these charges from infinity to d_0, the equilibrium distance in the crystal. Of course, the equilibrium distance itself is determined by the balance of attractive and repulsive forces. However, the repulsive forces are expected to increase very rapidly with decreasing distance and consequently make the minor contribution to ΔE (see Problem 4.14). The electrostatic energy is therefore quite a good measure of the value of ΔE for the atoms. The force F between the ions when at a distance r is e^2/r^2. If e is in e.s.u. of charge and r in cm, F is in dynes. In all our "atomic" calculations, we shall use electrostatic cgs units. In rationalized MKSA units, the force (in newtons) between two charges q_1 and q_2 (in coulombs) at a distance r metres *in vacuo* is $q_1 q_2 /(4\pi\varepsilon_0 r^2)$, where ε_0 is $1/(36\pi \times 10^9)$ farad m^{-1}. In cgs e.s.u., $\varepsilon_0 = 1/(4\pi)$. The energy ΔE which is gained on bringing the charges from a very large separation to the separation d_0 is

$$\int_{d_0}^{\infty} F \, dr = e^2 \int_{d_0}^{\infty} \frac{dr}{r^2} = \frac{e^2}{d_0} = \frac{(4.8 \times 10^{-10})^2}{2.81 \times 10^{-8}} = 8.2 \times 10^{-12} \text{ erg} \quad \text{(or 5.1 ev)}$$

if $d_0 = 2.81$ Å, the value for a sodium chloride crystal. This is a rough estimate of the sublimation energy of an ionic crystal and is correct in order of magnitude. We can see that this is a relatively large energy and that ionic crystals are held together by strong forces by calculating the temperature if this were a thermal energy. If $\Delta E \approx k T_{\text{sub}}$, where T_{sub} is a temperature such that the thermal energy is comparable with the sublimation energy,

$$T_{\text{sub}} = \frac{\Delta E}{k} = \frac{8.2 \times 10^{-12}}{1.38 \times 10^{-16}} = 60,000°\text{K}.$$

A more exact calculation for a sodium chloride crystal actually gives a higher electrostatic energy than the 5.1 ev calculated above. For the process in which the salt crystal is broken up into widely separated ions, which we write as "crystalline NaCl" $\rightarrow$ Na$^+$ + Cl$^-$, the electrostatic energy per ion pair is calculated to be 8.94 ev. The experimental value is 7.92 ev, so that the salt crystal can indeed be regarded as an array of ions in the appropriate structure. It is more usual to consider sublimation to atoms and this takes less energy since Na$^+$ + Cl$^-$ $\rightarrow$ Na + Cl + 1.40 ev. Therefore the energy of sublimation to atoms is 7.92 − 1.40 = 6.52 ev, still a large value. This is basically why crystals of salt are so much "tougher" than crystals of argon. Actually, salt *melts* at 1077°K which is a much lower temperature than 60,000°K. This is because on melting the ions are still quite close together so that the increase in energy on melting is much less than required to separate the ions entirely from each other (at first approximation molten salts consist of ions rather than atoms—they have a high electrical conductivity, for instance). If we suppose that on melting the ions increase their distance apart from d_0 to $d_0 + \Delta d$, then the energy required is

$$\int_{d_0}^{d_0 + \Delta d} F \, dr \qquad \text{rather than} \qquad \int_{d_0}^{\infty} F \, dr.$$

Since Δd is expected to be small compared with d_0, we have

$$\int_{d_0}^{d_0 + \Delta d} F \, dr \approx F(d_0) \, \Delta d = \frac{e^2}{d_0^2} \, \Delta d.$$

This is approximately $k T_{\text{m}}$. But we had $k T_{\text{sub}} \approx e^2/d_0$; therefore $T_{\text{m}} \approx (\Delta d/d_0) T_{\text{sub}}$. From the calculated value of T_{sub} and the measured value of T_{m}, we have

$\Delta d/d_0 \approx 1000/60{,}000 = 1/60$. Hence, in the molten salt, the ions are still quite close together.

ΔE can be estimated from surface tension or surface energy S, *if* we know the molecular diameter. To create a surface, we have to pull a layer of atoms apart (Fig. 4.2). The number of atoms per unit area is $1/d_0^2$. Therefore, the energy of a surface per unit area is $\Delta E(1/d_0^2)$, that is $S = \Delta E/d_0^2$ or $\Delta E = Sd_0^2$. Measurements of the surface tension, or surface energy S, of liquids show that its order of magnitude is 50 erg cm^{-2}. If $d_0 \sim 3\text{Å} = 3 \times 10^{-8}$ cm, we find using $\Delta E = Sd_0^2$ that $\Delta E \sim 50 \times 9 \times 10^{-16}$ erg $\sim 5 \times 10^{-14}$ erg and this is about what we found before. Actually, we should have used the surface energy of a solid rather than a liquid. However, the surface energy of a solid is not much different from that of a liquid and is much more difficult to measure. The surface energy of a solid tends to be higher than that of a liquid because the molecules in the solid are more closely packed and so more work must be done to separate the atoms so as to form a surface. In addition, the molecules in the liquid are more mobile and so can move more readily to accommodate themselves to the changes required to form a surface with smaller changes in energy. The surface energies of metals are in the range 1000 to 2000 erg cm^{-2}, of ionic crystals in the range 200 to 1000 erg cm^{-2}, and of molecular or atomic crystals in the range 50 to 200 erg cm^{-2}.

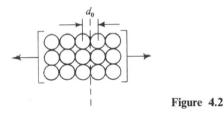

Figure 4.2

The more familiar experiments on the surface tension of liquids are more complicated. For instance, the capillarity effect which is a direct result of surface tension depends on *differences* in energy of interaction of like and unlike atoms. If the liquid climbs up the wall, as for water in glass, it may be regarded as evidence that the water molecules have a lower energy near the molecules of the glass than near each other. If the liquid is depressed, as for mercury in glass, the opposite is true. In either case, the system tends to the lower energy state and so the surface of the liquid and the height of the liquid in the tube take the well known forms. It is, however, rather difficult to get any numerical results about intermolecular forces from such experiments.

4.2 THE INTERACTION POTENTIAL IN SOLIDS

We see then that we can get an estimate of the two parameters ΔE and d_0 but what about the rest of the potential energy curve? We can get some idea of this from other effects, some of which depend on temperature. The atoms are in equilibrium at d_0 only if they are isolated and have been able to give up the energy ΔE on being brought together. If the pair of atoms are in a system at temperature T they will have an average energy of order kT and so the pair of atoms cannot be regarded as being stationary at the distance d_0. If the atoms are not at d_0, then their behaviour depends to some extent on their interaction at other distances and so information about $E(x)$ other than ΔE and d_0 should be obtainable.

Look at the potential energy curve more closely. Consider the value of $E(x)$, when x is not very different from d_0, which is given by the Taylor series

$$E(x) = E(d_0) + (x - d_0)\left(\frac{dE}{dx}\right)_{d_0} + \frac{1}{2!}(x - d_0)^2\left(\frac{d^2E}{dx^2}\right)_{d_0} + \cdots.$$

Clearly $E(d_0) \equiv -\Delta E$. As d_0 corresponds to a minimum in the value of $E(x)$ and the force is zero for that separation, we have

$$\frac{dE}{dx} = 0 \text{ at } x = d_0, \quad \text{that is} \quad \left(\frac{dE}{dx}\right)_{d_0} = 0,$$

$$\therefore \quad E(x) + \Delta E = (x - d_0)^2\frac{1}{2}\left(\frac{d^2E}{dx^2}\right)_{d_0} + (x - d_0)^3\frac{1}{6}\left(\frac{d^3E}{dx^3}\right)_{d_0} + \cdots.$$

The first term on the right has a harmonic oscillator form and is expected to be the most important one for values of x not too different from d_0. This term is sometimes called the parabolic term, since the curve of $E(x)$ versus x is a parabola if it is the only important one. For a harmonic oscillator, the force is proportional to the displacement $(x - d_0)$ and therefore equals $\kappa(x - d_0)$ say, as for a spring. This is the expression of Hooke's law of elasticity and κ is called the force constant. Therefore, using Newton's second law of motion (Section 5.2), we have

$$m\ddot{x} = -\kappa(x - d_0)$$

or

$$m(\overbrace{x - d_0}^{\cdots}) = -\kappa(x - d_0)$$

or

$$m\ddot{y} = -\kappa y \quad \text{where} \quad y = x - d_0.$$

The solution to this equation is

$$y = A\cos\sqrt{\frac{\kappa}{m}}t + B\sin\sqrt{\frac{\kappa}{m}}t$$

where A and B are constants, as can be verified by differentiation and substitution. The angular frequency of vibration is $\omega_{\text{vib}} = \sqrt{\kappa/m}$ or the frequency of vibration in HZ* is

$$\nu_{\text{vib}} = \frac{1}{2\pi}\sqrt{\frac{\kappa}{m}}.$$

---

* HZ stands for hertz and is the name of the unit of frequency which has recently replaced cycles per second.

The potential energy is

$$\int_0^y -F \, dy' = \int_0^y \kappa y' \, dy' = \tfrac{1}{2}\kappa y^2 = \tfrac{1}{2}\kappa(x - d_0)^2$$

since the force $F = -\kappa y$. Hence, comparing this last relation with the equation for $E(x) + \Delta E$, we see that the first term in the expansion is of the same form. Equating the two coefficients of $(x - d_0)^2$ we see that

$$\kappa = \left(\frac{d^2 E}{dx^2}\right)_{d_0},$$

and this is the force constant for the vibration of atoms with the interaction $E(x)$. Hence, if we know ν_{vib} and m, we can calculate $(d^2 E/dx^2)_{d_0}$. In fact,

$$\left(\frac{d^2 E}{dx^2}\right)_{d_0} = (2\pi\nu_{vib})^2 \left(\frac{m}{2}\right)^*.$$

We can obtain ν_{vib} experimentally from spectroscopic measurements. In order of magnitude, ν_{vib} is between 10^{12} Hz and 10^{13} Hz for a substance such as argon. The mass of the argon atom, $m = 40 m_p \approx 7 \times 10^{-23}$ g (m_p is the proton mass). Hence

$$\left(\frac{d^2 E}{dx^2}\right)_{d_0} \sim (2\pi \times 2 \times 10^{12})^2 \times \tfrac{7}{2} \times 10^{-23} \sim 6000 \text{ erg cm}^{-2}$$

$$= 6 \times 10^{-13} \text{ erg Å}^{-2},$$

since 1 Å $= 10^{-8}$ cm. We see from this that, if x changes from the equilibrium value of about 4 Å by 0.1 Å, the energy $E(x)$ changes by

$$\tfrac{1}{2}(x - d_0)^2 \left(\frac{d^2 E}{dx^2}\right)_{d_0} = \tfrac{1}{2}(0.1)^2 6 \times 10^{-13} \text{ erg} \approx 0.3 \times 10^{-14} \text{ erg}.$$

For argon, ΔE is $\sim 2 \times 10^{-14}$ erg; hence we could easily have a vibration of amplitude 0.1 Å and in fact such amplitudes of vibration are actually found in solid argon. Strictly speaking, we have to deal with a large number of atoms all vibrating and interacting with each other and this is a very difficult "many-body problem" (Chapter 15). We ought really to consider the vibration of all the some 10^{23} atoms in the piece of crystal. Nevertheless, it turns out that there is a sense in which most of the vibration of a whole crystal is very similar to the vibration of an isolated pair of atoms which we have discussed.

We can also get a crude estimate of the force constant κ by measuring the axial modulus of elasticity M. For the axial modulus, the transverse dimensions are fixed and the solid allowed to change its length in only one axis, so that actually some other forces besides the tensile forces F are needed. This is how M differs from the more familiar Young's modulus where the sample is left free to contract

---

* We must use the effective or reduced mass, which is $m/2$ for the example to be discussed (see Section 5.3).

laterally as it is stretched in one axis. Thus

$$M = \frac{\text{Axial stress}}{\text{Axial strain}}$$

for constant lateral dimensions. This modulus can be seen to depend on κ, since to measure M we just pull the atoms slightly apart. Assume that we have a simple cubic crystal and that the atomic separation is initially d_0. From the definition of the axial modulus of elasticity,

$$M = \frac{F/A}{\delta l/l} \ .$$

We need only look at a line of atoms in Fig. 4.3 in this simple case. Then $A = d_0^2$ and if $\delta l/l = \delta x/d_0$, F is just the force to increase the distance between two atoms by δx, that is $F = \kappa \, \delta x$.

$$\therefore \quad M = \kappa \, \frac{\delta x/d_0^2}{\delta x/d_0}, \qquad \text{that is } \kappa = M d_0.$$

The tables of measured values of M show that for many substances M is of order of 10^{11} dyn cm^{-2} and we know that d_0 is about 4×10^{-8} cm. We therefore have

$$\kappa \text{ or } \left(\frac{\mathrm{d}^2 E}{\mathrm{d}x^2}\right)_{d_0} \approx 4000 \text{ dyn cm}^{-1} \text{ (or erg cm}^{-2}),$$

as before. The agreement between this value of $(\mathrm{d}^2 E/\mathrm{d}x^2)_{d_0}$ and the one obtained from the vibration frequency is too good for such crude calculations. However, they should agree in order of magnitude. Alternatively, we could use this deduced value of κ to get $\nu_{\text{vib}} \sim 10^{12}$ Hz.

A more refined analysis shows that we can get some information about the repulsive forces from the bulk compressibility as might well be expected since we then force the atoms up the repulsive part of $E(x)$, but this is too difficult to deal with here. The value of $(\mathrm{d}^2 E/\mathrm{d}x^2)_{d_0}$ is usually more characteristic of the repulsive forces rather than the attractive forces, since the former usually vary more rapidly with distance at the equilibrium separation (see Problem 4.15).

It must be emphasized at this point that it is difficult to deduce any really reliable values of particle properties from bulk properties such as the elastic moduli. The materials which are usually measured are not single crystals and, even if they were, such crystals may be very imperfect. They contain impurities and imperfections which may either decrease or increase the strength of the crystal.

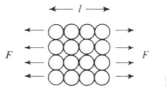

Figure 4.3

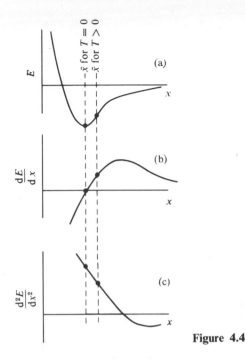

Figure 4.4

Generally speaking, the moduli of elasticity of solids are a good rough guide to intermolecular forces but only if due account is taken of the enormous variety of the internal constitution of materials. It would be quite misleading, for instance, to make simple deductions from a comparison of the moduli of a metal and a polymer.

The elastic properties involved here are for small deformations. In actually using materials, the behaviour for large deformations is usually important and that is a very different matter.

So far we have not taken much note of temperature. We know that materials expand on heating. What can we deduce from the observed temperature coefficient of the elastic modulus or from the coefficient of linear expansion? Clearly, at higher temperature, the molecules are on average further apart. Moreover, as the temperature increases the interacting atoms have increasing mean energy. Because of the asymmetry of the interaction energy curve, the mean separation increases, as discussed in more detail below. In first approximation, the relevant value of d^2E/dx^2 is expected to be that at the mean position at the given temperature. For our general interaction energy curve we see from Fig. 4.4 that d^2E/dx^2, and hence the force constant of the vibration κ, decreases with increasing x for values of x near d_0. The mean value of x increases with increasing temperature, as shown below in our discussion of the coefficient of thermal expansion; therefore κ decreases with increasing temperature. Hence ν_{vib} decreases and the axial modulus M decreases with increasing temperature. This is in agreement with experiment,

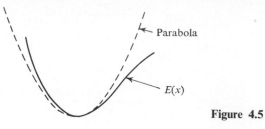

Figure 4.5

since moduli of elasticity are observed to decrease with increasing temperature. The temperature coefficient is about -10^{-4} deg^{-1}. We could get some idea of the variation of d^2E/dx^2 with x from this result.

Now let us look more closely at the coefficient of thermal expansion. As the temperature rises, the vibration *amplitude* increases because there is more thermal energy. However, if the vibration is simple harmonic, this does not increase the *mean* separation of the atoms or molecules. If $(x - d_0) = a \cos \omega t$, then $\overline{(x - d_0)} = \overline{a \cos \omega t} = 0$. This is only true if the energy is determined by the parabolic $(x - d_0)^2$ term in the expansion of $E(x)$ about the separation d_0 and this is only true for vanishingly small amplitudes of oscillation. We therefore have to investigate the effect of the next term in the expansion for $E(x)$ which is

$$(x - d_0)^3 \frac{1}{6}\left(\frac{d^3E}{dx^3}\right)_{d_0}.$$

The actual curve for $E(x)$ (Fig. 4.5) is lower than the parabolic curve for positive values of $(x - d_0)$ and higher than the parabolic curve for negative values of $(x - d_0)$. Therefore $(d^3E/dx^3)_{d_0}$ must be negative, as can also be seen by direct differentiation of the $E(x)$ curve (see Problem 4.4) or from the fact that the slope of d^2E/dx^2 in Fig. 4.4(c) is negative in the region of $x = d_0$. Since the energy is lower to the right of d_0 than for the same distance to the left, the atom will on average be to the right of d_0 and this effect will be greater the greater the amplitude of vibration, i.e. the higher the temperature. Thus we expect the coefficient of thermal expansion of solids to be positive. It will be low at low temperatures and will increase with increasing temperature. This is observed to be so although it tends to be constant at high temperatures.

We can make a rough estimate of the effect as follows. The vibration in the potential well is such that the atoms spend more time at the ends than in the middle as shown in Fig. 4.6 (see Problem 4.6). Hence, in calculating the mean position, the ends are very important. A first approximation to the mean position is $d_T = (d_l + d_r)/2$ where d_l and d_r are the extreme positions to left and right, respectively. Now

$$E(x) - E(d_0) = (x - d_0)^2 \frac{1}{2}\left(\frac{d^2E}{dx^2}\right)_{d_0} + (x - d_0)^3 \frac{1}{6}\left(\frac{d^3E}{dx^3}\right)_{d_0} + \cdots$$

$$\equiv (x - d_0)^2 A^2 + (x - d_0)^3 B + \cdots,$$

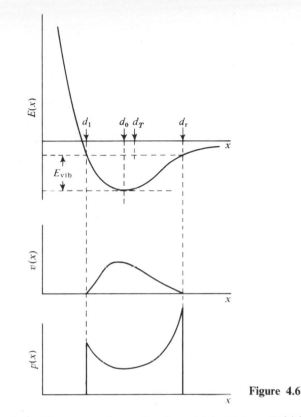

Figure 4.6

thus defining A and B. The two values of x for which $E(x) - E(d_0)$ is equal to E_{vib} are d_1 and d_r. We know that the second term is a small correction term if $(x - d_0)$ is not too large. A first approximation for d_1 and d_r is obtained by neglecting the correction term and so is given by the solutions of

$$E_{\text{vib}} = (x - d_0)^2 A^2, \qquad \text{that is} \qquad (x - d_0) = \pm E_{\text{vib}}^{1/2}/A.$$

Inserting this approximate solution in the correction term in the original equation, we get

that is

$$E_{\text{vib}} \approx (x - d_0)^2 A^2 \pm E_{\text{vib}}^{3/2} B A^{-3},$$
$$(x - d_0)^2 A^2 = E_{\text{vib}} \mp E_{\text{vib}}^{3/2} B A^{-3},$$

so that

$$(x - d_0) = \pm(E_{\text{vib}}^{1/2}/A)[1 \mp E_{\text{vib}}^{1/2} B A^{-3}]^{1/2} \approx \pm(E_{\text{vib}}^{1/2}/A)[1 \mp \tfrac{1}{2} E_{\text{vib}}^{1/2} B A^{-3}].$$

These two values of x are d_1 and d_r (see Fig. 4.6), so that

$$d_r + d_1 - 2d_0 = -(E_{\text{vib}}^{1/2}/A) E_{\text{vib}}^{1/2} B A^{-3} = -E_{\text{vib}} B A^{-4}.$$

But

$$d_T - d_0 = \tfrac{1}{2}(d_r + d_1 - 2d_0),$$

so that

$$d_T - d_0 = -\tfrac{1}{2}E_{\text{vib}}BA^{-4} = -\tfrac{1}{3}kT\left[\left(\frac{\mathrm{d}^3E}{\mathrm{d}x^3}\right)_{d_0}\right]\bigg/\left[\left(\frac{\mathrm{d}^2E}{\mathrm{d}x^2}\right)_{d_0}\right]^2.$$

In the last line, apart from inserting the explicit expressions for A and B, we have used the result that the total energy E_{vib} of a harmonic vibrator at temperature is kT, a result which we have already used in Section 2.3 and which is discussed in Section 11.4.

Alternatively, we may consider the force $F \equiv -\mathrm{d}E/\mathrm{d}x$, so that we have by differentiation of the equation for $E(x)$,

$$F = -2A^2(x - d_0) - 3B(x - d_0)^2.$$

Take mean values over the vibrational motion. We have $\bar{F} = 0$, since the particles have no resultant translational acceleration so there must be zero mean force acting on them. $\overline{(x - d_0)}$ is the mean position sought. We have that $\overline{(x - d_0)^2} = \tfrac{1}{2}kTA^{-2}$, since the mean *potential* energy of an harmonic vibrator at temperature T is $\tfrac{1}{2}kT$. Hence, substituting in the equation for F above, we have $\overline{(x - d_0)} = -\tfrac{3}{4}BA^{-4}kT$ whereas we found in the first method that $(d_T - d_0) = -\tfrac{1}{2}BA^{-4}kT$. The two results are of the same order of magnitude.

We are now in a position to calculate the coefficient of linear expansion α defined as $\alpha \equiv (1/l)(\delta l/\delta T)$ where δl is the change in an arbitrary length l of the sample for a temperature change δT. Since l is arbitrary, we can choose it to be d_T at temperature T; that is

$$\alpha = \frac{1}{d_T}\frac{\delta(d_T)}{\delta T} = -\left(\frac{k}{3d_0}\right)\left[\left(\frac{\mathrm{d}^3E}{\mathrm{d}x^3}\right)_{d_0}\right]\bigg/\left[\left(\frac{\mathrm{d}^2E}{\mathrm{d}x^2}\right)_{d_0}\right]^2,$$

where we have used the value of d_T given above. Hence the coefficient of thermal expansion α is predicted to be independent of temperature. Experimentally, α increases with temperature but rather slowly, especially at higher temperatures. Actually this is the "classical" result and so is expected to be in better agreement with experiment at higher temperature (see Section 11.4).

We can rearrange the expression for α to give

$$-\left(\frac{\mathrm{d}^3E}{\mathrm{d}x^3}\right)_{d_0} = \frac{3\alpha d_0}{k}\left[\left(\frac{\mathrm{d}^2E}{\mathrm{d}x^2}\right)_{d_0}\right]^2.$$

But we have

$$k = 1.4 \times 10^{-16}\ \text{erg deg}^{-1}, \qquad \left(\frac{\mathrm{d}^2E}{\mathrm{d}x^2}\right)_{d_0} \sim 4 \times 10^3\ \text{erg cm}^{-2},$$

$d_0 \sim 4 \times 10^{-8}$ cm and directly from experiment, $\alpha \sim 10^{-5}\ \text{deg}^{-1}$.

$$\therefore \quad -\left(\frac{\mathrm{d}^3E}{\mathrm{d}x^3}\right)_{d_0} \approx \frac{3 \times 10^{-5} \times 4 \times 10^{-8} \times (4 \times 10^3)^2}{1.4 \times 10^{-16}} = 1.4 \times 10^{11}\ \text{erg cm}^{-3}$$

$$= 1.4 \times 10^{-13}\ \text{erg Å}^{-3}.$$

Table 4.2

x, Å	$E(x)$ in units of 2×10^{-14} erg
3.9	$-1 + 0.1 + 0.001 - \cdots$
4	$-1 + 0 + 0$
4.1	$-1 + 0.1 - 0.001 - \cdots$
4.2	$-1 + 0.4 - 0.018 - \cdots$
4.3	$-1 + 0.9 - 0.03$

Hence to summarize a number of the preceding results, we have, for atoms like argon, that

$$\Delta E \sim 2 \times 10^{-14} \text{ erg}, \qquad d_0 \sim 4 \times 10^{-8} \text{ cm},$$

$$\left(\frac{d^2 E}{dx^2}\right)_{d_0} \sim 4 \times 10^3 \text{ erg cm}^{-2}, \quad \text{and} \quad \left(\frac{d^3 E}{dx^3}\right)_{d_0} \sim -1.4 \times 10^{11} \text{ erg cm}^{-3}.$$

(It must be emphasized here that all these results can only be expected to be correct in order of magnitude.) Hence, for atoms like argon, we have

$$E(x) \approx -2 \times 10^{-14} + (x - 4)^2 20 \times 10^{-14} - (x - 4)^3 2 \times 10^{-14} + \cdots$$

$$= 2 \times 10^{-14}[-1 + 10(x - 4)^2 - (x - 4)^3 - \cdots] \text{ erg},$$

where x is in ångströms. These terms are evaluated for x near d_0 in Table 4.2.

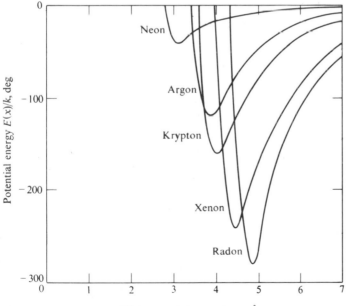

Figure 4.7. The interaction potential $E(x)/k$ in degrees for the rare gas atoms as deduced from experiment. N.B. The positive energy points of the curve have been omitted. [From G. L. POLLACK, *Scientif. Am.* **215,** 64 (1966).]

Hence the interaction energy curve is about right (see Figs. 4.1b and 4.7) but not really very accurate if x is much different from d_0. This inaccuracy is partly because of crude theories and partly because we really need higher terms in the expansion (see Problem 4.22). The interaction curve $E(x)$ is often represented by analytical formulae such as the six–twelve potential (Section 4.5 and Problem 4.13), the Morse potential (Section 4.4 and Problem 4.3), the Kihara potential (Problem 4.16), and so on. Actual curves of $E(x)$ derived from experiment for the rare gas atoms are shown in Fig. 4.7 (except for $E(x)$ positive).

We have emphasized how $E(x)$ can be obtained from simple macroscopic measurements. More precise information can be obtained from experiments on atomic beams (the principles of such experiments are discussed in Chapter 7) and from precise experiments on gases (as for Fig. 4.7).

It should be emphasized again that many of the macroscopic properties we have used will often depend on the detailed structure. Many materials are poly-crystalline, have microscopic flaws, impurities, etc., and even macroscopic flaws. In these cases, deduction of the nature and magnitude of the atomic forces may be considerably in error. We have nevertheless illustrated that we can get quite a good idea of the forces between atoms from simple macroscopic measurements.

4.3 UNSTABLE ASSOCIATIONS OF ATOMS OR MOLECULES—LIQUIDS

There is really no simple explanation of the behaviour of liquids, since the motion of molecules in liquids is essentially cooperative in a more complicated sense than it is in solids. Since the expansion on melting is only a few per cent, the atoms or molecules must be still close together. The expansion of solids on melting ranges from about 15% for the rare gas solids to 1.6% for lithium. Ice is unusual: it contracts by 8% on melting. Since the latent heat of fusion is only about one-tenth of the latent heat of sublimation, we might say that only about 1 in 10 of the bonds (ΔEs) in the solid are broken on melting, so that almost all the molecules are still pretty well held together in the liquid. Many theories about the nature of liquids depend on the role of the 5% or so "free volume", which is roughly the excess volume of the liquid as compared with the crystal and *not* the free space in the liquid. Even in a crystal, there is a lot of free space if we regard the atoms as hard spheres. For the maximal density close packing of hard spheres, the space inside the crystal is only 74% occupied by atoms. The maximal density of a non-crystalline arrangement of hard spheres corresponds to 63% of the space occupied. For this model, then, the expansion on melting is 17% which is very close to the experi-mental value for the inert gases whose atoms are well approximated by hard spheres, for this purpose.

In a crystal, x rays show that the atoms are arranged in a regular array, as we have already discussed. From such x-ray diffraction patterns, we can deduce that the neighbours of a given atom are most likely to be found at certain fixed distances corresponding to the crystal structure. The pattern shown in Fig. 4.8 is for the simplest possible crystalline solid, an atomic simple cubic crystal (which is very rare*). The first peak has an intensity of six corresponding to the six nearest neighbours to a given atom in the crystal structure, the next peak corresponds to the twelve second nearest neighbours, and so on. The breadth of the peaks is meant to give a diagrammatic representation of the effect of thermal vibrations. Since the atoms are vibrating, their distances apart are not exactly a, $\sqrt{2}a$, and so on, and so the probability peaks become broadened. For a solid, the positions of the atoms (or molecules) is regular out to large distances from any given atom and the crystal is said to have long-range order. The good definition of the x-ray scattering pattern is dependent on this long-range order, since the pattern is made up from scattering from a large number of atoms. If the peaks of Fig. 4.8 were smoothed out, they would give a curve approximating to a probability proportional to d^2, especially when d is large (see Problem 4.11). The probability distribution of Fig. 4.8 is characteristic of the simple cubic lattice and for other lattices the pattern may be quite different (Problem 4.17). For molecular crystals and mixed crystals, the pattern depends in general on which atom is chosen to be at the centre.

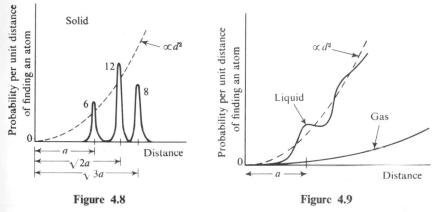

Figure 4.8   Figure 4.9

A similar x-ray experiment on a liquid gives a much less definite picture. There is still a good probability of finding an atom at a but further out the proba- bility soon becomes almost uniform and rises as d^2 as for a uniform fluid, as shown in Fig. 4.9. Thus, in a liquid, some vestige of structure remains but the situation is fundamentally different. We can no longer clearly identify particular atomic sites relative to the reference one. We can express this by saying that, in a liquid, the atoms have some short-range order but no long-range order. The short-range order persists, particularly at temperatures not far above the melting point, because the density is not much lower than in the solid so that the atoms must pack together quite closely and so tend to take up, as far as they are able, the structure in the solid. Over larger distances, the looseness of the structure, the free volume, allows an accumulated deviation from regularity corresponding to loss of long-range order. As the temperature of the liquid rises, the density falls

---

* α-Polonium metal has a simple cubic structure.

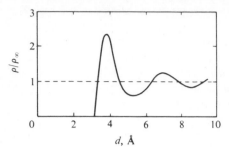

Figure 4.10. Adapted from D. G. HENSHAW, *Phys. Rev.* **105**, 976 (1957).

and the free volume increases. The x-ray pattern becomes more diffuse but in the probability pattern the nearest-neighbours peak tends to decrease in intensity rather than to move out to greater distances. It seems likely, therefore, that the nearest-neighbour atoms remain at much the same distance but the number of nearest neighbours decreases. An actual result for liquid argon at 84°K is shown in Fig. 4.10. In this figure, the effective density is plotted as a function of distance normalized to unity by using the macroscopic density (or the density for $d \to \infty$). This is the probability of Fig. 4.9 divided by d^2. The nearest-neighbour distance of about 3.9 Å for argon shows quite clearly and is one reason for using $d_0 = 3.9$ Å in some of our calculations on argon. (The actual method used to obtain the data of Fig. 4.10 was neutron diffraction, not x-ray diffraction, but the result is obtained in virtually the same way.)

It can be shown that for a low density gas at temperature T the probability distribution of Fig. 4.9 is proportional to $d^2 \exp(-E(d)/kT)$ where $E(d)$ is the interatomic potential discussed in Section 4.2. For a gas, no departure from the uniform fluid pattern is observable and of course the curve rises very much more slowly, since the density of a gas is usually so much lower than that of a liquid. For an "ideal gas", there are no forces between the molecules, $E(d) = 0$, and so there can be no structure and the probability distribution is exactly proportional to d^2 for all distances. It is said that there is no correlation between the positions of molecules in a perfect gas.

It is essential to understand that Figs. 4.9 and 4.10 represent the average environment for a given atom. We have pointed out in Section 2.3 that a molecule in a liquid suffers a "collision" roughly every 10^{-14} second. In the course of time, the actual number of nearest neighbours may vary quite widely from the mean value. In fact, it can be shown, as might be expected, that a fall in the number of nearest neighbours is accompanied by a rise in the number of second nearest neighbours and vice versa.

These results are consistent with the usual elementary explanations of the differences between solids, liquids, and gases (Fig. 4.11). It should be borne in mind that the diagrams in Fig. 4.11 represent an instantaneous picture of a rapidly varying situation. X-ray scattering data correspond to time averages of such pictures, since the time of scattering of x-ray photons is much smaller than the time for an atom to move appreciably and the exposure times are much longer. Although in the series solid, liquid, gas, the atoms tend on average to be further

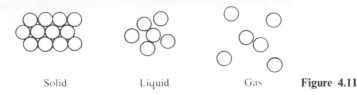

Solid   Liquid   Gas   **Figure 4.11**

apart, nevertheless they are subject, on occasion, to increasingly severe forces in the successive states solid, liquid, and gas because the "collisions" become more energetic.

With the help of computers, we can actually calculate the trajectories of a relatively small number of atoms with rather simple forces between them, say hard spheres or the 6–12 potential, and so get some idea of the difference in atomic motions as between solids, liquids, and gases by adjusting the density of the particles. One result of such calculations is shown in Fig. 4.12 where the trajectories shown are for the centres of the particles. For densities corresponding to the "solid", the atoms vibrate about one lattice site and the lattice is clearly distinguishable in Fig. 4.12(a). In the "liquid", some vestige of a lattice remains (Fig. 4.12b) and there is some short-range order but now the atoms can clearly move around but in a restricted way. In the "gas", no vestige of structure remains (Fig. 4.12c).

The viscosity of a liquid falls with increasing temperature whereas that of a gas rises. This again can be explained by the fact that, in a liquid, the molecules are close together whereas, in a gas, they are far apart.

The fact that a liquid flows is its most characteristic property and this is because, although the molecules are close together, they can move around each other relatively freely. When a molecule moves as the fluid is sheared, we should expect it to have to break several of the remaining "bonds" by which it is connected to its nearest neighbours. We can, in fact, estimate the energy involved in the flow process from the variation of the viscosity of the liquid with temperature. It is

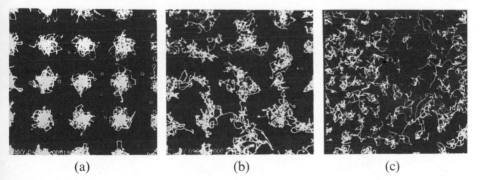

(a)   (b)   (c)

Figure 4.12. Trajectories of "hard sphere" atoms as calculated by computer and displayed on the screen of an oscilloscope. The densities of the particles and the energies were such that the three diagrams correspond to (a) a solid, (b) a liquid, and (c) a gas, respectively. [From T. WAINWRIGHT and B. J. ALDER, *Nuovo Cimento* suppl. **9,** No. 1, 116 (1958).]

found that this "activation energy" (see Problem 11.7) is about one-third of the latent heat of evaporation, for which all the bonds are broken. This is a plausible result.

In elementary treatments, the surface tension of a liquid receives considerable attention—possibly because it is relatively easy to measure, much easier than for a solid anyway. As discussed earlier (Section 4.1), the surface tension is related to intermolecular forces. In macroscopic terms, the surface tension, or rather surface energy, should be related to evaporation. In order to remove a molecule from the body of the liquid, we break all its bonds and must supply the corresponding energy, but merely to bring it to the surface breaks fewer bonds, say half as many. Consequently, the surface energy per molecule should be about half the energy of evaporation per molecule and this is found to be so.

4.4 STABLE ASSOCIATIONS OF ATOMS—MOLECULES

If we look at a molecule, we get the same sort of energy dependence on separation of the atoms as in a solid but the parameters have different values.

For a molecule to be stable at a temperature T, we must have $\Delta E \gg kT$, so that for a molecule stable at room temperature $\Delta E > 1.38 \times 10^{-16} \times 300 = 4 \times 10^{-14}$ erg or $\frac{1}{2}$ kcal mol^{-1}.

The energies of dissociation of common molecules (which are, of course, the stable ones!) are much greater than this, e.g.

Table 4.3

Dissociation	ΔE, kcal mol^{-1}
$H_2 \rightarrow H + H$	103.4
$HCl \rightarrow H + Cl$	102.7
$O_2 \rightarrow O + O$	34.9
$CH_4 \rightarrow C + 4H$	349.2

For a molecule, the energy curve is to a fair approximation given by the analytical formula

$$E(x) = \Delta E\{\exp\left[-2(x - d_m)/a\right] - 2\exp\left[-(x - d_m)/a\right]\},$$

and this is called a Morse curve. $E(x)$ has a minimal value of $-\Delta E$ at $x = d_m$ and the smaller "a" the sharper is the minimum. Note that d_m and not a is a measure of the size of a molecule.

The energy of interaction ΔE is now bigger and the separation for minimal energy d_m is somewhat smaller than for atoms which do not combine chemically. The scale of ordinates is larger but of abscissae is smaller. This means, for instance, that $(d^2E/dx^2)_{d_m}$ is bigger than for atoms which do not combine chemically. The $(d^2E/dx^2)_{d_m}$ value can be obtained from the vibration frequency of the *molecule*.

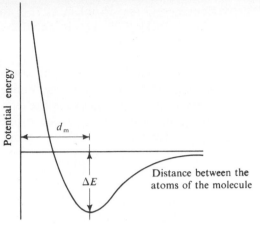

Figure 4.13

Although d^2E/dx^2 is bigger, the masses involved are similar. Therefore, because the frequency of simple harmonic vibrations of small amplitude is given by

$$v_{vib} = \frac{1}{2\pi}\sqrt{\frac{\kappa}{m}} = \frac{1}{2\pi}\sqrt{\frac{(d^2E/dx^2)}{m}},$$

the vibration frequencies are higher in molecules. They are typically 10^{14} Hz or more. This frequency, for electromagnetic waves, corresponds to a wavelength

$$\lambda = \frac{c}{v} \approx \frac{3 \times 10^{10}}{10^{14}} = 3 \times 10^{-4} \text{ cm} = 3 \text{ micron}.$$

This is in the infrared region of the spectrum. Such vibration frequencies can be measured by interaction with electromagnetic radiation if the molecules have an electric dipole moment which varies during the vibration as it does, for instance, for the hydrogen chloride molecule HCl. The interaction energy between an electric field $\mathbf{F}(t)$ and an electric dipole $\boldsymbol{\mu}$ is $-\boldsymbol{\mu} \cdot \mathbf{F}$.* For an alternating field, $F(t) = F_0 \cos \omega_r t$ (as in electromagnetic radiation) and a dipole moment with an alternating component, $\mu = \mu_0 + \mu_m \cos \omega_m t$, as for a vibrating polar molecule, the mean value of the interaction energy is $-\mu_0 F_0 \cos \omega_r t - \mu_m F_0 \cos \omega_r t \cos \omega_m t$. The average of the first term is zero and the average of the second term is zero unless $\omega_r = \omega_m$. Hence, by varying the frequency of the radiation ω_r, the vibration frequency of the molecule ω_m can be discovered. When $\omega_r \approx \omega_m$, the radiation is scattered or absorbed.

The values of $E(x)$ can only be properly explained by quantum mechanics, so we shall not go into this in detail here. We shall find however that the forces are all of the order of magnitude expected for *electrostatic* interactions.

---

* The scalar product $\mathbf{A} \cdot \mathbf{B}$ of two vectors $\mathbf{A}$ and $\mathbf{B}$ is $|\mathbf{A}| \, |\mathbf{B}| \cos \theta$, where $|\mathbf{A}|$ is the magnitude of $\mathbf{A}$ and θ is the angle between $\mathbf{A}$ and $\mathbf{B}$.

4.5 THE ORIGIN OF FORCES BETWEEN ATOMS AND MOLECULES

(i) Gravity

The gravitational forces are weak and negligible in all considerations of forces between atoms, as we now show.

The gravitational potential energy between two particles of mass m at distance d is Gm^2/d, where $G = 6.67 \times 10^{-8}$ dyn cm^2 g^{-2} (see Experiment 4). For two argon atoms at the equilibrium distance,

$$m = 40 \times 1.7 \times 10^{-24}\,\text{g} \quad \text{and} \quad d \sim 4\,\text{Å}.$$

Hence the gravitational energy is of order $6.7 \times 10^{-8} \times (40 \times 1.7 \times 10^{-24})^2/4 \times 10^{-8}$ erg $\approx 10^{-44}$ erg as compared with $\sim 10^{-14}$ erg from the observed forces between non-reacting atoms or molecules and much greater energies for atoms which form molecules (see Table 1.1). It is also clear that, although we do our experiments in the Earth's gravitational field, this has no observable effect on the properties of atoms and molecules, again because the gravitational force is so weak. We can show, for instance, that the acceleration of the electron in a hydrogen atom in its ground state is about 10^{21} times as great as the acceleration due to gravity (Problem 4.18). Gravity is a very weak force but is important in large-scale phenomena. The gravitational force between the Sun and the Earth is the most important force acting because the electrostatic forces are small, the two bodies being effectively uncharged.

(ii) The Covalent Bond

The chemical bond in a molecule is a very complicated thing and is a basic problem of chemistry. There are all sorts of bonds but we shall not go into the matter in detail.

We can easily see the reason for the chemical bond, i.e. the interatomic potential energy curve, in general. The bonded system, the molecule, has a lower energy than the separate atoms. Any mechanical system will get into its lowest energy state if it is able to do so. The atom can lose energy by radiating away electromagnetic energy because the electron in an orbit is an accelerating charge. It thus tends to lose its electrostatic potential energy. However, the electron does not fall into the nucleus. The atom has a lowest energy state in which it cannot radiate away any more energy because of the uncertainty principle and quantum mechanics and the electrons *cannot* get any nearer to the nucleus. It is not possible to enter into a discussion of quantum mechanics here but one of its simplest and most powerful results is Heisenberg's uncertainty principle (1927). This states that the product of the uncertainty in position Δx and the uncertainty in momentum Δp of a particle must always be greater than a particular value, namely $\hbar$.

$$\Delta x \times \Delta p \geq \hbar = h/2\pi,$$

where h is Planck's constant. (This relation is true for any particle.)

In the case of an electron in an atom, the uncertainty in the position of the electron is of the order of the radius of the electron's orbit and the uncertainty in its momentum is of the order of its classical momentum corresponding to its orbital velocity.

As the electron gets nearer the nucleus, Δx gets smaller and therefore Δp must get larger, since $\Delta x \, \Delta p$ has a minimal value. Since the actual momentum p must be at least as large as Δp, we see that p itself must get larger as Δx gets smaller, i.e. we expect that its kinetic energy (K.E.), $\frac{1}{2}mv^2 = p^2/2m$, increases. The total energy (K.E. + P.E.) will eventually increase in spite of the decrease in potential energy (P.E.), $-e^2/r$ (Fig. 4.14). This gives a minimum in the total energy which corresponds to the stable atom as can be seen from the following calculation.

We can assume that $p \approx \Delta p$ and $\Delta x \approx r$. Then, since $\Delta p \, \Delta x \approx h/2\pi$, we have $pr \approx h/2\pi$ or $p \approx h/(2\pi r)$ and so the kinetic energy is $p^2/2m_e = h^2/8\pi^2 m_e r^2$. Hence the total energy of the atom is given by

$$E \approx -e^2/r + (h^2/8\pi^2 m_e)(1/r^2)$$

E has a minimal (see Problem 4.19) value when $dE/dr = 0$ and this occurs for $r = h^2/(4\pi^2 m_e e^2)$. On substituting for the fundamental constants on the right, we find $r = 0.53$ Å. Since the uncertainty relation and our use of it is only approximate, this is only an estimate of the distance of the electron from the proton in a hydrogen atom. It turns out to be exactly the classical value which is derived below.

If we bring two hydrogen atoms together, the electron cloud tends to concentrate between the two protons because there it is attracted by both protons and

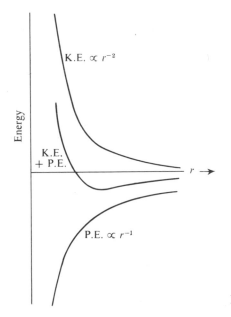

Figure 4.14

Figure 4.15

H   H   H$_2$

so we can have a lower electrostatic energy for the four particles as a group. The situation may also be thought of as the sharing of the electrons between the protons screening them and to some extent preventing them from repelling each other.

Look at the atom first. Suppose a mean radius for the orbit of the electron is r_0. Equating the centrifugal force to the electrostatic attraction, we have

$$\frac{mv^2}{r_0} = \frac{e^2}{r_0^2}.$$

Therefore $\frac{1}{2}mv^2 = \frac{1}{2}e^2/r_0$ and this is the kinetic energy of the electron. Again we would have to do work against the electrostatic attraction to pull off even a stationary electron from the distance r_0 of amount e^2/r_0. Hence we have that the energy of the atom is $-\frac{1}{2}e^2/r_0$ which is lower, of course, than the energy of a well separated stationary electron and proton which we have taken to be zero. But this energy is just the ionization energy of the hydrogen atom which we know to be 13.6 ev. (The ionization potential is 13.6 v.) Hence $\frac{1}{2}e^2/r_0 = 13.6$ ev or $r_0 = 0.53$ Å. This is the "classical" radius of the orbit of the electron in the hydrogen atom in its ground state—the first Bohr radius.

Let us assume that the kinetic energy of the electrons remains the same in the hydrogen molecule as it is in the separate atoms (a rather dubious assumption). However, the electrostatic potential energy will certainly be different since the charges are now rearranged and their interactions are different.

In order to allow for the fact that the electron is moving in an orbit in the classical sense and is a probability cloud of charge in the quantum-mechanical sense, let us very crudely approximate the hydrogen *atom* by a proton and two "half electrons" at distance r_0. If we really had such a charge distribution, the electrostatic potential energy would be

$$2 \times (-\tfrac{1}{2}e \times e)/r_0 + (-\tfrac{1}{2}e \times -\tfrac{1}{2}e)/r_{1/2},$$

where $r_{1/2}$ is the distance between the two half electrons. However, the second term must not be counted in our calculations, since it corresponds to the self-energy of the electron and as long as the electron is not destroyed (for example by annihilation with a positron) the self-energy is constant and does not come into calculations of changes in energy. The first term is the electrostatic potential energy $-e^2/r_0$ which was mentioned above.

Suppose we approximate the actual electron charge distribution in the hydrogen *molecule* by four charges $-\frac{1}{2}e$ positioned as shown in Fig. 4.16. This

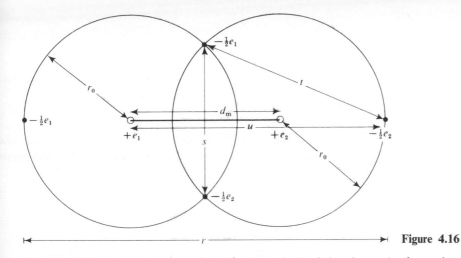

Figure 4.16

is a plausible first approximation, since the "overlap" of the charge in the region between the protons gives an increase in electron density in this region which we expected to find, as suggested by Fig. 4.14. We can now easily calculate the electrostatic potential energy of this system of static charges. However, we must bear in mind not to count the self-energy of the electrons, i.e. the interaction between the two $-\frac{1}{2}e_1$s or between the two $-\frac{1}{2}e_2$s where we have labelled the charges coming from hydrogen atoms 1 and 2.

We take the distance between the protons to be the known distance for the hydrogen molecule which can be found, for instance, from the moment of inertia as determined by Raman spectroscopy.* We have $d_m = 0.74$ Å and $r_0 = 0.53$ Å so that $s = 0.67$ Å. Similarly $t = 0.96$ Å, $u = 1.27$ Å, and $v = 1.80$ Å. The electrostatic potential energy is

$$\frac{-\frac{1}{2}e \times e}{r_0} \times 6 + \frac{e^2}{d_m} + \frac{(-\frac{1}{2}e)^2}{s} + \frac{(-\frac{1}{2}e)^2 \times 2}{t} + \frac{(-\frac{1}{2}e) \times e}{u} \times 2 + \frac{(-\frac{1}{2}e)^2}{v},$$

where, as usual, e is the magnitude of the electronic charge. This energy may be written in the form

$$-\frac{2e^2}{r_0} - \frac{e^2}{r_0}\left[1 - r_0\left(\frac{1}{d_m} + \frac{1}{4s} + \frac{1}{2t} - \frac{1}{u} + \frac{1}{4v}\right)\right] = -\frac{2e^2}{r_0} - \frac{e^2}{r_0} \times 0.15,$$

after substituting numerical values for r_0, d_m etc. The separate H atoms had an electrostatic potential energy of $-2e^2/r_0$. Therefore the fall in energy, which is the initial energy minus the final energy, is $(e^2/r_0) \times 0.15$. But we have shown above that $\frac{1}{2}(e^2/r_0) = 13.6$ ev. Hence the decrease in energy on formation of a hydrogen molecule from two separate hydrogen atoms is given by $0.15 \times 2 \times 13.6$

---

* See, for example, D. H. WHIFFEN, *Spectroscopy*, Longmans Green, London (1966), Chapters 7 and 9.

ev per molecule = 4.1 ev per molecule = 94 kcal mol^{-1}. This is obviously a very crude estimate and can only be regarded as an order of magnitude calculation. It is a much better answer than we have a right to expect. The correct answer is 103.4 kcal mol^{-1}. Nevertheless the physical ideas are correct. We have not, of course, shown that the energy is a minimum for the observed separation. This requires a much more refined analysis.

The sort of interaction between atoms to form a molecule just discussed is called a σ bond or a *covalent* bond. The origin of the energy is electrostatic but the rules for where the electrons can be, how fast they can move, how close they can be to each other and to the nuclei, and so on, are complicated and involve wave or quantum mechanics. Of course many, if not most, of the other properties of a molecule besides the energy are determined by the electron distribution.

Notice that even for the hydrogen molecule the chemical bond energy is only some $7\frac{1}{2}\%$ of the total electronic energy. This percentage is much smaller for atoms with more electrons—the chemistry takes place at the surface of atoms and the energy associated with the inner electrons is not much affected by the chemical bonds. Since the chemical bond energies represent only small changes in the energy of the atoms, they are quite difficult to calculate accurately. We can even see this from our rather crude electrostatic model of the hydrogen molecule as represented by Fig. 4.16. Quite small rearrangements of the electrons can change the bond energy considerably. In a proper calculation, we must obviously know rather precisely where the electrons are; in other words, we must know the electron wave functions very accurately.

For quantum-mechanical reasons, there is also a "state" in which the electrons tend *not* to be between the protons. This clearly has a higher electrostatic energy than the separate atoms and so does not lead to the formation of a molecule; it is called a repulsive state because the potential energy curve has no minimum and rises with decreasing separation of the atoms. Remembering that $F = -(\partial E/\partial x)$, we see that this corresponds to a repulsive force between the atoms. Both attractive and repulsive states can also occur for nuclear particles where of course we are concerned with nuclear forces rather than electrostatic forces. A proton and a neutron may repel each other rather than form a deuteron.

(iii) Ionic and Partially Ionic Bonds

The tendency for charge to be between the nuclei also operates for a molecule like HCl, for instance, but here the Cl atom tends to take the electron from the H atom and we get a bond which is said to be partially "ionic". We know that there is a tendency for the chlorine atom Cl to form a negative chloride ion Cl$^-$,

$$Cl + e^- \rightarrow Cl^- + 3.8 \text{ ev,}$$

as in salt crystals. The tendency to form ions in salts is so great that salt crystals are in good first approximation a conglomeration of ions and the principal forces between the particles are electrostatic, as we have already discussed. This is sometimes called an *ionic* bond whether in a crystal or a molecule. For the known separation d_m of the nuclei the electrostatic energy of this *ionic* bond is e^2/d_m. For HCl, $d_m = 1.28$ Å (from spectroscopy or electron diffraction) which gives for e^2/d_m the value 11.0 ev. Recalling that the ionization energy of the hydrogen atom is 13.6 ev, we have

$$H + Cl \rightarrow H^+ + Cl^- - 13.6 \text{ ev} + 3.8 \text{ ev}, \qquad \text{that is } -9.8 \text{ ev}.$$

$\therefore$ $H + Cl \rightarrow (H^+, 1.28 \text{ Å}, Cl^-) - 9.8$ ev $+ 11.0$ ev, that is $+1.2$ ev or about 30 kcal mol^{-1}, instead of 103 kcal mol^{-1} which is the experimental value. It is clear therefore that HCl is not just two ions H^+ and Cl^- at the correct distance 1.28 Å. (In passing, we notice that H^+ is just a proton. This is why the hydrogen positive ion plays such a unique and important role in chemistry.) Again, if HCl were H^+Cl^-, its electric dipole moment would be

$$e \times d_m = 4.8 \times 10^{-10} \times 1.28 \times 10^{-8} = 6.1 \times 10^{-18} \text{ e.s.u. of charge} \times \text{cm}$$
$$= 6.1 \text{ debye units}.$$

Actually, the experimental value is only 1.03 debye. Hence there is more involved for HCl than simple electrostatic attraction between ions. The bond must be largely covalent and this is why the bond energy is considerably higher than 30 kcal mol^{-1}.

(iv) Repulsive Forces

Such electrostatic effects also go far to explain the strong repulsive forces which arise on even closer approach of the atoms. For example, if we bring the protons nearer together in the hydrogen molecule, the electrons cannot get between them unless they have a large kinetic energy because of the uncertainty principle as we can see as follows. If the electrons are confined to the small space between the protons, Δx is small. Since $\Delta x \, \Delta p \approx \hbar$, if Δx gets smaller Δp must get bigger and so the kinetic energy $\sim \Delta p^2/2m$ gets bigger and this energy has to be supplied in compressing the molecule. In order to supply this energy, the force compressing the molecule must be able to do work as it moves. Hence there must be an opposing force and this is the repulsive force between the atoms. This effect has nothing directly to do with the electrostatic energy. However, compression of a molecule does, in fact, result in both a higher electron kinetic energy and a higher electrostatic potential energy. The rapid increase in energy of both sorts as the nuclei are pushed closer together corresponds to the repulsive forces.

(v) π Bonds and Metal Bonds

We can also get rather more complicated situations, particularly when the electrons in the molecules are rather more free to move than in the examples discussed so far. If an electron is free to move through a larger volume, its Δx is large and so its Δp can be small; hence its kinetic energy $\sim \Delta p^2/2m$ can be low. In many cases, it still suffers strong electrostatic attraction over its large orbit and so its potential

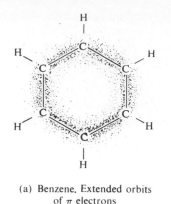

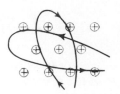

(a) Benzene. Extended orbits   (b) Metal. Extended orbits
        of π electrons   of the conduction electrons   **Figure 4.17**

energy may also be low. Hence such an electron may well have a very considerably lower energy than it did in one of the parent atoms and so may contribute importantly to bonding. This is the situation for the so called π electrons in benzene (Fig. 4.17a) and for the conduction electrons in metals (Fig. 4.17b). The former leads for instance to the special stability of the benzene molecule and the latter to the special bonding in metals.

(vi) Van der Waals' Forces

The attractive forces at larger distances between atoms which do not react, or between molecules, are complex and just as difficult to explain quantitatively. We shall give a qualitative explanation of their origin.

(a) Dipole–dipole interaction. If we have two polar molecules, they can attract each other because of their electric dipoles. Consider two hydrogen chloride molecules at a distance d apart and with their dipoles μ pointing as shown in Fig. 4.18(a). The electric field due at A to B is $2\mu/d^3$ (Gauss A position, see Problem 4.12). The energy of each dipole is $-\boldsymbol{\mu} \cdot \mathbf{F} = -\mu(2\mu/d^3)$. Hence the interaction energy is $-(2\mu^2/d^3) \times 2$ for the two dipoles oriented as shown in Fig. 4.18(a). Similarly, for the arrangement in which the dipoles point at right angles to the line joining them and in opposite directions, the energy is $-(\mu^2/d^3) \times 2$ (Gauss B position). Since the potential energy decreases with decreasing distance, the molecules are attracted to one another for these relative orientations of the dipoles. A molecular electric dipole is of order 1 debye $= 10^{-18}$ e.s.u. cm as we saw before. The actual dipole moment of HCl is 1.03 debye and the "diameter" of HCl is about

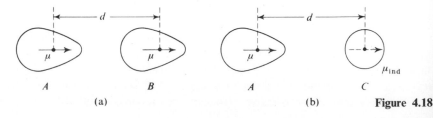

A B A C
                (a)   (b)   **Figure 4.18**

4.3 Å. Hence the dipolar attractive energy for two touching HCl molecules is of order

$$\frac{2\mu^2}{d^3} = \frac{2 \times 1.03^2 \times 10^{-36}}{4.3^3 \times 10^{-24}} \approx 2 \times 10^{-14} \text{ erg.}$$

This is correct in order of magnitude for an interaction energy ΔE between two molecules. Note that the interaction varies with the distance d between the molecules as d^{-3}. If the two molecules are dipolar, this is an important interaction but it should be noted that one is just as likely to get repulsion for different orientations of the dipoles. In fact, for random orientations, the average energy is zero. However, it often does happen that the low energy orientations are favoured. Since many molecules are not dipolar and since experimentally the attraction is usually found to depend on d^{-6}, we must seek other sources of the van der Waals' forces.

(b) Dipole–polarization interaction. A polar molecule and a non-polar molecule attract each other because the polar one can polarize the non-polar one (Fig. 4.18b). The electric field at molecule C due to the polar molecule A is $2\mu/d^3$. This polarizes C so that it has an induced electric dipole moment proportional to the field of magnitude

$$\mu_{ind} = \alpha F = \alpha \frac{2\mu}{d^3}$$

where α is the electric polarizability of molecule C. The interaction energy is

$$- F\mu_{ind} = - \left(\frac{2\mu}{d^3}\right)\left(\alpha \frac{2\mu}{d^3}\right) = - \alpha \frac{4\mu^2}{d^6}.$$

Molecular polarizabilities α are of order of magnitude 10^{-23} cm^3. (Note that this is roughly the volume of an atom; for example, the volume of an atom of radius 2 Å is $\frac{4}{3}\pi r^3 = \frac{4}{3}\pi(2 \times 10^{-8})^3 \approx 3 \times 10^{-23}$ cm^3.) For $\alpha = 10^{-23}$ cm^3, $\mu = 1$ debye (see Section 4.5iii), and $d = 4.3$ Å, the interaction energy is about 10^{-14} erg, which is the same order of magnitude as the dipole–dipole interaction (if there is one). However, this interaction varies as d^{-6}. This interaction is also present of course for two polar molecules. Note also that this is *always* an attractive force whatever the orientation of the dipole.

(c) Polarization–polarization interaction. An attraction is observed even between atoms or molecules without permanent dipole moments. This important interaction arises from the fact that the electrons in the molecules are in motion. Even for a non-polar molecule, or for an atom, although the mean position of the positive and negative charges coincide, this is not so for short intervals of time. For the hydrogen molecule at one moment, the electron may be at the point $\mathbf{r}$ with respect to the proton and so at that moment the electric dipole moment of the atom is $e\mathbf{r}$. Since $\mathbf{r}$ changes with time, and to emphasize this we write it as $\mathbf{r}(t)$, the dipole moment varies with time and so does the field produced by the dipole. Of course, if we average over a period of time which is long compared with the period of rotation of the electron, we have for the mean dipole momen $\overline{e\mathbf{r}(t)}$ which is zero. There are actually then fluctuating electric fields around ever molecule or atom. These fields are typically of the order of magnitude of tha produced by electric dipoles of strength about 1 debye unit (Problem 4.7). Not again that these fluctuating fields are produced mainly by the outer "chemical" electrons. The fields due to the inner electrons tend to cancel, since the position of the electrons are not correlated— in good first approximation.

The time-varying dipole polarizes any other molecule nearby (and vice versa and so we get an interaction energy similar in nature and in order of magnitude to the dipole–polarization interaction. The actual value can only be calculated using quantum mechanics because it depends on the motion of the electrons in the atoms. Nevertheless, it is clear that the interaction is always attractive and varies with distance as d^{-6}. This is often the most important interaction and is of course, present whether the molecules are polar or not. It therefore explains together with the dipole–polarization interaction, the attractive part of the 6–12 potential (Problem 4.13). It is sometimes called the London dispersion force.

In fact, there are all sorts of forces all with different laws d^{-n} and more compli cated ones because of angle dependences but we cannot go into the matter furthe here.

(d) Magnetic interactions. *Magnetic* energies of interaction are quite small. The magnetic moment of an electron (in a way because it is a spinning charge is one Bohr magneton, $\mu_B = eh/4\pi m_e c \approx 9 \times 10^{-21}$ erg gauss^{-1} (e is in electro static units) and this is the unit of atomic magnetism (see Problem 5.14). It may be determined by electron spin resonance (Experiment 9) or by magnetic suscepti bility (Experiment 17).

The magnetic dipolar interaction energy of two electrons at atomic distances is therefore of order

$$\frac{2\mu_B^2}{d^3} \approx \frac{2 \times 9^2 \times 10^{-42}}{4^3 \times 10^{-24}} \approx 3 \times 10^{-18} \text{ erg.}$$

This is very much smaller than the experimentally observed energies of interaction ΔE. Even so, the effect is often zero, since the molecule or atom often contains electrons in pairs with their moments opposed.

The magnetic moment generated by an electron moving in an orbit, which may be regarded as a current loop, is also of order one Bohr magneton. For a hydrogen atom and for the classical model, we have an electron circulating at a velocity $v = e/(m_e^{1/2} r_0^{1/2})$ at a distance $r_0 = h^2/(4\pi^2 m_e e^2)$ (see Section 4.5ii). The effective circulating current is $n'ev/c$ where n' is the number of charges per unit length which is $1/(2\pi r_0)$. This current encloses an area πr_0^2 so that the dipolar moment, which is the current times the enclosed area, is

$$(1/2\pi r_0) \times e \times (e/m_e^{1/2} r_0^{1/2}) \times \frac{1}{c} \times \pi r_0^2 = e^2 r_0^{1/2}/2cm_e^{1/2} = eh/4\pi m_e c,$$

which is one Bohr magneton. The resultant moment, however, is again often zero for a molecule, since the various electrons may orbit in opposite directions and their moments then tend to cancel. In any case, this interaction is also small.

Finally, the nuclei may or may not have magnetic moments. The magnetic moment of a nucleus, if any, is about two thousand times smaller. It is of order $eh/4\pi m_p c$, which is a fraction m_e/m_p of 1 Bohr magneton, so this interaction may also be neglected for atoms or molecules in good first approximation.

(vii) The Hydrogen Bond

There are some interactions which are not classed conveniently as either chemical bonds or as van der Waals interactions. Perhaps the most important is the hydrogen bond, the nature of which is not yet clear but which could be basically a simple electrostatic interaction between charges. The hydrogen atom in many molecules can be rather robbed of its electron and so may stick out of the molecule as a positively charged lump. On the other hand, for many molecules there are surface regions at which the electron density is relatively high and so there are local negative electric charges. Both circumstances occur, for instance, in the water molecule where, to some extent, the electrons withdrawn from the hydrogen atoms reside on the far side of the oxygen atom. Two such molecules can therefore have a quite strong electrostatic interaction and form a bond of intermediate strength (5 kcal mol^{-1}). Such bonds are of considerable importance in many molecular systems and especially in determining the structure of biologically important substances such as DNA. They play an important part in determining the properties of water—the most important liquid.

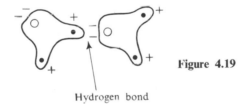

Figure 4.19

Hydrogen bond

PROBLEMS

4.1. Explain why it is that, if we removed one atom from an atomic crystal lattice, the crystal would tend to fall in and fill the hole whereas, if we removed an ion from an ionic lattice, the crystal would tend to deform so as to make the hole larger.

4.2. Explain why the surface tension of a liquid in equilibrium with its vapour may be expected to depend on the difference in density between the liquid and the vapour and so to approach zero at the liquid–vapour critical temperature.

4.3. The interatomic potential between two atoms is sometimes represented by a Morse curve

$$E(x) = \Delta E\{\exp\left[-2(x - d_m)/a\right] - 2\exp\left[-(x - d_m)/a\right]\}.$$

Show that $E(x)$ has a minimal value of $-\Delta E$ at $x = d_m$. Show that the frequency of small vibrations (simple harmonic motion) of two atoms of mass m about the minimum is given by $v = (\pi a)^{-1}(\Delta E/m)^{1/2}$. Draw a graph of the $E(x)$ curve for $\Delta E = 7.4 \times 10^{-12}$ erg, $d_m = 0.74$ Å, and $a = 0.5$ Å. These parameters are appropriate to a hydrogen molecule. If the proton mass is 1.6×10^{-24} g, calculate the vibration frequency of the hydrogen molecule.

4.4. Show that for the Morse curve (see Problem 4.3), $(d^3E/dx^3)_{d_m}$ is negative. What is the significance of this?

4.5. Look up the melting points and boiling points of water, hydrogen sulphide, hydrogen selenide, and hydrogen telluride and plot them against some suitable parameter. Why is water anomalous?

4.6. Show that the probability of finding a classical harmonic oscillator of amplitude a_0 in the range x to $x + \Delta x$ is given by

$$(\pi a_0)^{-1}[1 - (x/a_0)^2]^{-1/2} \Delta x \quad \text{for} \quad |x| \leq a_0.$$

Hence or otherwise show that it spends twice as long between $\frac{1}{2}a_0$ and a_0 as between 0 and $\frac{1}{2}a_0$.

4.7. Find the value of the instantaneous electric dipole moment of a hydrogen atom in its ground state on the Bohr model.

4.8. The so-called Hertzfeld–Meyer theory of melting states that, when the amplitude of vibration of the atoms is such that the force begins to decrease, if the amplitude increases further, then the substance melts. For the Morse potential (see Problem 4.3), find an expression for the melting temperature. (N.B. Assume that the mean energy at temperature T is kT and consider a pair of atoms only.)

4.9. Calculate the electrostatic potential energy per pair of a linear array of alternately positive and negative point charges q at equal distances d apart. Use this result to obtain a better estimate of the electrostatic energy per ion pair in a sodium chloride crystal than is given by assuming isolated pairs, as in Section 4.1.

4.10. As Problem 4.9, but calculate the interaction energy of an ion with its first, second, and third nearest neighbours only.

4.11. Show that, for any isotropic crystalline lattice, the most probable number of atoms per unit distance to be found at a distance d from a given point tends to $4\pi d^2 \rho_N$ as d increases, where ρ_N is the number density of atoms in the crystal.

4.12. Show that the interaction energy between two point dipoles $\boldsymbol{\mu}_A$ and $\boldsymbol{\mu}_B$ at separation $\mathbf{r}$ is given by

$$-\left[\frac{\boldsymbol{\mu}_A \cdot \boldsymbol{\mu}_B}{r^3} - \frac{3(\boldsymbol{\mu}_A \cdot \mathbf{r})(\boldsymbol{\mu}_B \cdot \mathbf{r})}{r^5}\right].$$

Show that this gives the correct answer for the Gauss A and B positions (Section 4.5vi).

4.13. The interaction energy between two molecules is sometimes expressed as $E(x) = -Ax^{-6} + Bx^{-12}$ where A and B are constants. This is called the 6–12 potential. Show that this potential has the usual form and find an expression for the equilibrium distance d_0 and the energy at the equilibrium separation $-\Delta E$. Show that $E(x)$ may be written in the form $\Delta E[(x/d_0)^{-12} - 2(x/d_0)^{-6}]$.

4.14. Show that, for the 6–12 potential (see Problem 4.13), the attractive part contributes numerically more to ΔE than the repulsive part.

4.15. Show that, for the 6–12 potential (see Problem 4.13), the contribution of the repulsive forces (Bx^{-12}) to $(d^2E/dx^2)_{d_o}$ is about twice as great and opposite in sign to the contribution due to the attractive forces.

4.16. The 6–12 potential (Problem 4.13) is sometimes thought to be unsatisfactory because the repulsion is not large enough for close approach of the atoms. This defect can be allowed for by a "hard core" correction, as in the Kihara potential

$$E(x) = \Delta E\left[\left(\frac{1-\delta}{x/d_0 - \delta}\right)^{12} - 2\left(\frac{1-\delta}{x/d_0 - \delta}\right)^6\right].$$

where $0 < \delta < 1$.

Show that the minimal value of $E(x)$ is $-\Delta E$ at $x = d_0$ and that there is a "hard core" of radius δd_0 (δ is often taken as 0.1).

4.17. Find the probability distribution corresponding to Fig. 4.8 for a face centred cubic lattice and a body centred cubic lattice.

4.18. Show that the acceleration of the electron in a hydrogen atom in the ground state is about 10^{21} times that due to gravity at the Earth's surface.

4.19. Show that, in Section 4.5, the distance $r = r_0$ corresponds to a minimum in the energy E of the hydrogen atom and not a maximum.

4.20. The 6–12 potential (see Problem 4.13) is sometimes written in the form

$$E(x) = \Delta E[(x/d_0)^{-6} - 1]^2.$$

Explain the difference between this form and that of Problem 4.13.

4.21. Use the uncertainty principle to show that an electron confined in a nucleus would have an energy enormously greater than the energy of any known β-emitting nucleus.

4.22. Find expressions for $(d^2E/dx^2)_{d_0}$ and $(d^3E/dx^3)_{d_0}$ for the 6–12 potential,

$$E(x) = \Delta E[(x/d_0)^{-12} - 2(x/d_0)^{-6}]$$

(see Problem 4.13). If $\Delta E = 2 \times 10^{-14}$ erg and $d_0 = 4 \times 10^{-8}$ cm find the values of $(d^2E/dx^2)_{d_0}$ and $(d^3E/dx^3)_{d_0}$ and compare them with the estimates used in preparing Table 4.2.

4.23. The 6–12 potential (see Problem 4.13) is sometimes written in the form,

$$E(x) = 4\Delta E[(\sigma/r)^{12} - (\sigma/r)^6]$$

Identify σ and explain its physical significance. Show that $d_0 = 2^{1/6}\sigma$.

CHAPTER 5

The dynamics of particles

Of matter in its ultimate essence and apart from
motion we know nothing whatsoever. SAMUEL BUTLER

5.1 SPACE, TIME, AND NUMBER

Mechanics is the study of the motion of things in space and time. We therefore
first want to be a little clearer about what we mean by space and time in physics.
This is rather difficult. Perhaps all we can say by way of a definition is that each
is something that is physically measurable according to a well-defined set of rules
and that we can find relations between space and time in defined experimental
circumstances which enable us to predict the results of experiments and to understand them.

As far as we are concerned for the moment, all we need for the measurement
of time is something *we believe* to be periodic, e.g. the rotation of the Earth, the
pendulum of a clock, the vibrations of a certain quartz crystal, or the period of
oscillation of a particular sort of light, in defined circumstances. We can then
measure longer times by measuring the number of integers and/or fractions of
the period we have chosen between the signals which mark the beginning and end
of the time interval to be measured. We must agree as to how the period of time is
to be identified before we can measure it. This last statement may appear so
obvious as to be superfluous. In elementary mechanics, this is true but when we
come to consider relativistic mechanics in Chapter 8 its importance will be better
appreciated.

The standard of time interval must be independent of the time at which it is
measured. We must be able to repeat an experiment and get the same answer—
unless something has changed in the meantime.

In much the same way, we must agree on a standard of length in terms of some
object whose length we believe to be constant (with time!) in given circumstances.
This may be, for instance, the standard metre bar or the wavelength of cadmium
light. Note that space and time are intimately connected in that we say that the
length standard is constant, i.e. it is independent of *time*. On the other hand, we
want a time standard which gives signals which can be used anywhere, i.e. is
independent of *position* (which we have to identify using the standard of *length*).

The *connexion* between space and time is *motion* and the fundamental connexion
between the two is revealed in relativity, which we discuss in Chapter 8 and 9.

There is no "natural" unit of length or time as there is for electric charge and, as we shall see, for angular momentum. As far as we know, length and time are not quantized. However, we shall find that there is a natural unit for velocity, the velocity of light *in vacuo*. If this were accepted, we could fix the unit of length (or time) if the unit of time (or length) were fixed. At the time of writing (1967), the standard of length is 1,650,763.73 wavelengths *in vacuo* of the $^2P_{10}-^5D_5$ transition of a ^{86}Kr atom and is called the metre. The standard of time is 9,192,631,770 vibrations of the 4,0 to 3,0 transition of the ground state of the ^{133}Cs atom and is called the second.

In order to establish our orders of magnitude once more, we may consider Table 5.1.

We can easily estimate the maximal and minimal distances and times. The longest distance is the observable radius of the universe. Light from large distances is believed to have suffered a Doppler shift in wavelength due to the velocity of recession of the source. The relative Doppler shift in wavelength due to a velocity v of the source in the line of sight is given by

$$\frac{\Delta\lambda}{\lambda} = \frac{v}{c}$$

where c is the velocity of light. Hence we can get v from measurements of the Doppler shift $\Delta\lambda$ (Fig. 5.1). It is found that out to distances R, which we can measure by some other means, we have $v = \alpha R$ and $\alpha = 3 \times 10^{-18}$ s^{-1} (the Hubble constant*), from astronomical observation. But the limiting velocity is c. This follows from relativity as discussed in Chapter 8. Therefore R has its maximal value R_{max} for $v = c$

$$\therefore \quad R_{max} \approx \frac{c}{\alpha} = \frac{3 \times 10^{10}}{3 \times 10^{-18}} = 10^{28} \text{ cm.}$$

(Strictly speaking the Doppler shift is $(v/c)(1 - v^2/c^2)^{-1/2}$ but this does not affect our order of magnitude estimate.)

The smallest known object is the proton (or neutron) and so $R_{min} \approx 10^{-13}$ cm. All lengths must lie within these limits.

For times, we have a similar situation. The longest time interval of any conceivable physical significance is that to send a signal clear across the universe and the signal must be carried by electromagnetic radiation.

$$\therefore \quad T_{max} \approx \frac{R_{max}}{c} = \frac{10^{28}}{3 \times 10^{10}} \approx 3 \times 10^{17} \text{ s} \quad (\approx 10^{10} \text{ years}).$$

The smallest time of physical significance is that for the fastest signal to cross the smallest object. Thus, electromagnetic radiation crossing a nucleus gives us the

---

* E. HUBBLE, *Proc. Natl. Acad. Sci.* **15**, 168 (1929).

Table 5.1

Distance, cm		Time, s		Mean life of
	10^{29}			
		10^{18}	Age of Universe	
Edge of universe			Age of Earth	^{238}U
	10^{26}			
		10^{15}		
			Earliest men	
	10^{23}			
Size of our galaxy		10^{12}	Pyramids	
				^{226}Ra
	10^{20}			
		10^{9}	Life of man	Triton
To nearest star				
	10^{17}			
		10^{6}	Moon goes round earth	
	10^{14}			
		10^{3}	Light from earth to sun	Neutron
To the sun				
	10^{11}			
		1	Tick tock	
To the moon				
	10^{8}			
		10^{-3}	Period of sound wave	
Mount Everest				
	10^{5}			
		10^{-6}	Period of radio wave	Muon
Height of a man				
	10^{2}			$\pi^{\pm}$ meson
		10^{-9}		
			Light travels one foot	
	10^{-1}			
		10^{-12}	Period of molecular rotation	
Dust				
A bacterium	10^{-4}			
		10^{-15}	Period of atomic vibration	
A virus	10^{-7}			π^{0} meson
Radius of an atom		10^{-18}	Light crosses an atom	
	10^{-10}			
		10^{-21}		
			Period of nuclear vibration	
Radius of a nucleus	10^{-13}			
		10^{-24}		
			Light crosses a nucleus	
				Strange particle

The scales of time and distance are arranged so that we get distance from time and vice versa by using the velocity of light. This emphasizes the close connexion of the two, at least at either end of the scale. [Adapted from FEYNMAN.]

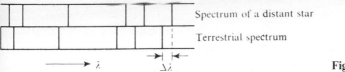

Figure 5.1

minimal time interval

$$T_{min} = \frac{R_{min}}{c} = \frac{10^{-13} \text{ cm}}{3 \times 10^{10}} \approx 3 \times 10^{-24} \text{ s}.$$

While we are talking of orders of magnitude, we could also make a list of the number of particles in things and this is given in Table 5.2.

Table 5.2

Number of particles	Object
10^{80}	Universe
10^{70}	
	Galaxy
10^{60}	
	Sun
10^{50}	Earth
10^{40}	
10^{30}	
	Human body
10^{20}	
	Living cell
10^{10}	
	DNA molecule
	Polymer molecule
10^{0}	Proton

5.2 NEWTON'S LAWS OF MOTION

Newton's laws of motion are of basic importance not only because of the results which are directly derived from them but because mechanics is the model situation which is generalized when we have to deal with more complicated phenomena. We shall not be concerned to demonstrate the plausibility of Newton's laws of motion; suffice it to say that they are not obvious and indeed are in direct contradiction with the superficial view of normal experience.

1) An object, if not acted on by forces, continues to move at constant velocity (i.e. zero acceleration) in a straight line. $\mathbf{a} = 0$ when $\mathbf{F} = 0$.

This is really rather obscure, since it does not say what a force is or what a straight line is. In fact, a force is supposed to be present if the body does not continue at constant velocity in a straight line and the second law gives a numerical measure of the departure from this simple behaviour. An inertial frame of reference is one for which a body not acted on by forces moves with uniform velocity.

2) Force = rate of change of momentum, or $\mathbf{F} = d\mathbf{p}/dt$ (note that this is a vector relation.)

In Newtonian mechanics, we put $\mathbf{p} = m\mathbf{v}$ and define a new quantity, the inertial mass m, but we must know how to measure force, length, and time in order to determine it. We can write

$$\mathbf{F} = \frac{d}{dt}(m\mathbf{v}) = m\mathbf{a}.$$

The last relation is usually true. It is true in non-relativistic mechanics unless there is an obvious reason why the mass may vary, as for instance in a rocket ejecting gases.

We note in passing that later experience shows us that momentum $\mathbf{p}$ is a more useful concept than acceleration $\mathbf{a}$, just as energy is more useful than force.

A force always produces a rate of change of momentum. In cases where this does not appear to be so, a closer consideration shows that the total force on a particle is different from the force initially referred to. We often think of the gravitational force on a body at rest on the surface of the Earth. However, the total force on the body is zero because of the supporting forces, and the momentum does not change. The gravitational force is revealed by removing the support and then the rate of change of momentum is finite. The law is sometimes said to apply to *unbalanced* forces but this restriction is not really necessary provided we always take account of all the forces acting on the particle.

These laws are only true in an unaccelerated or inertial reference frame as defined by the first law. They are not true in a frame which is accelerating or rotating relative to an inertial frame. If we measure relative to an inertial frame there are no so-called pseudo-, or fictitious, forces (e.g. centrifugal force, Coriolis forces, etc.). If we *do* measure relative to a non-inertial frame, i.e. one which is accelerating, then we can introduce pseudo-forces in order to explain the dynamics *as if* we were using an inertial frame.

Note that for particles the motion is completely determined by the initial *position* and *momentum* (or velocity) and by the forces acting on the particle. Thus, from the second law,

$$F_x = \frac{dp_x}{dt}, \quad \text{so that} \quad p_x = \int F_x\, dx, \quad \text{that is} \quad p_x(t_2) - p_x(t_1) = \int_{t_1}^{t_2} F_x(t)\, dt,$$

where we consider only the x component for the moment. The momentum change in a period of time depends on the force acting over that period of time. For the simple case of a constant force, the change in momentum is just $F \times (t_2 - t_1)$.

At any time t later than t_1, we have

$$p_x(t) - p_x(t_1) = \int_{t_1}^{t} F_x(t')\, dt'.$$

If we put

$$p_x = m\frac{dx}{dt}, \quad \text{then} \quad x = \frac{1}{m}\int p_x\, dt,$$

so that

$$x(t_2) = \frac{1}{m}\int_{t_1}^{t_2} p_x(t'')\, dt'' + x(t_1).$$

Substituting the expression for $p_x(t)$ in this equation, we find

$$x(t_2) = \frac{1}{m}\int_{t_1}^{t_2} dt'' \int_{t_1}^{t''} F_x(t')\, dt' + \frac{1}{m}\, p_x(t_1)[t_2 - t_1] + x(t_1).$$

Thus $x(t_2)$ depends on $x(t_1)$, $p_x(t_1)$, and $F_x(t)$, as stated above.

We know all we can about a particle at a given time t if we know $x(t)$ and $p_x(t)$ and also $y(t)$, $p_y(t)$, and $z(t)$, $p_z(t)$, that is $\mathbf{r}(t)$ and $\mathbf{p}(t)$. If we regard time as a parameter, we can imagine the particle moving in "phase space". In the simple case of motion in one dimension, this space has the coordinates x and p_x. For example, for a harmonic oscillator we have $x(t) = x_0 \cos \omega t$ and $p_x(t) = m\dot{x} = -m\omega x_0 \sin \omega t$ ($\dot{x} \equiv dx/dt$). Hence

$$x^2 + \frac{1}{m^2\omega^2}\, p_x^2 = x_0^2,$$

or

$$\left(\frac{x}{x_0}\right)^2 + \left(\frac{p_x}{m\omega x_0}\right)^2 = 1.$$

This is the equation of an ellipse. The "orbits" in phase space of a harmonic oscillator are therefore ellipses whose size increases with the amplitude of oscillation x_0. A point on the ellipse gives the values of the displacement and momentum at a given time. The passage of time corresponds to the point going around the ellipse (Fig. 5.2).

This representation of the motion is of considerable utility in more complex applications of mechanics and particularly in quantum mechanics and statistical mechanics. The area of the orbit of a harmonic oscillator in phase space A is $\pi m\omega x_0^2$. Since the energy of the oscillator E is $\frac{1}{2}m\omega^2 x_0^2$ and the period of oscillation

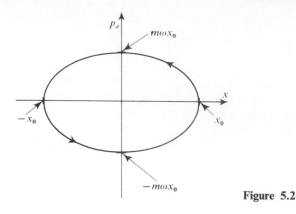

Figure 5.2

T is $2\pi/\omega$, we see that $A = ET$. ET, and therefore A, has the dimensions (see Section 5.6) of action which are the same as those of Planck's constant h. One way of introducing quantum ideas into mechanics, i.e. quantum mechanics, is to say that action is quantized in units of h and so for an oscillator this restricts the possible amplitudes of oscillation to those given by $A = nh$ where n is an integer. For the particular case of the one-dimensional harmonic oscillator, this means that for an oscillator of angular frequency ω, when $T = 2\pi/\omega$, the values of the energy E are restricted to $E = A/T = nh/(2\pi/\omega) = n\hbar\omega$.

The equations on page 63 are in principle sufficient to solve all mechanical problems! However, we frequently get into difficulty with the forces. We see we had to know $\mathbf{F}(t)$ to get $\mathbf{r}(t)$ and $\mathbf{p}(t)$. But the $\mathbf{F}(t)$ are often part of the answer! For example, in a simple pendulum, part of the force $\mathbf{F}$ on the bob is the tension in the string, which itself depends on the motion. Consequently, it would be good to reduce the necessity for a knowledge of the forces. This proves to be very generally true. A considerable help to this end is provided by Newton's third law.

3) Action equals reaction.

This conventional terse expression of the third law is retained deliberately. Its full meaning and power will be appreciated only in using it in the analysis of particle dynamics given below. Here again, we often find confusion in elementary treatments of mechanics and the difficulties are usually due to the fact that we consider bodies, which are not really simple, and only parts of larger mechanical systems. A treatment in terms of particles avoids these difficulties entirely. We emphasize therefore that we regard Newton's third law as applying to particles and hence ultimately only to fundamental forces between particles. The law is true for every pair of particles independently. (This is for central forces, "real" particles may interact with non-central forces but we ignore this difficulty for the moment.) For two particles 1 and 2 the force on 1 due to 2 is defined as $\mathbf{F}_{12}$ and similarly the force on 2 due to 1 is $\mathbf{F}_{21}$. We have, according to Newton's third law, $\mathbf{F}_{12} = -\mathbf{F}_{21}$. Note the vector relation (Fig. 5.3). Consider a *pair* of isolated

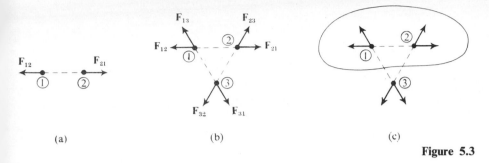

(a)   (b)   (c)

Figure 5.3

particles, say 1 and 2. Since $\mathbf{F}_{12} = -\mathbf{F}_{21}$ (from the third law), $\mathbf{F}_{12} = \mathbf{F}_1 = d\mathbf{p}_1/dt$
($\mathbf{F}_1$ is the total force on 1, etc.) and $\mathbf{F}_{21} = \mathbf{F}_2 = d\mathbf{p}_2/dt$ (from the second law), we
have

$$\frac{d\mathbf{p}_1}{dt} = -\frac{d\mathbf{p}_2}{dt} \quad \text{or} \quad \frac{d}{dt}(\mathbf{p}_1 + \mathbf{p}_2) = 0 \quad \text{or} \quad \frac{d\mathbf{P}}{dt} = 0$$

where $\mathbf{P} = \mathbf{p}_1 + \mathbf{p}_2$. Note that only *internal* forces are involved in this example.
Hence $\mathbf{p}_1 + \mathbf{p}_2$ is constant or $\mathbf{P}$ is constant, that is $\mathbf{P}$ is independent of time.
Hence *whatever* $\mathbf{F}_{12}$ may be, $(\mathbf{p}_1 + \mathbf{p}_2)$ is constant if no external forces are involved.

For three particles, we get the situation shown in Fig. 5.3(b). By the third law,
we have $\mathbf{F}_{12} = -\mathbf{F}_{21}$, $\mathbf{F}_{13} = -\mathbf{F}_{31}$, and $\mathbf{F}_{23} = -\mathbf{F}_{32}$. In the case of these three
isolated particles, we have

$$\frac{d\mathbf{p}_1}{dt} + \frac{d\mathbf{p}_2}{dt} + \frac{d\mathbf{p}_3}{dt} - \mathbf{F}_1 + \mathbf{F}_2 + \mathbf{F}_3$$

$$= (\mathbf{F}_{12} + \mathbf{F}_{13}) + (\mathbf{F}_{21} + \mathbf{F}_{23}) + (\mathbf{F}_{31} + \mathbf{F}_{32})$$

$$= (\mathbf{F}_{12} + \mathbf{F}_{21}) + (\mathbf{F}_{13} + \mathbf{F}_{31}) + (\mathbf{F}_{23} + \mathbf{F}_{32})$$

$$= 0.$$

because of the third law, that is $\mathbf{F}_{12} = -\mathbf{F}_{21}$, etc. Hence

$$\frac{d}{dt}(\mathbf{p}_1 + \mathbf{p}_2 + \mathbf{p}_3) = 0 \quad \text{or} \quad \frac{d\mathbf{P}}{dt} = 0,$$

that is $\mathbf{P} = $ constant. In general, for any number of particles,

$$\mathbf{P} \equiv \sum_i \mathbf{p}_i = \text{constant}.$$

We can see that this is *not* true if external forces are involved by looking at
two only of the above three particles, say 1 and 2 as shown in Fig. 5.3(c). We have

$$\frac{d\mathbf{p}_1}{dt} = \mathbf{F}_{12} + \mathbf{F}_{13} \quad \text{and} \quad \frac{d\mathbf{p}_2}{dt} = \mathbf{F}_{21} + \mathbf{F}_{23}.$$

$$\therefore \quad \frac{d}{dt}(\mathbf{p}_1 + \mathbf{p}_2) = \mathbf{F}_{12} + \mathbf{F}_{21} + \mathbf{F}_{13} + \mathbf{F}_{23}$$

$$= \mathbf{F}_{13} + \mathbf{F}_{23},$$

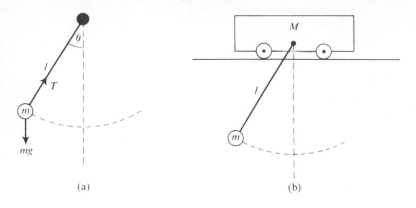

(a)   (b)   Figure 5.4

since $\mathbf{F}_{12} = -\mathbf{F}_{21}$; $(\mathrm{d}/\mathrm{d}t)(\mathbf{p}_1 + \mathbf{p}_2)$ thus is not zero in general, so that $\mathbf{p}_1 + \mathbf{p}_2$ is not conserved, in general, if the system is not isolated.

Hence we have, for *isolated* systems, *conservation of linear momentum.* For the usual simple pendulum experiment (Fig. 5.4a), momentum is not apparently conserved. The force at right angles to the string is $-mg \sin \theta$ and the acceleration is $\ddot{x} = l\ddot{\theta}$; therefore, by the second law, $-mg \sin \theta = ml\ddot{\theta}$.

$$\therefore \quad \ddot{\theta} \approx -(g/l)\theta \text{ for small } \theta \text{ (see Problem 5.31).}$$

This gives simple harmonic motion, for which $\theta = \theta_0 \cos \omega t$, where $\omega = \sqrt{g/l}$. At $t = 0$, $\theta = \theta_0$ and $\dot{\theta}$, which is $-\omega\theta_0 \sin \omega t$, is zero. Therefore the velocity of the bob is zero and $p \equiv mv$ is zero at this moment. But at time $t = (1/\omega)(\pi/2)$, $\theta = 0$ and $\dot{\theta} = -\omega\theta_0$ so that $v = l\dot{\theta} = -\omega l\theta_0$ and $p_{\max} = m\omega l\theta_0$ which is not zero. Hence the momentum of the bob varies with time; its momentum is not conserved. However, we must remember that the string has pulled on the support so that momentum is given to or received from the support, according to the position of the bob. Suppose we have instead of the pendulum with a fixed support a pendulum which is supported from a trolley of mass M, as shown in Fig. 5.4(b). If $M \gg m$, the motion of the bob (mass m) will not be much affected and so we shall still have $p_{\max} \approx m\omega l\theta_0$ for $\theta = 0$. However, M will have momentum of amount p_M, and since

$$\sum_i \mathbf{p}_i = 0, \quad \text{that is } \mathbf{p}_m + \mathbf{p}_M = 0,$$

then

$$p_M = m\omega l\theta_0 \quad \text{or} \quad v_M = \frac{m}{M} \omega l\theta_0.$$

A so-called "rigid support" is for $m/M \rightarrow 0$. We still have here a "rigid support" as far as the vertical direction is concerned and really the changes in vertical momentum are taken up by the Earth for which ratio m/M is very small indeed! This is just a more complicated case than Fig. 5.3(c) of looking at *part* of a system when we *must* allow for the influence of the external forces. This is not a trivial problem, since strictly speaking everything interacts with everything else in the univcrse und so there are no truly isolated systems. Nevertheless, it is often a very useful approximation to assume a system is isolated first and then correct afterwards for the small effect of the external forces if necessary.

Another example of an apparent violation of the law of conservation of momentum is the case of an electric charge accelerated in an electric field. Momentum is not apparently conserved here if we think in terms of the conventional picture shown in Fig. 5.5(a). The force on the charge q is $\mathbf{E}q$,

$$\therefore \quad \frac{d\mathbf{p}}{dt} = \mathbf{E}q,$$

$$\therefore \quad \mathbf{p} = \int_0^t \mathbf{E}q \, dt + \mathbf{p}_0 = \mathbf{E}qt + \mathbf{p}_0.$$

Where does the increase in momentum $(\mathbf{p} - \mathbf{p}_0)$ come from? It must come from the field itself, or from the agency producing the field (e.g. the charges on a condenser). The momentum comes from the charges in the plates and in the external circuit. The difficulty arose because we did not have a "closed system". A possible form of the complete system is shown in Fig. 5.5(b). It is clear that if the charge q moves there must be a reaction back somewhere. If q is a positive charge, it moves to the right and in so doing it tends to attract more negative charge to the right-hand condenser plate and the positive charge on the left-hand plate is less repelled and so can increase. Both these effects correspond to a current in the direction of the battery electromotive force and explains where the energy acquired by the charge q comes from. The momentum is transferred by the interaction forces of q with the charges on the plates and so a momentum balance can be achieved.

It may be noted that mass does not strictly speaking come into Newton's laws at all but it is clearly a useful concept. In particular, mass does not appear in the third law, but we can use the third law to compare masses by studying the result of a collision. In a collision between two particles of mass m_1 and m_2, the accelerations are $\mathbf{a}_1$ and $\mathbf{a}_2$ and, since the forces are equal and opposite by the third law, we have $m_1\mathbf{a}_1 = -m_2\mathbf{a}_2$. If we define the standard of inertial mass to

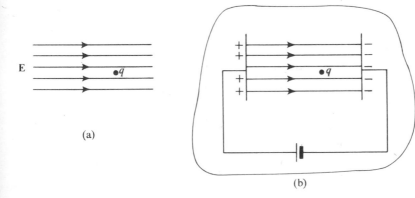

(a)

(b)   **Figure 5.5**

be that of the first particle, we can do the above experiment, i.e. measure $\mathbf{a}_1$ and $\mathbf{a}_2$ and hence find the mass of the second particle from the relation $m_2 = -(|\mathbf{a}_1|/|\mathbf{a}_2|)m_1$ and so on for any other particle. The standard of mass is that of the international kilogramme which is kept at Sèvres, France. It is not compared with other masses by collision experiments! However, comparisons are made with it by the use of gravity (see Section 5.9). Note that this is not an "atomic" standard like those of length and time and so it is more likely to change in an unpredictable manner. So far, we have not yet found it worthwhile to define the standard of mass as the mass of a given number of a given sort of atom because we have faith in the Sèvres kilogramme and because no-one knows a practicable way of counting out some 10^{23} atoms.

Having defined mass, length, and time, all other mechanical units are fixed. It should be noted that the definitions in terms of kilogramme and metre rather than gramme and centimetre in itself confer no special advantage on the MKS as opposed to the cgs system of units; we would only need to move the decimal points the appropriate distances.

From the defining relation $\mathbf{F} = m\mathbf{a}$, the unit of force is fixed. It is the newton in the MKS system and the dyne in the cgs system. The newton is 10^5 dynes. Since $\mathbf{F} = d\mathbf{p}/dt$, this also fixed the unit of linear momentum.

5.3 THE CENTRE OF MASS

Consider a simple isolated system of two particles of masses m_1 and m_2 moving along the line joining them with velocities v_1 and v_2, as in Fig. 5.6(a).

Consider what combined property of the whole may be associated with the known conservation of *total* momentum. Is there any sense in which these two particles behave as one particle? Suppose that we define the velocity of the pair of particles by the relation

Total momentum = total mass × "velocity of total".

Clearly, the obvious choice for a mass to represent the object is $(m_1 + m_2)$, so we have

$$m_1v_1 + m_2v_2 = (m_1 + m_2)v_{cm}, \qquad \text{that is } v_{cm} = \frac{m_1v_1 + m_2v_2}{(m_1 + m_2)}.$$

The numerator is a constant because of conservation of linear momentum; hence v_{cm} is a constant for this example. Note that v_{cm} is a constant *whatever* the forces between the particles.

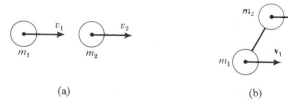

(a)   (b)   **Figure 5.6**

Again, if X is the "position" of the pair of particles and x_1 and x_2 those of m_1 and m_2, then $\dot{X} \equiv v_{cm}$ so that we can write the expression above in the form

$$\dot{X} = \frac{m_1\dot{x}_1 + m_2\dot{x}_2}{(m_1 + m_2)}.$$

This may be integrated to give

$$X = \frac{m_1 x_1 + m_2 x_2}{(m_1 + m_2)} + \text{a constant.}$$

In the special case where $x_1 = x_2 = x$, i.e. there is one body of mass $m_1 + m_2$, we have $X = x + $ a constant. It is clearly sensible to put this constant equal to zero, so that the coordinate describing the position of the combined particle is at the particle. Therefore, for two particles, X is the position given by

$$X = \frac{m_1 x_1 + m_2 x_2}{(m_1 + m_2)},$$

or in general for any number of particles,

$$X_{cm} = \frac{\sum\limits_i m_i x_i}{\sum\limits_i m_i}.$$

The point so defined is called the centre of mass. In general, the centre of mass is not fixed in space, since $\dot{X}_{cm} = v_{cm}$ is not necessarily zero. We have similar relations for the Y and Z coordinates, when the velocities have any value whatever, so that the vector position of the centre of mass is given by

$$\mathbf{R} = \sum_i m_i \mathbf{r}_i / \sum_i m_i,$$

and the velocity of the centre of mass is

$$\mathbf{v}_{cm} = \sum_i m_i \mathbf{v}_i / \sum_i m_i.$$

Another special case of interest is when the masses are rigidly connected and moving without rotation. Then $\mathbf{v}_1 = \mathbf{v}_2 = \mathbf{v}$, say (see Fig. 5.6(b)), so that

$$\mathbf{v}_{cm} = \frac{m_1\mathbf{v} + m_2\mathbf{v}}{(m_1 + m_2)} = \mathbf{v},$$

which again shows that our definition is a sensible one.

Centre of gravity is the same as centre of mass provided the gravitational field is uniform, since weight is proportional to mass (see Section 5.9).

If the system of particles is not isolated, i.e. if there are external forces, the linear momentum $\sum\limits_i m_i \mathbf{v}_i$ is not conserved and consequently $\mathbf{v}_{cm}$ varies with time. In other words, the centre of mass is accelerated. For each particle $\mathbf{F}_i = m_i(d\mathbf{v}_i/dt)$.

Since $\sum_i \mathbf{F}_i$ is the external force $\mathbf{F}_{ext}$, all internal forces vanishing in pairs because of Newton's third law, we have

$$\mathbf{F}_{ext} = \sum_i m_i \frac{d\mathbf{v}_i}{dt} = \frac{d}{dt}\left(\sum_i m_i \mathbf{v}_i\right) = \frac{d}{dt}\left(\mathbf{v}_{cm}\sum_i m_i\right) = \left(\sum_i m_i\right)\frac{d\mathbf{v}_{cm}}{dt}.$$

This is Newton's second law of motion for a particle of mass $M(=\sum_i m_i)$ acted on by a force $\mathbf{F}_{ext}(=\sum_i \mathbf{F}_i)$ giving it an acceleration $d\mathbf{v}_{cm}/dt$.

The motion of the centre of mass is obviously what we consider if we study the translational motion of the body *as a whole*. The total mass $\sum m_i$ arises naturally and is an obvious choice. The choice of a suitable velocity is not so obvious but an appropriate one is $\mathbf{v}_{cm}$ as given above. If we only consider the motion of the set of particles as a whole, we can therefore treat the motion as that of one particle and the internal degrees of freedom are irrelevant. We have an example of what we might call a quasi particle.

In considering the motions of the particles *relative* to the centre of mass, we can think firstly of rotations, which are discussed in Section 5.7, where the moment of inertia corresponds to the mass, and secondly of changes in the separations of the particles. In the latter, the idea of reduced mass arises, and is now discussed.

Consider the motion of two particles relative to the motion of their centre of mass. In the frame of reference whose origin is at the centre of mass and moves with it, the total momentum is zero by definition, since $\mathbf{v}_{cm} = 0$, that is $m_1 \dot{\mathbf{r}}_1 + m_2 \dot{\mathbf{r}}_2 = 0$. Further, because $\mathbf{R} = 0$, we have $m_1 \mathbf{r}_1 + m_2 \mathbf{r}_2 = 0$. Consider the equation of motion for the distance $\mathbf{r}_{12} = \mathbf{r}_1 - \mathbf{r}_2$ between the particles. Because of the relation above, we can eliminate $\mathbf{r}_2$ to give

$$\mathbf{r}_1 = \left(\frac{m_2}{m_1 + m_2}\right)\mathbf{r}_{12}.$$

The force on particle 1 is $\mathbf{F}_{12}$ (there are no external forces), so that

$$\mathbf{F}_{12} = m_1 \ddot{\mathbf{r}}_1 = \left(\frac{m_1 m_2}{m_1 + m_2}\right)\ddot{\mathbf{r}}_{12}.$$

We now find an expression for the force on particle 2,

$$\mathbf{F}_{21} = -\mathbf{F}_{12} \text{ (third law)} = -\left(\frac{m_1 m_2}{m_1 + m_2}\right)\ddot{\mathbf{r}}_{12} = \left(\frac{m_1 m_2}{m_1 + m_2}\right)\ddot{\mathbf{r}}_{21},$$

since $\mathbf{r}_{12} = -\mathbf{r}_{21}$ by definition.

The equation of motion is the same for both particles and is formally the equation of motion, using the second law, for a particle of mass $m_r \equiv m_1 m_2/(m_1 + m_2)$ which is called the reduced mass (because it is smaller than either m_1 or m_2). In the special case in which the two masses are equal, $m_1 = m_2 = m$ and $m_r = \frac{1}{2}m$. We used this result in Section 4.2 in connexion with the vibration of two interacting atoms. If, on the other hand, $m_2 \gg m_1$ then $m_r \approx m_1$ and moreover, since $\mathbf{r}_2 = -(m_1/m_2)\mathbf{r}_1$, we have $|\mathbf{r}_2| \ll |\mathbf{r}_1|$. In this special case, the system therefore behaves as if the particle 2 is fixed and particle 1 moves relative to it. This is a good approximation, for instance, for the Earth moving round the Sun or an electron moving round a nucleus.

5.4 ENERGY

We also introduce the idea of energy in terms of a conservation law. The conservation law is again only true if we include *all* the contributions—in this case to the energy.

The energy concept arises also, like momentum, from the forces. We are led to consider not only $\int F_x \, dt$, which is a momentum, but also $\int F_x \, dx$—what else is there to do?

$$\int_{x_i}^{x_f} F_x \, dx = \int_{x_i}^{x_f} \left(\frac{dp_x}{dt}\right) dx = \int_{p_i}^{p_f} dp_x \left(\frac{dx}{dt}\right) = \int_{p_i}^{p_f} dp_x \left(\frac{p_x}{m}\right)$$

$$= \frac{1}{m} \int_{p_i}^{p_f} p_x \, dp_x = \frac{1}{2m}(p_{x_f}^2 - p_{x_i}^2) \quad \text{or} \quad \tfrac{1}{2}mv_{x_f}^2 - \tfrac{1}{2}mv_{x_i}^2.$$

The subscript i indicates the initial value and f the final value. We identify $p^2/2m$ or $\tfrac{1}{2}mv^2$ as *kinetic* energy or energy of motion T, since in this simple case it depends on the velocity and in particular it is zero if the velocity is zero. We have, therefore,

$$\int F_x \, dx = \text{change in } T_x,$$

where we have used the subscript x to indicate that this is the kinetic energy associated with the x coordinate.

We now introduce a rather more subtle idea. Suppose we could find a function V having dimension of energy such that $F_x = -(\partial V/\partial x)$. Since V may be a function of several variables, for example $V(x, y, z)$, we usually write $-(\partial V/\partial x)$ rather than $-(dV/dx)$ to emphasize that in the differentiation with respect to x we must regard y and z as constants.

$$\therefore \quad -dV_x = F_x \, dx \quad \text{and} \quad \int F_x \, dx = -\text{change in } V_x$$

(we have put V_x instead of V because we are only considering changes in x for the moment).

$$\therefore \quad -\text{change in } V_x = \text{change in } T_x, \quad \text{or} \quad \text{change in } V_x + \text{change in } T_x = 0.$$

It is clear that we can carry out the same process for the other two cartesian coordinate directions and get two further contributions to the kinetic energy, $\int F_y \, dy$ and $\int F_z \, dz$. Corresponding to these, there are two further quantities

V_y and V_z. If we put $T = T_x + T_y + T_z$ and $V = V_x + V_y + V_z$, we have

$$\text{Change in } T + \text{change in } V = 0.$$

V is called the potential energy (P.E.) and is *defined* by $\mathbf{F} = -\text{grad } V$ (that is $F_x = -(\partial V/\partial x)$, etc.) We have, then,

$$\text{Change in } (V + T) = 0.$$

Since this is true for each particle, it is true for any number of particles considered as a whole—provided, of course, a function V can be found for each particle. If we put $U = V + T$, then we may write

$$\frac{dU}{dt} = 0$$

(compare this relation with that given in Section 5.2 for the momentum of a system of particles, $d\mathbf{P}/dt = 0$, except that U is a scalar quantity and not a vector). Hence $(V + T)$ is constant or U is constant. U is sometimes called the total energy but more often just "the energy". We see that if the potential energy decreases, the kinetic energy must increase and vice versa.

This constancy of U is true (as for momentum) for a closed system if we take *all* forms of energy into account. It is always possible in principle to find a function V such that

$$F_x = -\frac{\partial V}{\partial x}, \quad F_y = -\frac{\partial V}{\partial y}, \quad \text{and} \quad F_z = -\frac{\partial V}{\partial z}.$$

For the explicit conditions under which this is possible, see Problem 5.23. It should be noted that, for a system of particles, the potential energy is in general a function of all the coordinates of all the particles. In order to find the force on the ith particle in the v direction, we calculate $-(\partial V/\partial v_i)$.

Note that the change in kinetic energy when a particle moves under a force $\mathbf{F}$ along a path in space from $\mathbf{s}_1$ to $\mathbf{s}_2$ is

$$\int_{s_1}^{s_2} \mathbf{F} \cdot d\mathbf{s},$$

where $\mathbf{F} \cdot d\mathbf{s}$ is the scalar product of the two vectors $\mathbf{F}$ and $d\mathbf{s}$. The integral just written represents

$$\int_{x_1}^{x_2} F_x \, dx + \int_{y_1}^{y_2} F_y \, dy + \int_{z_1}^{z_2} F_z \, dz.$$

The unit of energy may be fixed by the relations

$$T = \int \mathbf{F} \cdot d\mathbf{s} \quad \text{or} \quad \mathbf{F} = -\text{grad } V$$

and is the joule in the MKS system and the erg in the cgs system. One joule $= 10^7$ erg.

If such a function V can be found, the system in question is called a conservative system, i.e. *energy is conserved*. This means that, if the system is in a given state, the potential energy V is the same no matter how it got there. Mathematically, this means that V is a function *only* of the coordinates of the particles. It does not depend, for instance, on the velocity of the particles. It is clear then that frictional forces, for instance, are non-conservative. For a conservative system, if we go from point r_1 to point r_2, the change in V is just $V(r_2) - V(r_1)$, independent of the path traversed in going from r_1 to r_2 (see Problem 5.29). This simple result has far reaching consequences which cannot be explored here.

Notice that the pendulum problem of Section 5.2 can be solved by energy considerations, even with a rigid support, since although it is not an isolated system negligible energy goes out to the support if $M \gg m$. We had $v_{M \max} = (m/M)\omega l \theta_0$. Therefore the maximal energy of M in horizontal motion is $\frac{1}{2}Mv_{M \max}^2 = \frac{1}{2}(m^2/M)(\omega l \theta_0)^2$ which can always be made small if $m \ll M$. Hence we need only consider the bob. We have $T = \frac{1}{2}mv^2 = \frac{1}{2}m(l\dot\theta)^2$ and $V = mgh = mgl(1 - \cos \theta)$,

$$\therefore \quad V + T = \tfrac{1}{2}ml^2\dot\theta^2 + mgl(1 - \cos \theta) = \text{a constant},$$

since the energy leaving the system through the support is negligible. Since $\dot\theta = 0$ for $\theta = \theta_0$, θ_0 being the amplitude of oscillation, we can determine the constant.

$$\text{constant} = mgl(1 - \cos \theta_0),$$
$$\therefore \quad \tfrac{1}{2}ml^2\dot\theta^2 = mgl(\cos \theta - \cos \theta_0)$$
$$\text{or } \dot\theta^2 = 2(g/l)(\cos \theta - \cos \theta_0)$$
$$\approx 2(g/l)(1 - \theta^2/2 - 1 + \theta_0^2/2) = (g/l)(\theta_0^2 - \theta^2),$$

for small θ_0. This equation for $\dot\theta$ corresponds to $\theta = \theta_0 \cos \omega t$ with $\omega = (g/l)^{1/2}$, since if this is so we have $\dot\theta = -\omega\theta_0 \sin \omega t$, so that

$$\dot\theta^2 = \omega^2\theta_0^2 \sin^2 \omega t = \omega^2\theta_0^2(1 - \cos^2 \omega t) \approx \omega^2\theta_0^2[1 - (\theta/\theta_0)^2] = \omega^2(\theta_0^2 - \theta^2).$$

This is the expression for $\dot\theta$ given above if $\omega^2 = g/l$. This is an example in which energy is conserved but momentum is not conserved. Such cases are always approximations, as in the present instance where the support for the pendulum is "rigid". Because the support is rigid, no work can be done on it, since in the expression $F_x \Delta x$, Δx is zero. However, the support can still exchange momentum with the bob, since in the expression $F_x \Delta t$ both F_x and Δt are non-zero. Such approximation in which the conservation laws are violated must be treated with great care.

It is sometimes said that when friction is involved the system is not conservative—as we did above. This is because we are looking at *part* of the system and we say energy is *lost* by friction. However, if we also look at the pieces being rubbed against, we have both that energy is conserved and $F = -\text{grad } V$, even though it would be impossible in practice to find V and to calculate the frictional force in this way. Of course momentum is also conserved. We can only say that energy is lost by friction and so is not conserved if we look at a part of the system, in the case of Fig. 5.7(a) at the block and pulley only. This may well be convenient to do in practice, since we can often simply represent the complex frictional V by a frictional force $\mathbf{F_f}$ which is easier to deal with but is clearly not a fundamental force between particles. The peculiar nature of $\mathbf{F_f}$ is seen when we note that it always acts in the opposite direction to the relative velocity of the two rubbing surfaces and is usually assumed to be independent of that velocity—$\mathbf{F_f}$ therefore has a discontinuity at $\mathbf{v} = 0$ as shown in Fig. 5.7(b).

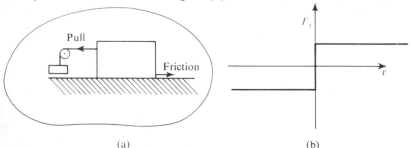

(a)   (b)   **Figure 5.7**

The idea of mechanical motion thus throws up the useful concepts of energy and momentum as alternatives to talking about forces. In a sense, a force is just something which is associated with momentum and energy, both kinetic and potential energy.

It turns out that it is almost always preferable to consider energy rather than forces. The reasons are:

1) Energy is a scalar quantity, whereas force is a vector quantity.

2) The idea of force leads to conceptual difficulties in all but elementary circumstances—it even does in Newton's equations! The difficulty with force is acute in relativity and in quantum mechanics. On the other hand, energy carries over nicely.

3) Energy is a quantity which is conserved whereas force is not and so energy is of more fundamental interest.

We are well on the way to removing forces but before we do so we shall just list all the ones we know of, in order of strength. They are gravitational, magnetic (really electric), electric, weak, and nuclear—these are all of them!—and they are all conservative.

5.5 CONSERVATION LAWS

Why are conservation laws important?

1) Because we can find out a lot without going into details, e.g. it is sometimes possible to say that something is impossible without any detailed calculation at all.

2) Mechanical conservation laws largely remove the need for knowledge of the details of forces.

3) Conservation laws are always connected with invariance which is probably a more fundamental idea. The relation of conservation laws to invariance is shown in Table 5.3.

Table 5.3

Conservation of		Invariance to
Linear momentum		Displacement in space
Angular momentum		Rotation in space
Energy⎱		Time
Mass ⎰ is equivalent to		
Charge		Zero of electric potential
Parity		Inversion in space
Baryons (neutron, proton, etc.)		?
Leptons (electron, μ meson, etc.)		?

5.6 DIMENSIONS

It is appropriate here to introduce a brief discussion of dimensions. Notice that energy × time has the same dimensions as momentum × distance. We have

$$\text{Energy} \times \text{time} = \text{force} \times \text{distance} \times \text{time} = M \frac{L}{T^2} \times L \times T = \frac{ML^2}{T},$$

since

$$\text{Force} = \text{mass} \times \text{acceleration}.$$

Again,

$$\text{Momentum} \times \text{distance} = \text{mass} \times \text{velocity} \times \text{distance} = M \frac{L}{T} \times L = \frac{ML^2}{T}.$$

Hence it is plausible that, *if* energy is related to time, *then* momentum is related to space, and so there is a plausible connexion between at least two of the items in Table 5.3. Apart from this rather intuitive application, dimensional analysis is useful in two distinct ways.

It is clear that all terms in an equation relating physical quantities must have the same dimensions and this is a very useful check that may reveal manipulative mistakes. Secondly, dimensional analysis may allow the deduction of a *possible* physical law provided we already have a reasonable understanding of the problem and provided it has a simple solution. These two conditions are not often satisfied! Thus we may expect the period $\mathscr{T}$ of a pendulum to depend on its length *l*, the mass of the bob *m*, and the acceleration due to gravity *g*. We then postulate that

$\mathcal{T} \propto l^a m^b g^c$. Then we can write the dimensional equation

$$T = L^a M^b (LT^{-2})^c = L^{a+c} M^b T^{-2c}$$

where the notation is obvious and we bear in mind that the numerical factor of proportionality is dimensionless. Homogeneity of dimensions (i.e. the dimensions on both sides of the dimensional equation must be the same) then requires that $a + c = 0$, $b = 0$, and $-2c = 1$, i.e. $c = -\frac{1}{2}$, $a = +\frac{1}{2}$, and $b = 0$. Therefore

$$\mathcal{T} \propto (l/g)^{1/2}$$

and is independent of m. This result is quite wrong! $\mathcal{T}$ in fact depends in a complicated way on θ_0, the amplitude of swing; however, for small amplitudes, the result *is* correct. The amplitude of swing θ_0 did not appear because it is dimensionless. In other cases, the exponents (a, b, etc.) may be overdetermined but nevertheless there may be some useful restrictive relations between them. Again, any function such as sin, exp, and so on does not appear, since such functions must be dimensionless quantities (see Problem 5.15); moreover the argument of sin, exp, etc., must be dimensionless. The latter is obvious for sin θ where θ is an angle, since an angle is the ratio of two lengths and so is dimensionless.

The solution of problems by the method of dimensions is not unique and is often useless. However, if it does give an answer it gives it quickly and it is often worth trying (see Problem 5.1). If we consider only mechanics, we can readily write down the dimensions of any quantity arising in terms of mass, length, and time (M, L, and T). Consequently, if we fix the units of mass, length, and time, we have fixed the units of all other mechanical quantities. However, if we also consider thermal and electrical (or magnetic) systems we need extra dimensional quantities. For example, in thermal systems it is convenient to use temperature Θ as a further dimensional quantity. All thermal quantities can then be expressed in terms of M, L, T, and Θ. For instance, Boltzmann's constant has dimensions $ML^2T^{-2}\Theta^{-1}$. The temperature *unit* is defined as the degree Kelvin and is such that the triple point of water is $273.16°$K. (The triple point is defined on page 29.)

5.7 ANGULAR MOMENTUM OR MOMENT OF MOMENTUM

Angular momentum is a useful extension of the idea of linear momentum but it is really nothing new. We depart from the idea of a simple particle for the moment. We have to introduce the idea of rotation. Suppose we have the situation shown in Fig. 5.8(a). Unless $\mathbf{v}_1 = \mathbf{v}_2$, the line joining the two particles turns and we have rotation. We shall consider rotation for a set of interacting particles forming a "body". Notice this is not necessarily, or even usually, a "rigid" body; the distances $\mathbf{r}_{ij} (= \mathbf{r}_i - \mathbf{r}_j)$ between the particles may, in general, vary with time. The velocities $\dot{\mathbf{r}}_i$ can correspond to a rotating body and the external forces can amount to a torque (which is defined below). In the simple special case shown in Fig. 5.8(b), the total force is $(\mathbf{F} + -\mathbf{F}) = 0$. Therefore the centre of mass, if initially stationary,

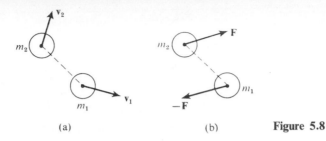

(a)   (b)   **Figure 5.8**

remains stationary (see Section 5.3) but the "body" *rotates*. It is often convenient to take the origin of coordinates at the centre of mass so that $\mathbf{R} = 0$ or $\sum_i m_i\mathbf{r}_i = 0$.

We define a torque, or moment of force, on a particle, $\mathbf{T}_i$, as $\mathbf{r}_i \times \mathbf{F}_i$.* Notice that, if $\mathbf{F}_i$ and $\mathbf{r}_i$ are parallel, $\mathbf{T}_i = 0$, which makes sense. Note that the origin 0 from which the $\mathbf{r}_i$ are measured may be any fixed point and is not necessarily the centre of mass of the body. We can write $|\mathbf{r}_i \times \mathbf{F}_i|$ as either $F_i(r_i \sin \phi)$ or $r_i(F_i \sin \phi)$ (see Fig. 5.9a). Thus the magnitude of the torque is either the force times the perpendicular distance from 0 to the line of action of the force, or the distance r_i from 0 to the particle times the component of the force perpendicular to r_i (Fig. 5.9a). We define an angular momentum $\mathbf{J}_i$ as $\mathbf{r}_i \times \mathbf{p}_i$. Since $|\mathbf{r}_i \times \mathbf{p}_i| = p_i(r_i \sin \psi)$, this is the moment of the momentum and hence the alternative, and better, name for angular momentum (Fig. 5.9b).

Note that angular momentum does not have the same dimensions as linear momentum—another reason for preferring the name "moment of momentum".

Since, by Newton's second law, $\mathbf{F}_i = d\mathbf{p}_i/dt$, we have

$$\mathbf{T}_i = \mathbf{r}_i \times \frac{d\mathbf{p}_i}{dt} = \frac{d}{dt}(\mathbf{r}_i \times \mathbf{p}_i) - \frac{d\mathbf{r}_i}{dt} \times \mathbf{p}_i.†$$

But

$$\frac{d\mathbf{r}_i}{dt} \times \mathbf{p}_i = \mathbf{v}_i \times \mathbf{p}_i = \mathbf{v}_i \times (m\mathbf{v}_i) = m(\mathbf{v}_i \times \mathbf{v}_i) = 0 \quad (\text{since } \theta = 0).$$

Therefore,

$$\mathbf{T}_i = \frac{d}{dt}(\mathbf{r}_i \times \mathbf{p}_i) = \frac{d}{dt}\mathbf{J}_i.$$

---

* The vector product of two vectors $\mathbf{A}$ and $\mathbf{B}$, which we write $\mathbf{A} \times \mathbf{B}$, is a vector at right angles to both $\mathbf{A}$ and $\mathbf{B}$ with the magnitude $|\mathbf{A}|\,|\mathbf{B}| \sin \theta$, where θ is the angle between the vectors $\mathbf{A}$ and $\mathbf{B}$.

† Note that

$$\frac{d}{dt}(\mathbf{A} \times \mathbf{B}) = \left(\mathbf{A} \times \frac{d\mathbf{B}}{dt}\right) + \left(\frac{d\mathbf{A}}{dt} \times \mathbf{B}\right);$$

the order of the vectors must be preserved but otherwise the rule is as for differentiation of a product of scalars.

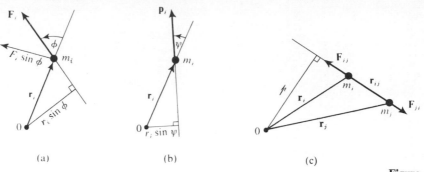

Figure 5.9

For a set of particles, we have $\sum \mathbf{T}_i = (d/dt) \sum \mathbf{J}_i$. We may write this in the form

$$\mathbf{T} = \frac{d\mathbf{J}}{dt}, \qquad \text{where } \mathbf{T} = \sum_i \mathbf{T}_i \quad \text{and} \quad \mathbf{J} = \sum_i \mathbf{J}_i.$$

The interest in considering the group of particles as a whole is that the resultant torque $\mathbf{T}$ involves only external forces. The contribution to $\mathbf{T}$ of all forces between particles vanishes because, by Newton's third law, these forces are equal and opposite in pairs. The magnitude of the torque due both to the action of particle i on particle j and that due to particle j on particle i is

$$|(\mathbf{r}_i \times \mathbf{F}_{ij} + \mathbf{r}_j \times \mathbf{F}_{ji})| = |\mathbf{F}_{ij}|\rho - |\mathbf{F}_{ji}|\rho = 0$$

where ρ is the perpendicular distance to the line joining particles i and j (Fig. 5.9c). More formally,

$$\mathbf{T} \equiv \sum_i \mathbf{r}_i \times \mathbf{F}_i = \sum_i \mathbf{r}_i \times \left(\mathbf{F}_{ii} + \sum_j \mathbf{F}_{ij}\right),$$

where $\mathbf{F}_{ii}$ is the external force on particle i.

$$\therefore \quad \mathbf{T} = \sum_i \mathbf{r}_i \times \mathbf{F}_{ii} + \sum_{i,j} \mathbf{r}_i \times \mathbf{F}_{ij}.$$

But, in the last term, we can exchange the labels i and j, since the sum is over both, so that

$$\sum_{i,j} \mathbf{r}_i \times \mathbf{F}_{ij} = \sum_{i,j} \mathbf{r}_j \times \mathbf{F}_{ji}.$$

Hence

$$\sum_{i,j} \mathbf{r}_i \times \mathbf{F}_{ij} = \tfrac{1}{2}\Big[\sum_{i,j} \mathbf{r}_i \times \mathbf{F}_{ij} + \sum_{i,j} \mathbf{r}_j \times \mathbf{F}_{ji}\Big] = \tfrac{1}{2}\Big[\sum_{i,j} \mathbf{r}_i \times (\mathbf{F}_{ij} + \mathbf{F}_{ji}) - \mathbf{r}_{ij} \times \mathbf{F}_{ji}\Big] = 0,$$

since $\mathbf{F}_{ij} = -\mathbf{F}_{ji}$ by Newton's third law, $\mathbf{r}_j = \mathbf{r}_i - \mathbf{r}_{ij}$, and $\mathbf{r}_{ij}$ is parallel to $\mathbf{F}_{ji}$. Hence

$$\mathbf{T} = \sum_i \mathbf{r}_i \times \mathbf{F}_{ii},$$

that is $\mathbf{T}$ is just the *external* torque (cf. $\sum \mathbf{F}_i = \mathbf{F}_{\text{ext}}$ in Section 5.3).

The relation $\mathbf{T} = (d\mathbf{J}/dt)$ is analogous to $\mathbf{F} = (d\mathbf{P}/dt)$, but is for rotation. Note that if $\mathbf{T} = 0$, i.e. there is no external torque, then $\mathbf{J}$ is constant. *Angular momentum is conserved* for an isolated system.

What is analogous for rotation to mass for translation? This is a little difficult to do properly in three dimensions so we do it for effectively two dimensions so that we can talk about a simple rotation about an axis. $\mathbf{F}_i$, $\mathbf{r}_i$, and $\mathbf{p}_i$ are now in the same plane but $\mathbf{T}_i$ and $\mathbf{J}_i$ are perpendicular to it. If $\mathbf{F}_i$ and $\mathbf{r}_i$ are defined to be in the xy plane, then $F_{iz} = 0$ and $z = 0$. $\mathbf{T}_i \equiv \mathbf{r}_i \times \mathbf{F}_i = \mathbf{k}(xF_y - yF_x)$, where $\mathbf{k}$ is a unit vector in the z direction. Again, $\mathbf{J}_i \equiv \mathbf{r}_i \times \mathbf{p}_i = \mathbf{k}(xp_y - yp_x) = \mathbf{k}J_{iz}$, where J_{iz} is the z component of the vector $\mathbf{J}_i(J_{ix} = J_{iy} = 0)$.

$$\therefore \quad J_{iz} = xp_y - yp_x = m_i(x\dot{y} - y\dot{x})$$

for each mass m_i. We have, quite generally (see Fig. 5.10a),

$$x = r \cos \theta \qquad \therefore \quad \dot{x} = -r \sin \theta \dot{\theta} + \dot{r} \cos \theta,$$

and

$$y = r \sin \theta \qquad \therefore \quad \dot{y} = r \cos \theta \dot{\theta} + \dot{r} \sin \theta.$$

$$\therefore \quad x\dot{y} - y\dot{x} = +r^2\dot{\theta} = +r^2\omega$$

where ω is the angular velocity. Substituting in the formula for J_{iz}, we have

$$J_{iz} = m_i r_i^2 \omega_i.$$

If ω is the same for all particles, as, e.g., for a rigid body, then

$$\therefore \quad J_z = \sum_i J_{iz} = (\sum_i m_i r_i^2)\omega = I\omega \qquad \text{where } I = \sum_i m_i r_i^2.$$

The relation is more complicated in the general three-dimensional case where the angular momentum vector $\mathbf{J}$ and the angular velocity vector $\boldsymbol{\omega}$ are not necessarily parallel to one another. The factor connecting $\mathbf{J}$ and $\boldsymbol{\omega}$ is then a tensor rather than a scalar quantity. $\mathbf{J}$ and $\boldsymbol{\omega}$ are parallel, that is the moment of inertia is a scalar quantity, if the body is symmetrical about its axis of rotation.

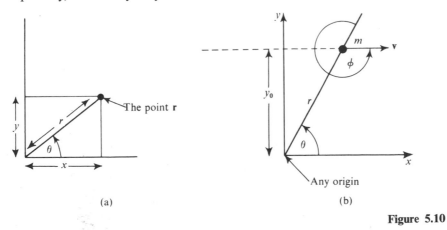

(a)

(b)

Figure 5.10

It should be noted that the moment of inertia I is clearly, in general, a quantity which may vary with time and only in special cases is the quantity referred to above a constant of the motion and a useful quantity.

As an example of variable moment of inertia, consider a single particle of mass m moving at uniform velocity v (there are therefore no forces acting on it) (see Fig. 5.10b). According to the definition, $J_z \equiv (\mathbf{r} \times \mathbf{p})_z = rp_x \sin \phi = rp_x \sin \theta = -y_0 p_x$, where $p_x = mv$, so that the angular momentum $\mathbf{J}$ is constant. This is as expected, since there are no external forces acting. On the other hand, we can show that $J = I\omega$. We have

$$I = mr^2 \quad \text{and} \quad \omega \equiv \dot{\theta} = \frac{1}{r^2}(x\dot{y} - y\dot{x}) = -\frac{y_0 \dot{x}}{r^2},$$

since $\dot{y} = 0$. (Note that both I and ω vary with time, since r varies with time.) We have

$$I\omega = mr^2 \times \left(-\frac{y_0 \dot{x}}{r^2}\right) = -my_0\dot{x} = -y_0(m\dot{x}) = -y_0 p_x,$$

so that $J = I\omega$ as we expected, even though I is a variable quantity. Clearly, the angular momentum about *any origin* is constant for this isolated system.

Notice that, although mass cannot be changed, moment of inertia can. In the simple example of Fig. 5.10(b), the moment of inertia is mr^2 which depends on the choice of origin and time.

In an isolated system, $\mathbf{J}$ is constant and therefore $I\omega$ is constant. For instance, consider a pair of similar spinning weights as in Fig. 5.11(a) where the separation $2r$ may vary. The centre point is the centre of mass because then $\sum_i m_i \mathbf{r}_i = m\mathbf{r} + m(-\mathbf{r}) = 0$. The moment of inertia I about the centre of mass is $\sum_i m_i r_i^2 = 2mr^2$. But $I\omega$ is constant; therefore $mr^2\omega$ is constant. Therefore $\omega = \text{constant}/mr^2$ or $\omega \propto 1/r^2$. If the weights are drawn in towards the centre, the rate of rotation increases—the spinning skater effect. Some care is required for non-rigid bodies where ω is not necessarily the same for all parts or all particles.

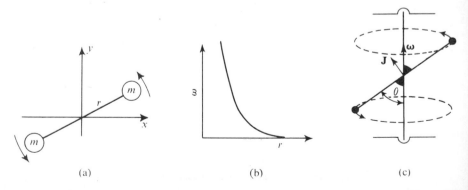

(a)   (b)   (c)

Figure 5.11

We recall that for translational motion we have $\mathbf{F} = d\mathbf{p}/dt$ and, if $\mathbf{p} = mv$, then

$$\mathbf{F} = m\frac{d\mathbf{v}}{dt} + \mathbf{v}\frac{dm}{dt}.$$

In the case of angular motion, $\mathbf{T} = d\mathbf{J}/dt$ and, if $\mathbf{J} = I\omega$,

$$\mathbf{T} = I\frac{d\omega}{dt} + \omega\frac{dI}{dt}.$$

Although, as we have seen, the relation between $\mathbf{T}$ and ω is in general complex, it is always true that $\mathbf{T} = d\mathbf{J}/dt$ provided $\mathbf{T}$ and $\mathbf{J}$ are measured from a point fixed in an inertial frame (or about the centre of mass). We have just considered the dumb-bell rotating freely about its centre of mass and in this case $\mathbf{J}$ and ω are parallel, there are no external forces and so $\mathbf{T} = 0$ and $\mathbf{J}$ is a constant. If we try to make the dumb-bell rotate about any other axis, we have to apply external torques to force it to do so and we can imagine this to be achieved, for instance, by the arrangement shown in Fig. 5.11(c), where the mass of the tie-rods and the rigid link between them is small compared with that of the balls. We also ignore gravitational forces. The system is constrained to rotate as indicated, so that the angular velocity vector ω is vertical. However, from the definition $\mathbf{J}_i = \mathbf{r}_i \times \mathbf{p}_i$, we see that $\mathbf{J}$ is perpendicular to the line joining the balls and in the plane of this line and ω. $\mathbf{J}$ changes its direction in time but ω does not. Since $\mathbf{J}$ changes, there must be an external torque applied to the system given by $\mathbf{T} = d\mathbf{J}/dt$. This must be provided by the supports and from the relation given the axis of $\mathbf{T}$ must be parallel to $\Delta\mathbf{J}$ which in this case is perpendicular to $\mathbf{J}$. Clearly, this torque can be provided by the forces due to the restraining bearings. We have an unbalanced system which is often thought of in terms of centrifugal forces. The restraining torque $\mathbf{T}$ is zero if $\theta = 90°$, since then $\mathbf{J}$ is constant (and incidentally parallel to ω) and so $d\mathbf{J}/dt = 0$. $\mathbf{T}$ is also zero if $\theta = 0°$, since then $\mathbf{J}$ is zero (if the balls are particles) and so again $d\mathbf{J}/dt = 0$.

The principle of the conservation of angular momentum leads to some elegant analyses of mechanical behaviour. One example is the deduction of Kepler's second law of planetary motion. This law states that equal areas of an orbit are swept out in equal times. This is obvious for a circular orbit but not for a hyperbola or an ellipse. For planetary motion, we can ignore the movement of the sun, since it is practically the centre of mass* and there are no external forces if we ignore the relatively small forces due to other planets. We therefore have rotation effectively about the centre of mass. We use the fact that angular momentum about the Sun is conserved (Fig. 5.12). The area ΔA of the orbit swept out by the path of the planet in the small time Δt is

$$\tfrac{1}{2}r^2\,\Delta\theta + \tfrac{1}{2}r\,\Delta\theta\,\Delta r.$$

---

* Mass of Sun = 333,000 × mass of Earth (see also Problem 5.25).

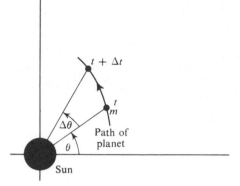

Figure 5.12

The second term is in the limit infinitesimal compared with the first and so may be neglected. Therefore

$$\frac{dA}{dt} = \tfrac{1}{2}r^2 \frac{d\theta}{dt}.$$

Also $I = mr^2$ so that

$$\text{Angular momentum} \equiv I\omega = (mr^2)\omega = mr^2 \frac{d\theta}{dt} = \text{constant,}$$

because of the conservation law.

$$\therefore \quad \frac{dA}{dt} = \text{constant,} \qquad \text{that is } A = c_1 t + c_2, \text{ where } c_1 \text{ and } c_2 \text{ are constants.}$$

Equal areas are swept out in equal times, which is Kepler's second law.

Notice that, from a general mechanical law, conservation of angular momentum, we have derived a general property of the motion, $dA/dt = \text{constant}$, without having to go into *details* of the motion. Note also that the observation that Kepler's second law is true supports Newton's laws of motion, since the conservation of angular momentum is based on Newton's laws. The result is true for planets, which move in ellipses with the Sun at one focus and for the classical picture of an atom where the electrons move in ellipses about the nucleus at one focus. It is physically plausible because the planet (electron) moves faster when it is nearer the Sun (nucleus). The orbits are similar because in both cases an inverse square law of force operates.

We can also consider rotational kinetic energy. As for angular momentum, this is not really a new concept but it is a useful quantity. We have, starting from the usual expression for the kinetic energy,

$$T = \sum_i \tfrac{1}{2}m_i v_i^2 = \tfrac{1}{2}\sum m_i(r_i\omega)^2 = \tfrac{1}{2}\omega^2 \sum m_i r_i^2 = \tfrac{1}{2}I\omega^2,$$

if ω is the same for all the particles, e.g. for a rigid body rotating about its centre of mass. This formulation is less useful than the corresponding one for momentum. In the simple example of the rotating dumb-bell of variable length, we found $\omega \propto r^{-2}$ and also we have $I \propto r^2$. Therefore $\frac{1}{2}I\omega^2 \propto r^{-2}$, although $I\omega$ is constant. The increase in energy with decreasing r corresponds to the work done in pulling the *rotating* weights in towards the centre. Here once more the calculation of the forces and accelerations involved would be a major operation but the general result, the final angular momentum, is obtained immediately from the conservation law. However, if we ask for more details, for instance exactly how a given internal pull brings the weights in a specified amount, then we should find it necessary to use more than just conservation laws.

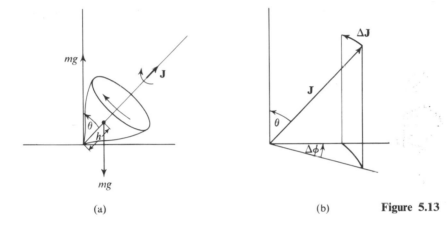

(a)   (b)   **Figure 5.13**

An important application of the formula $T = dJ/dt$ is to analyse the precession of a spinning top. Since $T = dJ/dt$,

$$T \approx \frac{\Delta J}{\Delta t} \quad \text{or} \quad \Delta J \approx T \, \Delta t.$$

The torque in this case is due to the weight of the top and the reaction of the supporting surface. Clearly, from Fig. 5.13(a), $|T| = mg(h \sin \theta)$ and T is directed into the paper at the moment chosen for Fig. 5.13(a). Since $\Delta J = T \, \Delta t$, ΔJ is also into paper at that moment and it is at that moment, as always, parallel to T. The *magnitude* of J does not change during the motion, because

$$\frac{d}{dt} (J \cdot J) = 2J \cdot \frac{dJ}{dt} = 2J \cdot T = 0$$

The last step results because J and T are at right angles.

$$\therefore \quad J \cdot J = |J|^2 = \text{constant}.$$

Suppose the top precesses by an angle $\Delta\phi$ about a vertical axis in a small time Δt, then (see Fig. 5.13b)

$$\Delta\phi = \frac{|\Delta\mathbf{J}|}{|\mathbf{J}| \sin\theta} = \frac{|\mathbf{T}|\,\Delta t}{|\mathbf{J}| \sin\theta}.$$

$$\therefore \quad \frac{\Delta\phi}{\Delta t} = \frac{|\mathbf{T}|}{|\mathbf{J}| \sin\theta} = \frac{mgh \sin\theta}{|\mathbf{J}| \sin\theta} = \frac{mgh}{|\mathbf{J}|}, \quad \text{that is } \omega_{\mathrm{p}} \equiv \frac{d\phi}{dt} \equiv \frac{mgh}{|\mathbf{J}|}.$$

This precession, independent of the angle θ, of systems with angular momentum subject to a torque is very widespread and important particularly in atomic phenomena, in atomic structure and therefore also in understanding the structure of molecules. It is the basic idea of magnetism and of the spin resonance experiments (9 and 11).

Elementary particles, all periodic atomic motions, and indeed all isolated rotating bodies have an angular momentum which is quantized. It is zero or an integral multiple of $h/4\pi = 0.52 \times 10^{-27}$ erg s. Because of this, angular momentum considerations are of fundamental importance and not just a useful elaboration of the concept of linear momentum as they are in Newtonian mechanics.

5.8   FORCES

We can now profitably summarize our views about forces. We have assumed that all the forces on particles are one- or two-body ones, that is $\mathbf{F}_i = \mathbf{F}_{ii} + \sum_j \mathbf{F}_{ij}$

(Sections 5.2 and 5.7). A typical one-body force $\mathbf{F}_{ii}$ is that produced by an electric field on a charged particle. A typical two-body force $\mathbf{F}_{ij}$ is the interaction between two particles, $E(x)$ (see Chapter 3). The two-body forces are assumed to be central and conservative. The latter is true for all the fundamental forces which were enumerated at the end of Section 5.4. When this is not true, the reason can usually be traced to some violation of our basic assumptions, most often because we are not dealing with particles. Thus the force on one atom due to two adjacent ones is not equal to the sum of the forces which each adjacent one would produce separately. This is clearly because an atom is not a particle and is less likely to be approximated by a particle at distances comparable to its diameter. The interaction between two bricks is not central or conservative because they are not particles and have a complex internal structure. In the second place, the classical laws of dynamics break down when the rate of propagation of the force cannot be regarded as infinite. As we shall see in Chapter 8, no signal can travel faster than the velocity of light and consequently a force on a particle A due to a particle B a distance d away must correspond to the state of particle B at a time at least d/c earlier. This is the most common explanation of paradoxes such as the breakdown of Newton's third law for the interaction of two charges or two dipoles.

We have only considered forces of interaction of particles which depend on position and, in the next chapter, on velocity. It can be shown by relativistic arguments that these are the only two types of forces which can arise (spin-dependent forces are met with but arise from combined quantum-mechanical and relativistic considerations).

5.9 GRAVITATION

The gravitational force on a particle is found experimentally to be proportional to the inertial mass of the particle. The gravitational force and the ability of *any* force to accelerate a piece of matter are two quite different things and the proportionality of the gravitational and the inertial masses is a very remarkable result. The proportionality can be demonstrated for macroscopic pieces of matter by a simple experiment (Fig. 5.14). We take two bodies A and B, which in general may have different masses, and join them by a sufficiently rigid rod of sufficiently small mass. In the first part of the experiment, we find the point X where pulling does not rotate the rod (in the absence of gravity of course, e.g. on a low-friction horizontal table). In the second part, we balance the rod so that it is horizontal and find the point of balance X'. Experiment shows that X and X' are the same point and therefore the inertial and gravitational masses are proportional to one another. The difference between the two types of mass is obscured to some extent by the fact that it is usual to use the same unit for both. The experimental result for the gravitational interaction is well known in terms of the attraction of two particles of inertial mass m_1 and m_2 at distance d, where the force is measured to be Gm_1m_2/d^2. G is a universal constant which must be determined by experiment (see Experiment 4), since we have already defined mass, length, and time. The dimensions of G are $L^3M^{-1}T^{-2}$. We have already shown that, for interaction between atoms at close range, the gravitational forces are quite negligible compared with the electrical ones. However, for large, effectively neutral, bodies such as the objects of everyday life, the planets, and the stars the gravitational forces dominate. Familiar objects cannot carry large charges without special arrangement, since even a relatively small charge produces electric fields which cause breakdown of the air and so the charge is rapidly neutralized or never developed. The fact that the gravitational force has an inverse square dependence on distance makes the dynamics of bodies subject to gravitational forces rather similar to that of charged bodies under electrostatic forces and vice versa. The important differences between gravitational and electrostatic forces are that we always have

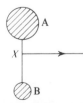

(a) Acceleration   (b) Gravity and
    and no gravity   no acceleration   **Figure 5.14**

gravitational *attraction* (it may be that antimatter repels matter) and we canno'
screen out a gravitational field as we can an electric field.

In the very special case where one attracting body is the Earth and we measure
the force on another body at the surface of the Earth, we can characterize the
amount of material in that body by its weight. For a body of gravitational mass m
the force on it is given by

$$F = GmM_E/R_E^2 = mg, \quad \text{where} \quad g = GM_E/R_E^2.$$

Clearly, the weight of a body is much less fundamental than its mass. It varies
from place to place on the Earth and is much less on the Moon. Moreover, weight
is a vector quantity and as far as we know mass is a scalar.

Looking at inertial mass more closely, we realize it is not really a local phenomenon. In order to measure inertial mass, we must be able to define an inertia'
frame of reference and to do this we refer to the "fixed" stars. Hence the loca
property of inertial mass must depend in some way on the large-scale universe
In the same way, the gravitational force certainly depends on the presence of other
matter and so may also be associated with the rest of the universe. We begin to
see a connexion between the two types of mass. Another connexion is that a
uniform acceleration and a uniform gravitational field cannot be distinguished
by physical measurements. It is interesting that the question of the relation between
inertial and gravitational mass arose at an early stage since Newton's laws of
motion were derived in connexion with the dynamics of celestial bodies.

The law of gravitation and Newton's second law of motion together imply
the proportionality of inertial and gravitational masses. Consider the attraction
of the Earth, of mass M_E and radius R_E, for two bodies A and B. We can measure
their gravitational masses from the force of attraction of the Earth on them.

$$F_A = GM_{AG}M_E/R_E^2$$

and similarly, for M_{BG}, we have $F_A/F_B = M_{AG}/M_{BG}$. But F_A and F_B are just the
observed weights of the two masses W_A and W_B, so that $W_A/W_B = M_{AG}/M_{BG}$
We now observe that the weight of a body causes an inertial mass M_{AI} to have an
acceleration g, that is $W_A = M_{AI}g$ and $W_B = M_{BI}g$, so that $W_A/W_B = M_{AI}/M_{BI}$
Hence $M_{AI}/M_{BI} = M_{AG}/M_{BG}$. Hence $M_I \propto M_G$ for any body; the gravitational
and inertial masses are proportional to one another, as we set out to show.

Of course, every experiment which includes acceleration under gravity
involves the ratio of inertial to gravitational mass. For example, if we make the
distinction between the two types of mass, we have for the period of a simple
pendulum

$$T = 2\pi \sqrt{\frac{M_I l}{M_G g}}.$$

Newton performed the first experiments which showed that T is the same whatever
the density or the material of which the bob is composed so that $M_I \propto M_G$. It is
therefore simplest to define the two units so that $M_I = M_G$. The standard of

mass is actually one of gravitational mass, since comparisons are rather simpler to perform than for inertial mass; we do the experiment of Fig. 5.14(b) rather than that of 5.14(a).

It is now known from experiment that the proportionality between gravitational and inertial mass is correct to at least one part in 10^{11}.*

PROBLEMS

5.1. Show by dimensional analysis that the viscous force on a sphere of radius a travelling at velocity v through a liquid of viscosity η could be proportional to $\eta a v$. (Complete answer is $6\pi\eta a v$ and is true for streamline flow.) Show that the force could also be proportional to $a^2 v^2 \rho$, where ρ is the density of the fluid. Give a physical explanation of the difference between these two results.

5.2. The moment of inertia of a body of mass M about an axis through its centre of mass is I_{cm}. Show that the moment of inertia about a parallel axis a distance R away is $I_{cm} + MR^2$.

5.3. Suggest a method for measuring the radius of the Earth.

5.4. From the values of the universal gravitational constant G, the acceleration due to gravity at the surface of the earth g_E, and the Earth's radius R_E, calculate the mass of the Earth. What is the mean density of the Earth?

5.5. Given the universal gravitational constant, the mass of the earth, the lunar month, and that the Moon's diameter subtends an angle $\frac{1}{2}°$ at the Earth, calculate the radius of the Moon.

5.6. A particle in an elliptic orbit has speed v_1 or v_2 when it is at one end or the other of the major axis of the ellipse and it is then at distance r_1 or r_2 from the centre of attraction. Use Kepler's second law to show that $v_1/v_2 = r_2/r_1$.

5.7. A force $\mathbf{F}$ is applied to a fixed point in a rigid body which can rotate about another point in the body fixed in space and the force $\mathbf{F}$ is at right angles to the axis of rotation. Show that, if the force $\mathbf{F}$ is in the xy plane,

$$F_x \Delta x + F_y \Delta y = (xF_y - yF_x)\Delta\theta,$$

i.e. the work done by the force is the torque times the angle of rotation.

5.8. Show that, for motion in a plane, the kinetic energy of a particle at the point $\mathbf{r}(t)$ is given by $\frac{1}{2}m\dot{r}^2 + \frac{1}{2}\mathbf{J}^2/I$, where $\mathbf{J}$ is the angular momentum and I the moment of inertia about the origin.

5.9. The present-day abundances of the uranium isotopes ^{238}U and ^{235}U are in the ratio 138:1. The half-life of ^{235}U is 7×10^8 years and of ^{238}U is 4.5×10^9 years. Presumably then, long ago there was relatively more ^{235}U. Assume that, at the time the uranium was trapped in the Earth's crust, the relative abundances were equal. Hence obtain an estimate of the age of the Earth.

5.10. A spacecraft weighing 100 metric tons is projected into stable orbit close to the Earth's surface in an easterly direction above the equator. Estimate the increase in the period

---

* R. H. DICKE, *Scientif. Am.* December (1961).

of revolution of the Earth in seconds during the time that the space craft is in orbit. $(I = \frac{2}{5}MR^2$ for a uniform sphere; a metric ton is 1000 kg.)

5.11. Show that a thin spherical shell of matter produces a gravitational force at points outside the shell as if all its mass were concentrated at the centre of the sphere and that it produces no gravitational force inside itself. Hence, or otherwise, show that the variation in density, if any, of the Earth cannot be detected by gravimetric measurements *outside* the Earth provided the density distribution is spherically symmetric.

5.12. It is thought that the Earth may have an outer layer, the mantle, which is less dense than the inner material, the core. Show how measurements of the acceleration due to gravity as a function of depth, given in the table, indicate that this might be so. (Use the result of Problem 5.11.)

g, cm s^{-2}	981	985	989
Depth, km	0	33	100

5.13. The difference in acceleration due to gravity g, as between the north pole and the equator, is found to be about 5 cm s^{-2}. Assume that most of this difference is due to the fact that the Earth is rotating and hence obtain a value for the radius of the Earth. Where is g greater, at the north pole or at the equator?

5.14. The electron is known to have an angular momentum $\frac{1}{2}(h/2\pi)$. Consider as a possible model for the electron a dumb-bell consisting of two point masses $\frac{1}{2}m_e$ each carrying a charge $\frac{1}{2}e$ separated by a fixed distance $2a$. Note that the rotating charges constitute an electric current i which generates a magnetic field which at distances much greater than a corresponds to a dipole moment μ, given by $\mu = \pi a^2 i$. Hence show that the magnetic moment of the electron is $eh/8\pi m_e c$ e.m.u. independent of a, which is just half the experimentally observed value.

Show that the more plausible assumption of an electron with a spherically symmetric distribution of charge gives the same result.

5.15. Explain why the argument x in sin x, log x, exp x, etc., must be dimensionless.

5.16. Show that the escape velocity of a projectile from the surface of a spherical body of mass M and radius R is $(2GM/R)^{1/2}$. Show that this is 11 km s^{-1} for the Earth. What is it for the Moon?

5.17. The classical picture of the excitation of an electron in an atom to a higher orbit by electromagnetic radiation shows that this will be most effectively done by radiation which is circularly polarized about an axis which is the axis of the electronic orbit. Explain this and explain why this means that the electromagnetic radiation must have an associated angular momentum (quantum mechanically, the angular momentum of a photon is $\hbar$).

5.18. The two components of a double star move in concentric circles with radii in the ratio R. What is the ratio of their masses?

5.19. A particle collides elastically head-on with a stationary particle. After the collision, the originally stationary particle is moving faster (slower) than the first. What can be said about the masses?

5.20. What is the height of a Syncom satellite orbit? (Such a satellite appears stationary from the Earth.)

5.21. Show that the reduced mass $m_1m_2/(m_1 + m_2)$ is less than m_1 or m_2 (hence the name!).

5.22. Show that, for two particles of masses m_1 and m_2 at r_1 and r_2 moving with velocities $\dot{r}_1$ and $\dot{r}_2$, (a) the kinetic energy, $\frac{1}{2}m\dot{r}_1^2 + \frac{1}{2}m_2\dot{r}_2^2$, can be written as $\frac{1}{2}M\dot{R}^2 + \frac{1}{2}\mu\dot{r}^2$ and (b) the angular momentum about the origin can be expressed as $MR \times \dot{R} + \mu r \times \dot{r}$, where $M = m_1 + m_2$, $\mu = m_1m_2/(m_1 + m_2)$, R is the position of the centre of mass, and r is the distance between the particles.

5.23. For a conservative system, the forces must be derivable from a potential V such that $F = -\mathrm{grad}\ V$, that is $F_x = -(\partial V/\partial x)$, $F_y = -(\partial V/\partial y)$, and $F_z = -(\partial V/\partial z)$. Show that this is so provided curl $F = 0$, i.e. if $\partial F_x/\partial y - \partial F_y/\partial x = 0$, $\partial F_y/\partial z - \partial F_z/\partial y = 0$, and $\partial F_z/\partial x - \partial F_x/\partial z = 0$.

5.24. Find out if the following forces are conservative (see Problem 5.23):

a) $F_x = ay$, $F_y = az$, $F_z = ax$
b) $F_x = ax + by^2$, $F_y = az + 2bxy$, $F_z = ay + bz^2$.

5.25. Show that the centre of mass of the Sun and the Earth is inside the Sun.

5.26. Explain the statement "weight is a variable vector quantity and mass is a constant scalar quantity".

5.27. Compare the magnitudes of the orbital and spin angular momenta of the Earth.

5.28. Show that, in any elastic collision between any two particles as viewed in the centre of mass system of coordinates, the velocities of the particles are reversed by the collision.

5.29. The force field of Problem 5.24(b) is conservative. Show explicitly that the work done, $\int F \cdot ds$, on a particle moving from the origin, O, $(0, 0, 0)$, to C, $(\beta, \alpha, 0)$ is the same whether it goes by straight paths from O to A, $(0, \alpha, 0)$ to C or from O to B, $(\beta, 0, 0)$ to C.

5.30. Show that, for a thin hoop, the moment of inertia about a perpendicular axis through the centre is twice that for an axis in the plane of the hoop through the centre.

5.31. Use a table of sines to find the largest angle θ ($|\theta| < \pi/2$) for which $\sin \theta = \theta$ to an accuracy of 1% (N.B. θ is, of course, in radians).

5.32. In the kinetic theory of gases, it is shown that $D\rho/\eta = 1$ and $KM/\eta C_v = 1$, where D is the coefficient of self-diffusion, ρ is the density, η is the viscosity, K is the thermal conductivity, M is the molecular weight, and C_v is the molar specific heat at constant volume (see Chapter 7). Show that these two relations are dimensionally correct.

5.33. Show that the equation K.E. $= \frac{1}{2}mv^2$ is dimensionally correct.

5.34. Show that the equation $E^2 = p^2c^2 + m^2c^4$ is dimensionally correct. (E is an energy, p is a momentum, c is the velocity of light, and m is a mass; see Section 8.6.)

5.35. Show that the moment of inertia of a hydrogen molecule about an axis through its centre of gravity and perpendicular to the line joining the nuclei is about 0.5×10^{-40} g cm^2. What is the corresponding value for hydrogen deuteride?

5.36. It is stated in Chapter 1 that the reaction

$$O_3 \rightarrow O_2 + O + 17 \text{ kcal mol}^{-1}$$

can occur spontaneously. Does it require the presence of another body to conserve momentum?

5.37. Find the order of magnitude of the maximal force between two isolated argon atoms (use data given in Chapter 4). Hence show that the maximal acceleration of two argon atoms may be of order $10^{14}g$, where g is the acceleration due to gravity at the Earth's surface.

5.38. Show that the force $\mathbf{F} = -\kappa x\mathbf{i}$ for a simple harmonic oscillator ($\mathbf{i}$ is a unit vector in the x direction) is conservative, i.e. show that curl $\mathbf{F} = 0$ (see Problem 5.23 for definition of curl). Find the potential energy function V for this case from the relation $\mathbf{F} = -\text{grad } V$.

5.39. In the problem considered in Section 5.7, Fig. 5.10 (b), the torque on the freely moving particle is zero so that we expect $(d/dt)(I\omega) = 0$. Show explicitly that this is true using the expressions for I and ω.

5.40. Show that the acceleration due to gravity g at the Earth's surface is consistent with the measured quantities G, M_E, and R_E.

5.41. Show that the acceleration due to gravity at height h ($\ll R_E$) above the Earth is the fraction $2h/R_E$ smaller than at the surface.

CHAPTER 6

Dynamics of particles
in electromagnetic fields

I selected the bodies with the smallest atomic weight and ordered them
according to the magnitude of their atomic weights. MENDELÉEFF

6.1 ELECTRIC FIELD—the cathode ray oscilloscope

Suppose an electron or a nucleus, or indeed any particle, with charge q passes
through a region in which there is an electric field $\mathbf{E}$, whose direction is transverse
to the initial motion of the particle, as for instance in a cathode ray oscilloscope
(Fig. 6.1). Before entering the field, the momentum in the x direction is $p_x = mv_x$
and the particle is moving in the x direction. The force on the particle when
between the plates is $\mathbf{E}q$ in the direction of $\mathbf{E}$ and hence effectively perpendicular
to its motion. If q and E are in cgs electrostatic units, the force Eq is in dynes.
If q is in coulombs and E is in volts per metre, then the force Eq is in newtons.*

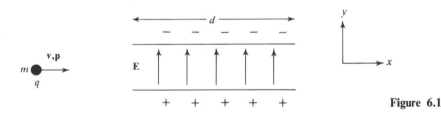

Figure 6.1

In this section, we shall quote results where necessary in both cgs (or gaussian)
units and in MKS units. In atomic physics, it is still most usual to use cgs units
but in electricity and magnetism there is a considerable advantage in using MKSA
or SI units. It seems likely that in the foreseeable future many different systems of
units will remain in use and we must learn to deal with them all, tedious as this may
be. The reason why there are many systems of units is that, if we are working in
a given field, the overriding consideration, apart from accuracy, is convenience
and conciseness, and so the most convenient and concise system of units will be
used. Thus people who deal with electromagnetic waves essentially *in vacuo* tend
to use gaussian units, since in this system both the permittivity and permeability

---

* We remind the reader that 1 coulomb $= 3 \times 10^9$ e.s.u. of charge, 1 volt $= 1/300$ e.s.u. of
potential difference, and one newton $= 10^5$ dynes.

of free space are unity. Quantum mechanicians tend to use a system in which $\hbar$ is taken to be unity and relativists one in which c is unity.

We continue our discussion of the motion of a charged particle projected into a transverse electric field. We note that the time of passage through the plates during which the particle is subject to $\mathbf{E}$ is d/v_x whatever the transverse velocity acquired. The particle therefore accumulates in passing through the plates a momentum in the y direction given by $p_y = Eq(d/v_x)$ and hence a transverse velocity given by $v_y = Eqd/mv_x$. Usually, the time spent inside the plates is short compared with the time in free flight afterwards and so it is v_y which determines the resultant deflexion rather than any *details* of what happened while the particle was subject to the field. In a distance D, the particle gets off the centre line (Fig. 6.2b) due to its transverse velocity v_y by a distance $v_y \times D/v_x = EqdD/mv_x^2$. But if the accelerating potential difference for the charged particles in the "gun" is V_0, we have $\frac{1}{2}mv_x^2 = qV_0$. If the potential difference between the plates with separation s is V_p, $E = V_p/s$. Thus the transverse deflexion T is

$$\left(\frac{V_p}{s}\right)\left(\frac{qdD}{2qV_0}\right) = \left(\frac{V_p}{V_0}\right)\left(\frac{dD}{2s}\right).$$

Hence the deflexion does not depend on the charge or the mass of the particles! It is a good exercise to explain physically why this is so. Typical values in a cathode ray tube, for which the particles involved are electrons, are $V_p = \sim 10$ v, $V_0 \sim 500$ v, $d \sim 2$ cm, $D \sim 20$ cm, $s \sim \frac{1}{2}$ cm. Hence, using the formula just given, we get for the deflexion

$$T = \frac{10 \times 2 \times 20}{500 \times 2 \times \frac{1}{2}} \approx 1 \text{ cm.}$$

The path of any, otherwise free, charged particle in a uniform electric field is a parabola just as it is for a projectile under the influence of gravity near the Earth's surface (Problem 6.12).

Another special case of interest is when a charged particle passes from a region of one uniform electric potential to a region of different uniform electric potential.

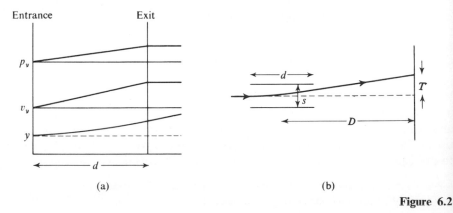

(a)   (b)

Figure 6.2

In the regions of uniform potential, the particle is not accelerated, since there is no field. We have $\mathbf{E} = -\mathrm{grad}\ V$. The vector grad V has cartesian components $(\partial V/\partial x, \partial V/\partial y, \partial V/\partial z)$; thus, if V is a constant independent of x, y, and z, grad $V = 0$. For a charge q, we may write $\mathbf{E}q = -\mathrm{grad}\ qV$ and then this expression is the exact analogue of the mechanical relation $\mathbf{F} = -\mathrm{grad}\ V$ of Section 5.4 when we remember that here V is the potential energy *per unit charge* whereas there V was the potential energy. However, where the potential changes with position, there must be a field. If the change is "rapid enough", the change in potential can be regarded to a sufficiently good approximation as equivalent to a parallel plate condenser through which the particle passes without mechanical hindrance. The change in the kinetic energy of the charged particle is due to the electric field in the "condenser" and the change in potential is $(V_1 - V_2)$, so that $\frac{1}{2}mv_2^2 - \frac{1}{2}mv_1^2 = q(V_1 - V_2)$. Alternatively, we may write this equation in the more interesting form

$$\tfrac{1}{2}mv_2^2 + qV_2 = \tfrac{1}{2}mv_1^2 + qV_1$$

or

$$\text{K.E.}_2 + \text{P.E.}_2 = \text{K.E.}_1 + \text{P.E.}_1$$

which simply expresses conservation of energy. The total energy is constant. Notice that if $v_2 > v_1$, $V_2 < V_1$ for q positive. Also $v_1 \sin \alpha_1 = v_2 \sin \alpha_2$ because there is no transverse force (see Fig. 6.3) and so the path of the particle can be determined. This is just like the Newtonian form of Snell's law for the diffraction of light, $\sin \alpha_1/\sin \alpha_2 = v_2/v_1$. Hence a change of potential for a beam of charged particles is like a change of refractive index for a ray of light. Because of this analogy, we often speak of the arrangements for manipulating electrons in electron microscopes, in radio valves such as klystrons, etc., as electron optics and of the manipulation of beams of ions, as for example in the mass spectrograph, as ion optics. The calculation of trajectories in other than the simplest field configurations is complex and must in practice be done by computer. Deflexion of charged particles by electrostatic fields is used in many instruments, e.g. cathode ray oscilloscopes, some electron microscopes, some television tubes, etc.

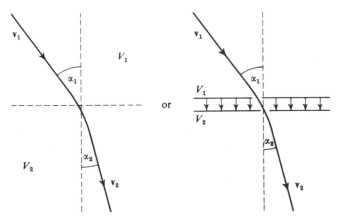

Figure 6.3

6.2 MAGNETIC FIELD—the mass spectrograph

In a steady magnetic field, the force on a moving charge is $\mathbf{F} = q(\mathbf{v}/c) \times \mathbf{B}$.*
This is the same effect as the force on a current in a magnetic field. In this expression, if q is in e.s.u. of charge, B is in gauss, and $\mathbf{v}$ and c are in cm s^{-1}, then
F is in dynes. This corresponds to the gaussian system of units. In MKSA units,
this would be written $\mathbf{F} = q\mathbf{v} \times \mathbf{B}$ where q is in coulombs, $\mathbf{v}$ is in m s^{-1}, B is in
wb m^{-2}†, and F is in newtons. It can be shown that this force may be derived
from the Coulomb "electrostatic" interaction of a moving charge by a relativistic
effect; the factor $\mathbf{v}/c$ may be rather loosely regarded as an indication of this. This
force has the unusual property that it is at right angles to both the velocity of the
charged particle and the field acting on it. We can show that this force does no
work as follows. The work done when the point of application of a force F_x
in the x direction moves dx is $F_x\,$dx or, in general, the work done is d$w = \mathbf{F} \cdot$ d$\mathbf{r}$.
If this work is done in time dt, the rate of working is

$$\frac{dw}{dt} = \frac{\mathbf{F} \cdot d\mathbf{r}}{dt} = \mathbf{F} \cdot \mathbf{v}.$$

In this case, $\mathbf{F} \cdot \mathbf{v} = q(\mathbf{v}/c \times \mathbf{B}) \cdot \mathbf{v} = 0$, since $\mathbf{v} \times \mathbf{B}$ is perpendicular to $\mathbf{v}$. The
speed $|\mathbf{v}|$, which is a scalar quantity, is constant but the velocity $\mathbf{v}$, which is a vector,
is not.

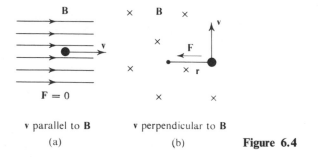

v parallel to **B**   v perpendicular to **B**

(a)   (b)   **Figure 6.4**

Look first at two extreme cases (Fig. 6.4). If $\mathbf{v}$ is parallel to $\mathbf{B}$, $\mathbf{F} = 0$ because
$\mathbf{v} \times \mathbf{B} = 0$. Thus in a uniform magnetic field a charge initially moving parallel
to the field continues to move parallel to it (Fig. 6.4a). If $\mathbf{v}$ is perpendicular to
$\mathbf{B}$ (Fig. 6.4b), the magnitude of the force on the charge is given by $F = q(vB/c)$.
Since the force is always perpendicular to the velocity, the particle will move in a
circle of radius r, such that the acceleration towards the centre v^2/r is produced
by the magnetic force. Thus

$$qvB/c = \frac{mv^2}{r} \qquad \therefore \quad r = \frac{mvc}{qB} = \frac{pc}{qB}.$$

---

* See first footnote on page 77.
† 1 wb m^{-2} = 10^4 gauss.

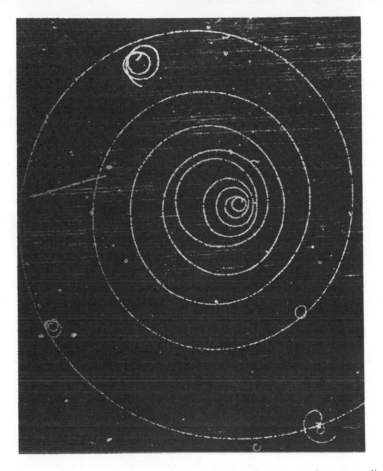

Figure 6.5. Cloud chamber photograph of the track of an electron moving perpendicular to a magnetic field. As the particle slows down the radius of curvature decreases and the electron spirals in until it is captured. The small spirals are either secondary or stray slow moving electrons. [From F. R. STANNARD *Phys. Educ.* **1** (1966).]

Hence particles moving parallel to a magnetic field tend to continue to move parallel to it, but particles moving perpendicular to a magnetic field travel in circular paths round it. Notice that deflexion of a charged particle moving perpendicular to a magnetic field is a measure of the *momentum* of the particle. It does not give the velocity unless we know the mass—which is often not known, especially in nuclear physics. The angular frequency ω_c is v/r, $\therefore$ $\omega_c = v/r = qB/mc$, that is q/m can be determined in this way. ω_c is called the cyclotron frequency and the effect is very common (see Problem 6.13). It is used, for instance, in a particle accelerator called the cyclotron. Notice that ω_c is independent of the particle velocity. Cloud chamber photographs of paths of charged particles moving perpendicular to a magnetic field are shown in Fig. 6.5.

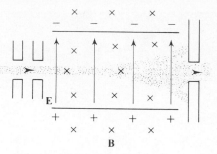

Figure 6.6

An important use of the force due to a steady magnetic field on a beam of charged particles is in the mass spectrograph.

Firstly, we need a beam of particles of uniform velocity. This can be achieved by crossed E and B fields, as used first by Thomson (Fig. 6.6). The force due to **E** is $q\mathbf{E}$ in the direction of **E**. The force due to **B** is $q(\mathbf{v}/c) \times \mathbf{B}$ which is $(q/c)vB$ at right angles to **v** and **B**. There is no force and therefore no deflexion for particles such that $qvB/c = qE$, i.e. with $v = cE/B$. Particles with velocity near this value emerge from the slit. Alternatively, the particles can be selected by a curved condenser. The velocity of a particle of mass m which emerges is given by $v = (VR_1q/dm)^{1/2}$ (see Fig. 6.7 and Problem 6.7). We then need a device which separates the particles of this given velocity in the first method, or with the known relation between their mass and velocity in the second method, into particles of given mass, i.e. of given momentum. This can be done with a uniform transverse magnetic field. The particles which follow a path of radius R_2, which is pc/qB, have a mass

$$m = qB^2/c^2ER_2$$

in the first method and

$$m = B^2qdR_2^2/VR_1c^2$$

in the second method. Isotopes were discovered from such experiments. Aston (1919) found, for instance, that beams of charged particles from neon gave lines

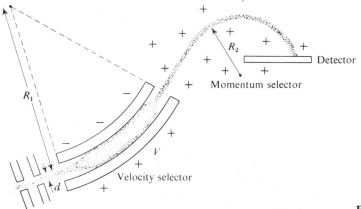

Figure 6.7

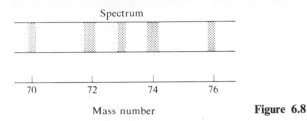

Figure 6.8

corresponding to masses 20 and 22 times that of the hydrogen atom with intensities in the ratio 10:1. The weighted mean of these masses is 20.2, which is the chemical atomic weight. J. J. Thomson had earlier (1912) observed these two lines of neon but his accuracy was not sufficient for him to realize that the stronger line is at 20 and not at 20.2. The "spectrum" of isotopes for germanium which spreads from 70 to 76 is shown in Fig. 6.8. The chemical value of the atomic weight is 72.60. This discovery is of tremendous significance in understanding atomic weights and of course the properties of the nucleus.

The masses of atoms from the mass spectrograph are very close to integral multiples of the mass of the hydrogen atom, even for large nuclei like uranium, as can be seen from Table 6.1.

The mass spectrograph can be used for the detection of chemical species. The substance to be studied is ionized by an electron beam or in an arc and the mass of the ions produced is measured. For instance, methane (CH_4) gives the ions CH_4^+, CH_3^+, and CH_2^+, and CH^+. If these are detected (at mass numbers 16, 15, 14, and 13) in correct proportions, then the original substance can be identified. The mass spectrometer is now so accurate that it can distinguish H_2 from D and ^{16}O from CH_4 and so on, where the differences in mass of such "doublets"

Table 6.1

Atom		Mass
	n (neutron)	1.00861
Hydrogen	^1_1H (proton)	1.00782
	^2_1H (deuteron)	2.01409
Helium	^4_2He	4.00259
Carbon	$^{12}_6C$	12.0000 (standard)
Nitrogen	$^{14}_7N$	14.00304
Oxygen	$^{16}_8O$	15.99488
	$^{17}_8O$	16.99908
	$^{18}_8O$	17.99910
Neon	$^{20}_{10}Ne$	19.99238
Uranium	$^{234}_{92}U$	234.0388
	$^{235}_{92}U$	235.0418
	$^{238}_{92}U$	238.0487

Table 6.2

$H_2 = 2.01564$	$^{16}O = 15.99488$	$^{12}CH = 13.00782$
$D = 2.01409$	$^{12}CH_4 = 16.03128$	$^{13}C = 13.00332$

are quite small, as can be seen in Table 6.2. Consequently, even quite large molecules can be *uniquely* identified simply from their mass or the mass of fragments of them (see Problems 6.3 and 6.4).

A mass spectrometer is also often used to detect and identify the products of nuclear reactions. For example, in some nuclear reactions both ^{3}He and ^{4}He nuclei are produced and we want to know the relative proportion of each.

A simple mass spectrometer may be used as a leak detector for vacuum systems. A little helium is blown round the suspected leak and helium is detected at the exhaust of the pumps when the leak has been located (Fig. 6.9).

In non-uniform magnetic fields, the motion of charged particles is complex but is often of great importance. Non-uniform magnetic fields are used for focusing the beam in particle accelerators so that the beam stays inside the field of the bending magnets and can be passed down a narrow pipe. The Van Allen radiation belts around the Earth are due to charged particles which have become trapped in the Earth's inhomogeneous magnetic field. The particles spiral around the lines of the Earth's field because of the force $(q/c)\mathbf{v} \times \mathbf{B}$ but as the field becomes stronger nearer to the surface of the Earth the spiral becomes tighter and finally the velocity of the particle in the direction of the line of force is reversed. The particle then spirals back until it is again "reflected" by the increase in field strength, as shown in Fig. 6.10. The particle once trapped has difficulty in escaping and so there is an accumulation of charged particles spiralling back and forth forming a radiation belt in a sort of doughnut whose axis of symmetry is the Earth's magnetic axis. A similar effect is employed in containing plasma by suitably "shaped" magnetic fields.

In many applications, both electric and magnetic fields are used at the same time and they are not necessarily either perpendicular to one another or uniform. The dynamics of the motion of the charged particle is then obtained from the

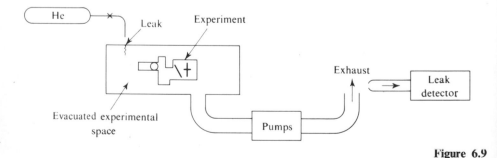

Figure 6.9

Lorentz force,

$$\mathbf{F} = q\left(\mathbf{E} + \frac{1}{c}\mathbf{v} \times \mathbf{B}\right),$$

and Newton's equations of motion. This can be a very involved calculation. In the expression quoted, we are thinking in terms of gaussian units, the most convenient ones for electromagnetism *in vacuo*. In MKSA units, we would write $\mathbf{F} = q(\mathbf{E} + \mathbf{v} \times \mathbf{B})$ where q is in coulombs and $\mathbf{B}$ is in wb m^{-2}. The Lorentz force just quoted is of fundamental importance. It might well be used, for instance, to identify and define the electric and magnetic fields $\mathbf{E}$ and $\mathbf{B}$ in free space by the measurement of the force $\mathbf{F}$ on a particle carrying a charge q. It represents the simplest and most direct relation between mechanics and electromagnetism and it is relativistically invariant (see Chapter 9).

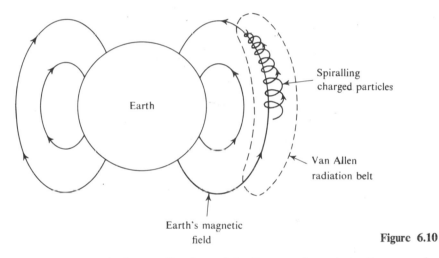

Spiralling
charged particles

Earth

Van Allen
radiation belt

Earth's magnetic
field

Figure 6.10

An important particular application of the Lorentz force is to the case of a metal or semiconductor subject to electric and magnetic fields at right angles to each other. In an electric field alone, the electrons tend to flow in the opposite direction to the field, since they are negatively charged, and we have the usual electrical conductivity. In a magnetic field alone, there is no observable flow of charge since the force $e\mathbf{v} \times \mathbf{B}$ is on average zero since the average of $\mathbf{v}$ is zero. However, in the presence of both $\mathbf{E}$ and $\mathbf{B}$, the velocity $\mathbf{v}$ has a non-zero mean value owing to the drift of the electrons and so the mean magnetic force, $e\mathbf{v} \times \mathbf{B}$, is no longer zero. The electrons tend to move to one side of the sample in a direction perpendicular to both $\mathbf{E}$ and $\mathbf{B}$. However, this displacement of charge tends to produce an electric field $\mathbf{E}_H$ which is perpendicular to $\mathbf{E}$ and $\mathbf{B}$ which eventually balances the effect of $e\mathbf{v} \times \mathbf{B}$. Hence a transverse potential difference is produced across the sample and this is called the Hall effect. From the magnitude of the Hall coefficient, we can deduce the density of the mobile charges which is a result of great interest in the study of metals and semiconductors.

6.3 UNCHARGED PARTICLES—the Stern–Gerlach experiment

If a particle is completely uncharged, it is not deflected in a uniform electric or magnetic field. However, if it has an electric (or magnetic) dipole moment, it can be deflected in a non-uniform electric (or magnetic) field. This is perhaps most important for magnetic dipole moments and leads us to consider the Stern–Gerlach experiment (1921).

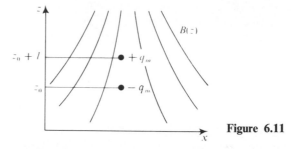

Figure 6.11

Consider a magnetic dipole in a non-uniform magnetic field. Start with two poles $+q_m$ and $-q_m$ a distance l apart (Fig. 6.11). The force on the dipole is $+q_m B(z_0 + l) - q_m B(z_0)$. We can write $B(z_0 + l) = B(z_0) + l(dB/dz)_{z_0}$ if l is small. Hence the force is $(q_m l)(dB/dz)_{z_0} = \mu_m(dB/dz)_{z_0}$. This result is exact if we let $l \to 0$ but with $q_m l$ remaining finite and equal to μ_m. In fact, it is believed that the magnetic moment is more properly to be regarded as due to an infinitesimal current loop rather than a dipole. There is no evidence for the existence of magnetic poles—the simplest thing that can be observed is the magnetic dipole. Since the force is proportional to (dB/dz) we conclude that there is no force on a dipole in a uniform field (see Fig. 6.12a) but that there is a resultant force in a field gradient (see Fig. 6.12b). In Fig. 6.12, the arrows indicate the direction of the force on a current element $I \, \Delta s$ in the field $\mathbf{B}$. This is proportional to $I \, \Delta s \times \mathbf{B}$ which is perpendicular to both Δs and $\mathbf{B}$.

Suppose we have a stream of these particles. If they take a time T to go through the inhomogenous field, they acquire a transverse momentum $FT = \mu_m(dB/dz)_{z_0}T$ and a transverse velocity $\mu_m(dB/dz)_{z_0}(T/m)$ and so will be deflected just like electrons in a cathode ray oscilloscope (Fig. 6.13a). In general, μ_m is not

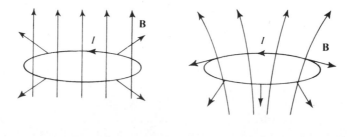

(a)   (b)   Figure 6.12

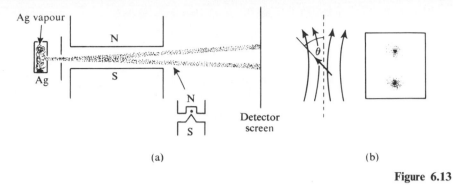

Figure 6.13

necessarily parallel to the field gradient. If the dipole moment is at an angle θ (Fig. 6.13b), we have a force and hence an acquired transverse momentum proportional to cos θ. Hence on the screen we will collect particles on a line with a length proportional to $\mu_m(dB/dz)_{z_0}(T/m)$ and so we can measure μ_m. In fact, Stern and Gerlach tried this experiment with silver atoms. They found that the extent of the spot corresponded to a value of μ_m of approximately 1 Bohr magneton = $eh/4\pi m_e c^*$ but that instead of the expected distribution (Problem 6.8) there were two separate spots! This must be because μ_m cannot have just *any* orientation θ. In fact, there are only two possible orientations for silver atoms, $\theta = 0$ or $180°$. Thus sometimes peculiar things happen to beams of particles in magnetic fields. This is an example of orientational quantization. The effect is due to the magnetic moment of the one special outer electron of the silver atom.

Thus we can manipulate particles, particularly if they are charged, and we can do experiments with beams of such particles in order to study their properties.

PROBLEMS

6.1. Suppose a radioactive material emits α, β, and γ rays in the direction of the X axis. The deflexion, if any, of the rays is observed (a) using a magnetic field in the YZ plane or (b) using an electric field in the YZ plane. If the pattern is similar in both cases, indicate the directions of the **B** and **E** fields.

6.2. Until recently, the physical scale of atomic weights was based on taking $^{16}O = 16.000 \ldots$ a.m.u. whereas the chemical scale was based on taking atmospheric oxygen as being $16.00 \ldots$ Given that atmospheric oxygen contains 0.204% of ^{18}O and 0.037% of ^{17}O, obtain a value for the correction factor (assume $^{18}O = 18.000 \ldots$ and $^{17}O = 17.000 \ldots$ on the physical scale).

6.3. A mass spectrograph shows a strong line at 84 a.m.u. If only C, H, and O are involved, show that possible molecular formulae are $C_6H_{12}^+$, $C_5H_8O^+$, or $C_4H_4O_2^+$. However, if these are the only possibilities, the molecule may be determined uniquely by comparing

---

* Since the energy of a magnetic dipole μ in a magnetic field **B** is $-\mu \cdot \mathbf{B}$, we can express μ in units of erg gauss^{-1} and this is the unit used here where e is in e.s.u. and h, m, and c are in cgs units. In MKS units, the magnetic dipole moment would be in joule wb^{-1} m^2.

the 84 a.m.u. signal with the weaker one at 85 a.m.u.   Show that, if the only low abundance isotopes involved are ^{13}C (1.1%), D (0.016%), ^{17}O (0.037%), and ^{18}C (0.204%), then for "C_6H_{12}" the 85 mass peak is 6.7% of the 84 and find the percentage "84" for C_5H_8O and $C_4H_4O_2$.

6.4. Under low resolution, the mass peak in a spectrograph at 28 a.m.u. may be due to CO^+, N_2^+, CH_2N^+, or $C_2H_4^+$. Show that a resolution of 1 in 3000 would be sufficient to remove the ambiguity.

6.5. The standard of atomic mass was changed from $^{16}O = 16.000 \ldots$ to $^{12}C = 12.000 \ldots$ As a result, the numbers representing masses on the ^{16}O scale were all reduced by 0.032% to give the ^{12}C scale. Explain why this is so and confirm that the percentage reduction is correct.

6.6. Charged particles, all with the same momentum, are projected across a uniform magnetic field and traverse a semicircle. The particles projected into the field have a small angular distribution α in the plane at right angles to the field. Show that the particles arrive at the other end of the diameter with a linear spread proportional to α^2, i.e. there is a focusing effect.

6.7. Derive the formula $v = (VRq/dm)^{1/2}$ for the velocity of particles with charge q and mass m which get through a curved condenser of radius of curvature R, spacing d, and potential difference V.

6.8. In the classical Stern–Gerlach experiment, the probability of the dipole being in $\Delta\theta$ at angle θ to the field gradient is $(1/2\pi) \Delta\theta$. Show that the deposit on the detector at position s has a density proportional to $(s_m^2 - s^2)^{-1/2}$ where s_m is the maximal deflexion. Note that this result is not easy to distinguish experimentally from the quantum result which is two lines near $\pm s_m$.

6.9. Show that a mass spectrometer fed with CO_2 would show lines from 12 to 49 a.m.u.. Which would be the strongest?

6.10. The atomic weight of hydrogen as derived from measurement on the gas as it occurs naturally is 1.0080 (on the ^{12}C scale). Show that natural hydrogen gas contains about 0.02% deuterium.

6.11. In an early form of mass spectrograph, a beam of particles with charge q and mass m and having a range of velocities, was passed through a region with electric and magnetic fields parallel to each other and to the beam of particles. The particles then coasted to a screen in a field-free region. Show that the particles fall on a parabola for a given value of q/m.

6.12. Show that the path of a charged particle, which is otherwise free, in a uniform electric field is a parabola.

6.13. Show that the cyclotron frequency (Section 6.2) for an electron in a magnetic field of 5000 gauss (0.5 wb m^{-2}) is 1.4×10^{10} Hz.

6.14. Show that positively charged particles approaching the Earth are deflected to the east.

CHAPTER 7

Collisions of particles

> ... so I said "why not let him see if any α-particles can be scattered
> through a large angle". RUTHERFORD

7.1 COLLISION CROSS-SECTION

Now let us look at collisions of particles in more detail. Particles arc unlikely
to have head-on collisions: there are all sorts, as for molecules in a gas. In a
liquid or a solid, the idea of collisions between the atoms or molecules is more
vague, since they are at no time moving freely to any useful approximation. A
situation which is easier to deal with is when we have a stream of particles im-
pinging on others, as, for instance, in Rutherford's experiment with α particles.
If we study collisions of particles, we can obtain information about the forces
between them. Let us take a simple case of collisions of hard spheres and suppose
we have the special case of a stream of moving ones of diameter d_1 hitting stationary
ones of diameter d_2. The distance b in Fig. 7.1 is called the impact parameter. For
hard spheres, if $b > [(d_1 + d_2)/2]$, there is no collision and, if $b < [(d_1 + d_2)/2]$,
the incident particle is deflected from its original path. Thus, if we had a stream
of particles of uniform density across its cross-section, the stationary particle will
just scatter out the particles within the circle of area $\pi[(d_1 + d_2)/2]^2$. The stationary particle acts as an opaque barrier of *radius* $[(d_1 + d_2)/2]$. If there are n
particles per unit area of the target and their density is such that they do not get
in each other's line of sight, then a *fraction* of the incident particles $n\pi[(d_1 + d_2)/2]^2$
will be scattered out and the incident beam will be weakened by this fraction. In
the special case where $d_1 \ll d_2$, this is $n\pi(d_2^2/4) = n(\pi r_2^2)$ and the effective scattering
cross-section is just the projected area of the scatterers. Hence, if there is reason
to think we are scattering small particles on big ones, the reduction in beam
intensity for a known density of target particles gives a value for r_2, the size of
the target particles. If the particles were not, in fact, hard spheres, we should still

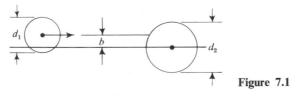

Figure 7.1

get an apparent value for the area of the scatterers and we would call this the effective scattering cross-section. It is clear that the undeviated beam will be attenuated exponentially. For a distance Δx and N target particles per unit volume, there will be $N \Delta x$ particles per unit area and the cross-sectional area for scattering per unit area of the target material is $\pi[(d_1 + d_2)/2]^2 \times N \Delta x$. If there are $\mathcal{N}$ incident particles per unit area per unit time, this is the fraction $\Delta \mathcal{N}/\mathcal{N}$ scattered in Δx so that

$$-\frac{\Delta \mathcal{N}}{\mathcal{N}} = \pi \left(\frac{d_1 + d_2}{2}\right)^2 N \Delta x \quad \text{or} \quad \mathcal{N}(x) = \mathcal{N}(0) \exp -\pi \left(\frac{d_1 + d_2}{2}\right)^2 Nx,$$

where $\mathcal{N}(0)$ is the number of incident particles per unit area at $x = 0$. We have done this thinking of hard spheres but, in fact, for any interaction between the particles we would get a law of the same form, that is $\mathcal{N}(x) = \mathcal{N}(0) \exp(-\mathcal{A}Nx)$ but $\mathcal{A}$ is now an effective collision cross-section. This experiment clearly only gives rather averaged information about the particle interactions. Moreover it gives only the effect on the original beam. We look at the particles actually scattered in Section 7.2. The probability of a particle being scattered in traversing a small distance Δx is proportional to the distance and is dimensionless, so we can write it as $\Delta x/l$. The probability of its getting to x is then $\exp(-x/l)$ (see Problem 7.22) so that the law of scattering may also be written

$$\mathcal{N}(x)/\mathcal{N}(0) = \exp(-x/l).$$

By comparison with the formula $\mathcal{N}(x)/\mathcal{N}(0) = \exp(-\mathcal{A}Nx)$, we see that

$$l = 1/\mathcal{A}N,$$

where $\mathcal{A}$ is the effective collision cross-section and N is the number of target scatterers per unit volume. The mean distance a particle travels before being scattered is

$$\int_0^{\infty} x \exp(-x/l)(dx/l) = l.$$

l is therefore called the "mean free path". If the velocity of the particle is v, then on the average it is scattered after a time l/v. For air at n.t.p., the mean free time l/v is of order $(m/3kT)^{1/2}(\pi d^2 N)^{-1}$ which is about 10^{-10} s. Such considerations arise in calculating the viscosity and other properties of a gas which is why we were able to estimate molecular diameters in this way in Chapter 2. The transport properties of a gas are viscosity η, self-diffusion D, and thermal conductivity K. They correspond to transport of momentum due to a velocity gradient, mass due to a concentration gradient, and energy due to a temperature gradient, respectively. The transport of all three quantities through a gas depends clearly on how fast the molecules can get through it, since they carry the momentum, the mass, and the energy. Evidently, therefore, all three ought to depend on the molecular mean free path l. The actual expressions for η, D, and K in terms of the mean free path are

$$\eta = \tfrac{1}{3}nm\bar{v}l, \qquad D = \tfrac{1}{3}\bar{v}l, \quad \text{and} \quad K = \tfrac{1}{3}n\bar{v}lc_v,$$

where n is the number of molecules of mass m per unit volume, $\bar{v}$ is the mean thermal velocity $((8kT/\pi m)^{1/2})$, l is the mean free path, and c_v is the specific heat per molecule. This can be easily seen, for instance, for the thermal conductivity. The thermal conductivity K is the amount of energy per unit time crossing unit area of a plane per unit temperature gradient dT/dz perpendicular to the plane. As already pointed out, the energy is carried by the gas molecules and if the mean free path is l then on average the molecules passing through the plane at angle θ to its normal come from a distance $l\cos\theta$ above (or below) it. The mean energy of those molecules passing through the plane is $E + l\cos\theta(dE/dz)$. The number of molecules per unit time which cross unit area of the plane in the directions between the ones defined by θ and $\theta + d\theta$ is $\tfrac{1}{2}n\bar{v}\cos\theta\sin\theta\,d\theta$. Consequently, the energy flow across the plane is $[E + l\cos\theta(dE/dz)]\tfrac{1}{2}n\bar{v}\cos\theta\sin\theta\,d\theta$. Integrating θ from 0 to π so as to include molecules approaching from any direction—above and below the plane—we find that the flow of energy is $\tfrac{1}{3}n\bar{v}l(dE/dz)$. But this is just $K(dT/dz)$, so that

$$K = \tfrac{1}{3}n\bar{v}l\,\frac{dE}{dT} = \tfrac{1}{3}n\bar{v}lc_v, \qquad \text{as stated above.}$$

Similar derivations can be made for the viscosity and self-diffusion coefficients (see Problem 7.20).

It is easy to show by combining suitable pairs of the above three equations for η, D, and K that $D\rho/\eta = 1$ and also that $KM/\eta C_v = 1$ where ρ is the gas density (mn), M is the molecular weight, and C_v is the molar specific heat. One of the advantages of thinking in terms of mean free path is that it is often a useful intermediary relating different phenomena, as in the example just quoted.

In a metal, the application of a potential difference causes a tendency of the electrons to flow in one direction. However, the electrons are scattered by collisions with each other and with any displaced metal ions and any impurities or imperfections in the crystal lattice and the steady flow tends to be attenuated. The measurement of electrical resistivity may therefore be regarded as a measure of the mean free path, or the collision cross-section for scattering, of the electrons. From measurements of electrical resistivity, the electron mean free path at room temperature in a metal appears to be about 1000 Å. It is clear from this that the electrons are not scattered by all the ions acting as hard spheres or the mean free path would be only a few ångströms (see Problem 7.1). It is, however, true that the electrons are scattered by thermal vibrations of the ions and each other but in a rather subtle way.

Flow of heat may be regarded in the same way. The thermal energy may be regarded as pseudo-particles flowing in the material. The transmission of heat tends to be prevented by scattering of these "phonons" by imperfections in the crystalline lattice. We therefore expect crystals with impurities and dislocations, or alloys, to have an enhanced thermal resistivity and this is found to be so.

In a metal, it seems likely that the flow of both heat and electricity is carried by the same particles, the electrons. In this case, we would expect the ratio of the thermal to the electrical conductivity of a metal to depend only on the ratio of the energy carried by the electron to the charge carried by it, i.e. on the ratio $\frac{1}{2}mv^2$ to e. Since $\frac{1}{2}mv^2 \propto T$ and e is independent of T, we therefore expect

$$\frac{\text{Thermal conductivity}}{\text{Electrical conductivity}} \propto T.$$

This temperature dependence is quite well obeyed for many metals and is known as the Wiedemann–Franz law.

The mean free path is often used because it frequently gives a good physical idea of what is happening without having to go into details. We would expect, for instance, considerable changes in the physical properties of a gas in a given vessel when the mean free path of the molecules becomes comparable with the size of the vessel. The mean free path for hydrogen gas at $0°\text{C}$ is about 1 cm at about 10^{-2} mm of mercury pressure. The apparent viscosity and thermal conductivity of the gas change quite suddenly with pressure at around this pressure and so must the techniques used for obtaining lower pressures than this in vessels and tubes a few cm in size. On the other hand, for pressures at which the mean free path is much less than the size of the vessel, the viscosity is independent of pressure. Doubling the pressure, and therefore the density, doubles n but halves l. Since $\eta \propto nl$, from the relation given above, the viscosity of the gas should be independent of pressure at constant temperature and this is found to be so experimentally—except, of course, at the low pressures discussed above and at very high pressures where the molecules are so close together that the simple kinetic theory does not apply. When the molecules are close together as in a liquid, the concept of a mean free path is less useful and transport of energy and momentum intimately involves the intermolecular forces $E(x)$ which we discussed in Chapter 4.

7.2 THE SCATTERING PATTERN

We estimate the proportion of particles scattered into any given solid angle for various interactions. Take the simple case in which the incident particles are much smaller than the target particles, that is $d_1 \ll d_2$. We shall also assume that both the target and incident particles are hard spheres and that the target particles are stationary.

If $m \ll M$, the velocity component $v \cos \phi$ of the projectile particle is reversed by the collision and so the velocity after impact is as shown in Fig. 7.2. The change in direction of the scattered particle θ is given by $\theta = \pi - 2\phi$ so that $\phi = \pi/2 - \theta/2$. If r_1 and r_2 are the radii of the incident and target particles, respectively, we have $r_1 \ll r_2$ so that $\sin \phi = b/r_2$ and therefore $\cos \theta/2 = b/r_2$. Differentiating

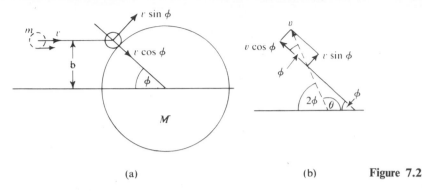

(a)   (b)   **Figure 7.2**

this relation we get $\Delta b/r_2 = -\frac{1}{2}\sin(\theta/2)\,d\theta$. Now consider the incident particles which are randomly distributed across the cross-section of the beam. If again there are $\mathcal{N}$ incident particles per unit area per unit time across the incident beam then $\mathcal{N} \times 2\pi b\,\Delta b$ particles are incident on the thin ring of thickness Δb and radius b for any given target particle and are scattered into the small range of angle $\Delta\theta$ at θ (more precisely into the solid angle formed by the two cones of angle θ and $\theta + \Delta\theta$). If again there are n target particles per unit area the number of incident particles scattered per unit area per unit time is $\Delta\mathcal{N} = n\mathcal{N} \cdot 2\pi b\,\Delta b$. Hence the fraction of incident particles scattered $\Delta\mathcal{N}/\mathcal{N}$ is $2\pi nb\,\Delta b$. Substituting for b and Δb using the expressions given above, this fraction is

$$-2\pi nr_2^2 \times \tfrac{1}{2}\sin\theta/2\cos\theta/2\,\Delta\theta = -\tfrac{1}{2}\pi nr_2^2\sin\theta\,\Delta\theta$$

(the negative sign is because as b increases, θ decreases). The relative number of scattered particles per unit angle at angle θ is therefore proportional to $\sin\theta$ (Fig. 7.3). The interesting thing is that we get maximal intensity in the transverse

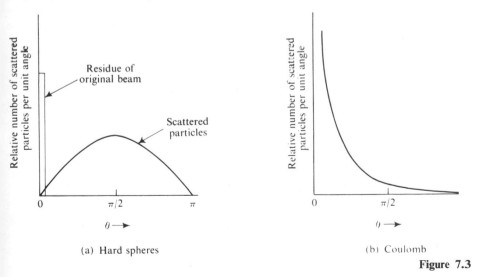

(a) Hard spheres   (b) Coulomb

Figure 7.3

direction, $\theta = \pi/2$, for hard spheres. Moreover, the curve is symmetrical about the direction $\theta = \pi/2$ so that there are just as many particles scattered backwards as forwards, i.e. there is no "persistence of velocity" in such collisions. r_2 could also be measured in this way. To get the number scattered into *all* angles, we have to sum over all angles. The number is therefore

$$\int_0^\pi - \tfrac{1}{2}\pi n r_2^2 \sin \theta \, d\theta$$

which equals $n\pi r_2^2$. This is the result for the total scattering cross-section which we obtained in Section 7.1.

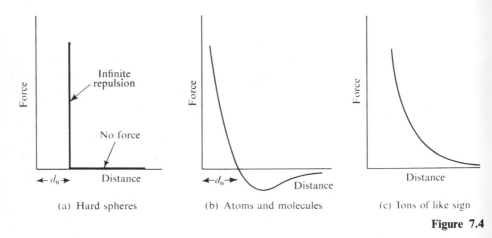

(a) Hard spheres   (b) Atoms and molecules   (c) Ions of like sign

Figure 7.4

The angular dependence of the scattering depends on the law of force between the particles. The hard sphere law of force is as shown in Fig. 7.4(a). We know that a more realistic law of force for atoms or molecules is that discussed in Chapter 4 in which there are both attractive and repulsive forces and is shown in Fig. 7.4(b). For two point charges, the law of force (Fig. 7.4c) is $F \propto (\text{distance})^{-2}$. This Coulomb repulsion for charges with the same sign gives a quite different dependence of scattering on angle. We find $b \propto \cot \theta/2$, instead of $b \propto \cos \theta/2$ and therefore the intensity is proportional to $(\sin \theta)/(\sin^4 \theta/2)$. Hence, for Coulomb scattering, most particles are only scattered by small angles (this is associated with the long range of the force) and this was observed in Rutherford's experiments. It has already been noted in Section 3.3 that very few particles were scattered by large angles. The very different results for Coulomb and hard sphere scattering is illustrated by comparing Figs. 7.3(a) and (b). It is clear from this how the scattering pattern reflects the law of force between the colliding particles. If the ions or charged particles are of opposite sign, then the particles attract one another but the scattering pattern is the same and it is instructive to explain physically why this is so (Problem 7.13). Of course, for very close approach, the repulsive forces become dominant whatever the relative signs of the charged particles.

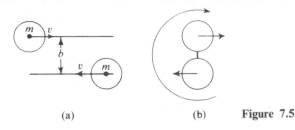

(a)   (b)   **Figure 7.5**

The impact parameter b controls the angular momentum associated with a collision. We see this by letting a pair of similar particles approach with impact parameter b (Fig. 7.5a). If at the moment they were passing they were suddenly rigidly connected (Fig. 7.5b), we would then have a rotating body with angular momentum mvb. Since the formation of the dumb-bell involved only internal forces, then the angular momentum is unchanged and is also mvb for the free particles. The angular momentum is thus proportional to the impact parameter b. This point of view is important in quantum-mechanical calculations where the angular momentum is quantized. (The angular momentum about a certain axis can only have the values nh where n is an integer.) This restricts the possible values of b and so affects the scattering. It also affects the probability of two atoms being able to form a molecule as a result of a collision. Since the molecule formed has quantized angular momentum, only certain values of b lead to molecules. In practice, at least a third body is required in a reaction to be able to balance momentum and energy so that it can also help to conserve angular momentum.

7.3 COLLISIONS IN GASES

Collisions are very relevant to the kinetic theory of gases. We have particles which are moving freely most of the time but with occasional collisions. For gases at usual pressures, collisions between two particles (binary collisions) are much more frequent than between three or more particles, although multiple collisions may play an important role in the preservation and attainment of equilibrium. Whatever the law of force between the particles, any tendency to have a flow of particles in any one direction is annulled by the scattering because head-on collisions are rather unlikely. Any particularly fast particles will tend to be slowed down and slow ones speeded up because, whatever the impact parameter, for identical particles the faster particle is more likely to lose energy (see Problem 7.17). The distribution of the magnitude of the velocity, the speed of the molecules, is shown in Fig. 10.8 as $p(v)$. The tendency to uniform velocity is apparent.

The molecules do not all have exactly the same velocity in equilibrium because in some few collisions fast molecules may gain energy and slow molecules may lose energy and also there are other than binary collisions. The actual dynamics of the collisions of particles in a gas is quite complex because of the form of the interaction potential which is discussed in Section 4.1. We can simplify the problem

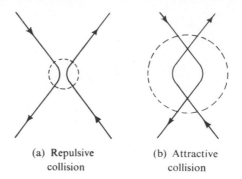

(a) Repulsive   (b) Attractive
    collision   collision   **Figure 7.6**

rather arbitrarily by considering two types of collisions, one in which the repulsive forces dominate, and the other in which the attractive forces dominate, as illustrated in Fig. 7.6. The former is a more or less head-on collision in which the direction of the molecules is only changed inside a rather small volume. The effect of this type of collision is mainly to produce an excluded volume effect on the possibilities for motion of the molecules as has already been discussed in connexion with the van der Waals b coefficient, in the factor $(V - b)$, in Section 3.1.

In the second type of collision, the molecules swing round each other. While in these curved paths, these molecules do not fully contribute to the pressure of the gas and so the external pressure P exerted by the gas is not as great as it would be if the molecules did not attract each other. The probability of such a collision in a given volume is proportional to the square of the number of molecules in that volume, i.e. to $1/V^2$. This is because the probability for each of the two molecules being there independently is proportional to $1/V$. In a real gas, therefore, the modification to the pressure term a/V^2 is, in first approximation, a measure of the attractive forces between the molecules.

Special techniques are required to study in detail the properties of collections of *large numbers* of particles, as in a gas, and we shall take this up in Chapter 10. However, it may be useful at this point to look in a little more detail at the effect of the intermolecular forces on the properties of a gas.

If the gas is perfect, we mean that it obeys the relation $PV = RT$. This relation is increasingly well obeyed for real gases at sufficiently low densities ρ. We might anticipate, therefore, that it would be possible to express the behaviour of a real gas, for not too high densities, in the form

$$\frac{PV}{RT} = 1 + B_2(T)\rho + B_3(T)\rho^2 + \cdots$$

$B_2(T)$ is called the second virial coefficient, $B_3(T)$ the third, and so on and they are expected to depend on temperature only. The first virial coefficient is the coefficient of ρ^0 which is unity. For the perfect gas, all the virial coefficients, except the first, are zero and $PV/RT = 1$. The forces between the molecules give non-zero virial coefficients, hence the name (Latin *vis, vires* = force).

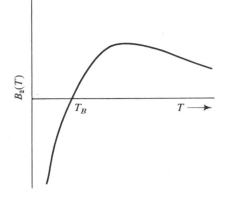

Figure 7.7

At low temperatures, molecules have less kinetic energy and are more likely to be found in arrangments with low potential energy, i.e. near $x = d_0$ and so, as for "attractive" collisions, the effective number of molecules is reduced and the pressure will be lower than it would otherwise be. Hence $B_2(T)$ should be negative at low temperatures. On the other hand, at high temperatures the molecules have much more kinetic energy and the effect of the minimum ΔE in $E(x)$ is much smaller and the molecules are more free except for rather violent "repulsive" collisions. Since these latter effectively reduce the volume available to the molecules (cf. $(V - b)$ in the van der Waals equation), the pressure is larger than it otherwise would be. Hence $B_2(T)$ should be positive at high temperatures. This is, in fact, found to be so experimentally as shown diagrammatically in Fig. 7.7. This result is an indirect confirmation of the form of the interaction potential between molecules we have assumed in Chapter 4 and elsewhere. It can be shown that $B_2(T)$ is related to the interaction potential $E(x)$ as follows

$$mB_2(T) = -2\pi \int_0^\infty [\exp(-E(x)/kT) - 1]x^2 \, dx.$$

For the hard spheres approximation, as in Fig. 7.4(a), this is readily shown to give $mB_2(T) = (2\pi/3)d_0^3$, independent of temperature. This is as expected for the van der Waals equation for hard spheres, which is

$$P(V - b) = RT \quad \text{or} \quad \frac{PV}{RT} = 1 + b/V + \cdots = 1 + 4(V_m/N_0m)\rho + \cdots,$$

since b is 4 times the volume V_m of the molecules (see Section 3.1). Hence $mB_2(T) = 4V_m/N_0 = 4 \times \frac{4}{3}\pi(d_0/2)^3 = (2\pi/3)d_0^3$ as above. Measurements of $B_2(T)$ are currently the simplest and most satisfactory way of obtaining the interatomic potential $E(x)$ through the equation given above. The values of ΔE and d_0 for the rare gas atoms, used in this book, have been obtained in this way (see also Fig. 4.7).

7.4 INELASTIC COLLISIONS

Inelastic collisions occur when the "particles" have internal structure, as for billiard balls or lumps of putty. Part of the kinetic energy can be converted into energy of elastic vibrations or into heat. If you hit *atoms* hard enough, you may get inelastic collisions, e.g. we may knock electrons off and naturally this has to be allowed for. Ionization by collision may be achieved experimentally by bombardment with electrons (Fig. 7.8), as for example in the mass spectrograph (Section 6.2). Even if we did not notice the increase in number of electrons, this could be detected from the fact that the collisions are no longer elastic and from an increase in the collision cross-section.

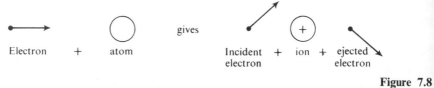

Electron   +   atom   gives   Incident   +   ion   +   ejected
                                               electron   electron

Figure 7.8

Another possibility is for some of the energy of the colliding particles to get stored in one or both of the colliding particles as potential energy. For example, suppose one particle has a spring, then end-on collisions put energy into the spring and this is how internal vibrations in molecules can be excited in a gas, say, as illustrated in Fig. 7.9.

Figure 7.9

If we have a ratchet in addition, the energy can get locked in, in a somewhat different way. If the collision is strong enough and the orientation is right, we may get the effect illustrated in Fig. 7.10. Part of the original kinetic energy is now locked in the system. In both cases, the collision is *inelastic*. For atoms, the lock may correspond to electronic excitation which has a *threshold*. The bump must be big enough and in the right direction or nothing happens. Both of these effects are found in nuclear collisions too. A type of collision which is important in chemistry is one in which a molecule is either formed or destroyed and the problem is one of calculating the probability of this happening. Suppose two atoms approach each other. If they *can* form a molecule, they *will* only do so if they can get rid of the kinetic energy relative to the centre of mass in some way. For example, they may do so by emitting electromagnetic radiation, or by putting the energy into internal vibrations, or by passing it on to a third molecule, and so on.

gives

Figure 7.10

Calculations of the rate of formation of molecules from atoms and vice versa are quite difficult to do. If we have say two gases interacting, the molecules or atoms are all moving about at various speeds in various directions and the collisions are different for different orientations of the two molecules. These matters arise in the theory of the kinetics of reactions which for gases depends on the collisions of particles.

Perhaps the best known inelastic collisions are the Franck and Hertz experiments (1914) in which electrons are used to excite atoms to higher electronic levels. Some of the kinetic energy of the electrons is converted to internal potential energy of the atoms.

PROBLEMS

7.1. Show that, if the scattering from the atoms in copper is responsible for the electrical resistivity, the electron mean free path would be about 5 Å. (For copper, the number of atoms per cm^3 is 8×10^{22} and the radius of Cu^+ is about 1 Å. Ignore Coulomb forces.)

7.2. If the scattering in Problem 7.1 is due to the displacement of the copper atoms due to thermal vibrations, show that the mean free path of electrons is about 100 Å at room temperature.

7.3. Compare the van der Waals equation $(P + a/V^2)(V - b) = RT$ and the virial equation* $PV = A + BP + CP^2 + \cdots$ for gases. Show that $A = RT$, $B = b - a/RT$, and $C = ab/R^2T^2$. At the Boyle temperature, $B = 0$ so that $T_B = a/Rb$ and the gas obeys Boyle's law rather well. Look up the values of a and b for argon and hydrogen and compare the theoretical T_B with the corresponding measured T_B which is $453°K$ and $103°K$ for argon and hydrogen, respectively.

7.4. A particle of mass M and charge Ze is projected at velocity v and impact parameter b towards a nucleus with mass M_n ($\gg M$) and charge $Z_n e$. Show that the deflexion of the particle is given by $2 \cot^{-1} (Mv^2/ZZ_n e^2)$. (HINT: Angular momentum about the target nucleus is conserved; consider the linear momentum along a direction bisecting the incident and deflected asymptotes. This is Rutherford's α particle scattering experiment.)

7.5. The D–D reaction is

$$^2_1H + {}^2_1H \rightarrow {}^3_2He + {}^1_0n + 3.3 \text{ Mev}.$$

This reaction has a maximal cross-section at about 0.1 Mev. Consider a head-on collision of a 0.1 Mev deuteron with a stationary one and show that there are three possible results: (1) a neutron is emitted forward with 2.85 Mev, or (2) backwards with 2.15 Mev, or (3) the collision is elastic.

7.6. A particle of mass m travelling at velocity $\mathbf{v}$ collides elastically (i.e. without loss of energy to internal degrees of freedom) with another particle at rest also with mass m. Show that, after the collision, the two particles move at right angles to one another for any $\mathbf{v}$ or m, except in the special case in which the collision is "head on".

---

* The virial equation can be written in terms of pressure as in Problem 7.3 or in terms of the density as is convenient for Problem 7.19.

7.7. In nuclear reactors, the fast neutrons produced are slowed down by a "moderator" which may be heavy water or graphite. Estimate the efficiency of heavy water and graphite as moderators by calculating the percentage loss of energy of a neutron in a head-on elastic collision with an initially stationary deuterium nucleus (^{2}H) or a carbon nucleus (^{12}C). (Assume that the fact that deuterium or carbon nuclei are chemically bound within the material is not important until the neutrons are slowed down.)

7.8. A possible chemical reaction is that of atomic deuterium with molecular hydrogen, i.e. the forward reaction might be written D + H$_2$ → DH + H. As a model for this reaction, consider the elastic collision of a deuterium atom travelling at velocity v directly towards and along the extension of the line joining the protons in the hydrogen molecule, which is initially at rest. If the reaction described above takes place, show that the velocity of the hydrogen deuteride molecule after the collision has the value 0.21 v. Why could the velocity, in fact, prove to be greater?

7.9. A beam of light passes through a region containing N scatterers per unit volume each of which scatters the light with a cross-section $\mathscr{A}$. Show that the intensity of the light as a function of distance x traversed is given by

$$I = I_0 \exp(-N\mathscr{A}x).$$

7.10. It was shown by Lord Rayleigh that the effective cross-section of the molecules in a gas which has a refractive index n and contains N molecules per cm^3, for scattering of light of wavelength λ, is

$$\frac{2}{3\pi} \frac{(n-1)^2}{N^2} \left(\frac{2\pi}{\lambda}\right)^4.$$

Estimate the value of Avogadro's number from the observation that the sky is blue! (The refractive index of air at ground level ≈ 1.0003.)

7.11. How close to an initially stationary free proton can an 8 Mev α particle get? (Assume only electrostatic forces operate.)

7.12. It was observed that the number of α particles scattered from a beam in a given time on to a detector at angle θ by a film of silver was as follows:

θ	7.5°	10°	15°	30°
No.	1710	508	93	5.3

Show that this corresponds to scattering by electrostatic repulsion (see Section 7.2).

7.13. A particle is projected towards a fixed stationary particle, but not head on. There is an inverse square law of force between them. Illustrate by means of a diagram the relation between the two different trajectories obtained, according as the force is attractive or repulsive.

7.14. An α particle collides with the following stationary particles: (a) a proton, (b) a helium 4 nucleus, (c) a fluorine nucleus. Show that the angle between the trajectories of the two particles after collision is (a) less than, (b) equal to, or (c) greater than, 90°, respectively.

7.15. Chadwick found in 1932 that neutrons striking protons imparted to them a maximal speed which was 7.5 times greater than the maximal speed imparted to nitrogen nuclei. Show that this implies that the neutron mass is about the same as that of the proton.

7.16. Consider again the collision in Problem 7.8. It could be inelastic, since some of the energy could be converted to energy of internal vibration of the HD molecule. Show that the velocity of the HD molecule then has the *minimal* value 0.21v and a maximal value 0.5v.

7.17. Consider the elastic collision of two identical particles. Show that the *faster* particle only increases its velocity as a result of the collision if (1) its initial velocity relative to the centre of mass has a component in the direction of motion of the centre of mass and (2) after the collision its velocity relative to the centre of mass is more in the direction of motion of the centre of mass.

7.18. Show that, if two particles of mass m_1 and m_2 collide elastically, the loss of energy δE of one particle relative to the total energy before collison E has a maximal value given by

$$\frac{\delta E}{E} = \frac{2(m_1 m_2)^{1/2}}{(m_1 + m_2)}.$$

7.19. Show that if the interaction potential between molecules is given by the 6–12 potential $E(x) = \Delta E[(x/d_0)^{12} - 2(x/d_0)^6]$ where ΔE and d_0 have values which are different for different molecules, then B_2/d_0^3 is a universal function of $kT/\Delta E$ for any gas, where B_2 is the density second virial coefficient* (Section 7.3).

7.20. Confirm the formulae $\eta = \frac{1}{3}nm\bar{v}l$ and $D = \frac{1}{3}\bar{v}l$, given in Section 7.1, by using the same method as for K but considering the flow of momentum and number of gas molecules.

7.21. Use the "mean free path" relations of Section 7.1 to show that the thermal conductivity of a gas is independent of pressure but that the diffusion coefficient varies inversely as the pressure.

7.22. Show that, if the probability of a particle colliding in a small distance Δx is $\Delta x/l$ (Section 7.1), then the probability of its travelling a distance x without colliding is $\exp(-x/l)$.

---

* See footnote to Problem 7.3.

CHAPTER 8

Particles at high velocity—relativity

> There is no difference between Time and any of the three dimensions
> of space except that our consciousness moves along it.   H. G. WELLS

8.1 INADEQUACY OF NEWTON'S LAWS

Newton's laws of motion were for a long time found to be valid experimentally. However, as soon as particles moving at very high velocities were available for experiment, deviations were found which are greater the higher the velocity. We look at the behaviour of particles "independently" first.

In Newton's second law of motion, we had

$$\mathbf{F} = \frac{d\mathbf{p}}{dt} \quad \text{and} \quad \mathbf{p} = m\mathbf{v},$$

so that

$$\mathbf{F} = \frac{d}{dt}(m\mathbf{v}) = m\frac{d\mathbf{v}}{dt} + \mathbf{v}\frac{dm}{dt}.$$

In Newton's scheme, it is assumed that m is a constant of the motion so that $dm/dt = 0$ and $\mathbf{F} = m(d\mathbf{v}/dt)$. This is the familiar relation, force = mass × acceleration.

As soon as electrons became available for experimentation, it was possible to accelerate these light particles to very high velocities without needing enormous energies. The kinetic energy, according to Newton, is $\frac{1}{2}mv^2$ and so, if m is small, so is the kinetic energy. According to this, we can get the speed of an electron up to two thirds of the velocity of light with a potential of about 100,000 v

$$(\tfrac{1}{2}m_e v^2 = \tfrac{1}{2}m_e \times \tfrac{4}{9}c^2 = \tfrac{2}{9}m_e c^2 = \tfrac{2}{9} \times 9.1 \times 10^{-28} \times (3 \times 10^{10})^2$$

$$\approx 1.8 \times 10^{-7} \text{ erg} \approx 10^5 \text{ ev} = 0.1 \text{ Mev.})$$

We have used the electron mass as determined at low velocities (Experiments 1 and 2). Even for a proton, the lightest nucleus, m is some 1800 times bigger and so we need about 180 Mev to accelerate the proton to a velocity two thirds that of light. This is much more difficult, since a difference of electrical potential of some hundreds of millions of volts cannot be obtained electrostatically, whereas 100,000 v is quite easy.

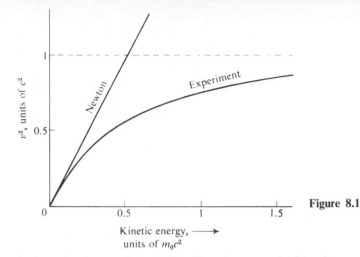

Figure 8.1

For Newtonian mechanics, we expect that if we increase the kinetic energy T of a particle then its velocity increases such that $v^2 \propto T$. The energy can easily be given to a charged particle, like an electron, by means of an electric field. If we let the electron "fall" through a potential difference V, we expect it to acquire an energy eV. However, it is not obvious that this is true for charges having *any* velocity. We can prove that the energy acquired is eV quite simply by stopping the fast electrons in a piece of matter and so converting their kinetic energy into heat. We must measure both the total heat produced and the total charge collected in a given time. It is found experimentally that the ratio, heat per unit time/charge per unit time, is numerically equal to V, the accelerating potential, whatever the velocity of the electrons. This is the correct result, since this ratio should be just eVn/en which is V, where n is the number of electrons per unit time in the beam. (It is a little more subtle to show that the Lorentz force (Section 6.2) is also correctly given by the usual formula for any particle velocity.)

It has been shown by measuring the kinetic energy (by heat production) and the velocity (by the time of flight over a known path) of an electron, by equipment shown schematically in Fig. 8.2, that there is a limiting velocity which is found

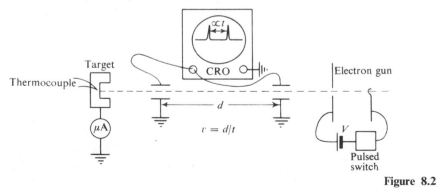

Figure 8.2

experimentally to be numerically equal to the velocity of light. This experiment relates kinetic energy to velocity (see Fig. 8.1).

We now consider also an experiment which relates *momentum* to velocity, since momentum turns out to be a more basic quantity.

One of the most direct tests of Newton's laws at high velocity was Bucherer's experiment (1909), although the technical aspects of the experiment have been criticized. In this experiment, e/m is measured for electrons as a function of their velocity. For a particle charge q at velocity **v** in a magnetic field **B**, the force on it is $q(\mathbf{v}/c) \times \mathbf{B}$, the Lorentz force due to a magnetic field. If **v** and **B** are perpendicular, the force is $q(v/c)B$. As shown in Section 6.2, such a particle moves in a circle of radius $r = pc/qB$ (Fig. 8.3). We measure the amount x that the particle is deflected in travelling a linear distance l across the magnetic field where l is such that θ is small.

$$x = r(1 - \cos \theta) \quad \text{and} \quad \sin \theta = l/r.$$

If l/r is small θ is small,

$$\cos \theta \approx 1 - \theta^2/2, \qquad \therefore \quad x \approx r\theta^2/2 = rl^2/2r^2 = l^2/2r = \frac{l^2 qB}{2pc},$$

that is

$$x = \left(\frac{l^2 qB}{2c}\right)\frac{1}{p}.$$

Hence, by measuring x, we get the momentum p. If we also measure the velocity v of the particle, we can then test if $p = mv$.

The velocity of the electrons was selected in Bucherer's experiment with crossed electric and magnetic fields as described in Section 6.2 for the mass spectrograph. Bucherer's apparatus is just a mass spectrograph adapted to measure particles with high velocity. Since the resultant force on the selected particles inside the velocity selector is zero, the particles all have the same velocity whatever their mass. Thus the mass does not appear in the expression for the selected velocity, $v = cE/B$. Incidentally, neither does the charge q, so the question of charge does not arise either.

Combination of the two experiments, velocity selection in crossed **E** and **B** fields followed by momentum selection in **B** alone, gives Bucherer's experiment

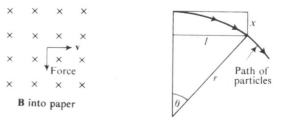

Figure 8.3

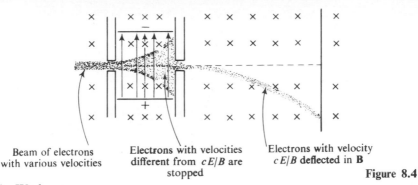

Beam of electrons | Electrons with velocities | Electrons with velocity
with various velocities | different from cE/B are | cE/B deflected in **B**
| stopped | **Figure 8.4**

(Fig. 8.4). We have

$$p = \frac{qBl^2}{2xc} \quad \text{and} \quad v = cE/B$$

so that

$$\frac{p}{v} = \frac{l^2qB^2}{2c^2xE},$$

where for an electron $q = e$ and all the quantities on the right-hand side are known. We can now plot p/v versus v (Fig. 8.5). If Newton was right, $p/v = m = $ a constant independent of v. This is practically so at low velocities, as was to be expected, but the apparent mass p/v increases with v and appears to increase without limit as $v \rightarrow c$. The apparent mass p/v is found to be given by the formula

$$m = p/v = m_0/(1 - v^2/c^2)^{1/2}$$

where c is *numerically equal to* the velocity of light, and m_0 is the familiar Newtonian mass for low velocities. This means that mass is velocity dependent and we ought to write $m(v)$. Similar results would be found for any material particle.

This experiment is consistent with the previous experiment on the velocity dependence of kinetic energy. If m increases with velocity, it is expected that the kinetic energy $\frac{1}{2}mv^2$ increases faster than v^2. However, this proves to be too

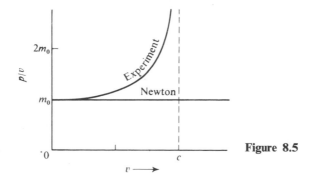

Figure 8.5

naive an approach and the kinetic energy is *not* $\frac{1}{2}m(v)v^2$ at high velocities (see Section 8.3).

The velocity of light c is a limiting velocity for material particles. Since, in normal circumstances, $v \ll c$, we have $m \approx m_0$ and the deviations from Newtonian mechanics are negligible. We now call m_0 the *rest mass* of the particle. It is a limiting value for low velocities.

In Einstein's theory of relativity, it is postulated that the limiting velocity is *exactly* that of light and this is a crucial matter. The experimental evidence we have given supports this postulate.

8.2 RELATIVISTIC CORRECTIONS

Let us consider in what circumstances relativistic corrections to Newtonian mechanics may be necessary.

The speed of the Earth in its orbit is about 3×10^6 cm s^{-1}, so that

$$\frac{v}{c} \approx 10^{-4} \quad \text{and} \quad 1/(1 - v^2/c^2)^{1/2} \approx 1 + 0.5 \times 10^{-8}.$$

There is only a very small effect, so small that it cannot be detected in astronomical observations.

For an electron in a hydrogen atom, we assume that the electron moves in an orbit of radius 0.53 Å. The electrostatic force is e^2/r^2 and centrifugal force is mv^2/r. These must be equal, so that

$$mv^2 = e^2/r, \quad \text{that is} \quad v = e/\sqrt{mr}.$$

Put

$$m = m_e = 9.1 \times 10^{-28} \text{ g}, \qquad e = 4.8 \times 10^{-10} \text{ e.s.u.},$$

and

$$r = 0.53 \times 10^{-8} \text{ cm},$$

so that

$$v = \frac{4.8 \times 10^{-10}}{[(9.1 \times 10^{-28})(0.53 \times 10^{-8})]^{1/2}} = 2.3 \times 10^8 \text{ cm s}^{-1}.$$

Hence,

$$\frac{v}{c} = \frac{2.3 \times 10^8}{3 \times 10^{10}} \approx \frac{1}{130} \text{ *}$$

and so

$$[1 - v^2/c^2]^{-1/2} \approx 1 + 0.5 \times 10^{-4}.$$

Therefore the motion is non-relativistic. The electrons in a television set are much more relativistic than they are in atoms! (see Problem 8.2). Hence, in atoms as a first approximation, we need not use relativistic mechanics. The same is true

---

* To be more precise, this ratio is α, where α is the fine structure constant, $e^2/4\pi\varepsilon_0 hc \approx 1/137$ (Problem 2.3).

of chemical bonds and most of chemistry (the main exception is nuclear chemistry). However, relativistic considerations are implicitly involved in matters concerning electromagnetic radiation—because it travels at the velocity of light! In accelerators, in cosmic rays, and in most nuclear physics experiments, the particles are usually relativistic. In the design of high-energy electron accelerators, the best first approximation is that the velocity of the electrons is the velocity of light c. For example, this is so in calculating the time for the electron to make one revolution of the machine. In the latest linear accelerator at Stanford, which is two miles long, the electrons take about $10 \, \mu s$ to go along it (Problem 8.4) so they travel almost at the velocity of light all the way.

8.3 MASS–ENERGY

Since mass depends on velocity $m(v)$, mass is not necessarily conserved in a collision of particles. Hence the mechanics of collisions of particles, and any other mechanics for that matter, is more complicated at relativistic velocities. For instance, if we apply a constant force F to a particle of rest mass m_0 and start it from rest, we have

$$F = \frac{dp}{dt} = \frac{d}{dt}(mv) = \frac{d}{dt}\{m_0 v[1 - v^2/c^2]^{-1/2}\}.$$

Therefore

$$d\{v[1 - v^2/c^2]^{-1/2}\} = (F/m_0) \, dt,$$

so that

$$v[1 - v^2/c^2]^{-1/2} = (F/m_0)t.$$

The particle still accelerates under the action of the force but approaches a limiting velocity of c as t increases (Fig. 8.6). The distance the particle moves from rest under a constant force is also very different from the Newtonian expression $\frac{1}{2}(F/m_0)t^2$ (see Problem 8.21).

Now consider the expression for the mass of a particle moving at velocity v,

$$m = m_0[1 - v^2/c^2]^{-1/2}.$$

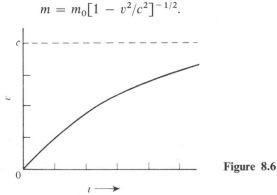

Figure 8.6

If $v/c \ll 1$, we can expand the square root using the binomial theorem, so that

$$[1 - v^2/c^2]^{-1/2} = 1 + \tfrac{1}{2}(v^2/c^2) + \cdots .$$

Therefore

$$m = m_0 + \tfrac{1}{2}m_0(v^2/c^2) + \cdots ,$$

or

$$mc^2 = m_0c^2 + \tfrac{1}{2}m_0v^2 + \cdots .$$

We recognize $\tfrac{1}{2}m_0v^2$ as the Newtonian kinetic energy corresponding to the rest mass m_0. We note that the term m_0c^2 is independent of velocity and only depends on the rest mass m_0. Since one of the terms on the right, $\tfrac{1}{2}m_0v^2$, is recognized as an observable energy of the particle, we suggest therefore that there is an *energy* associated with the rest *mass* m_0, that is $E_0 = m_0c^2$. Consequently, it seems reasonable to consider mc^2 as the *total* energy of the particle for *any* velocity, even if v is comparable with c. We can regard m_0c^2 as potential energy in the usual mechanical sense. Then the total energy (mc^2) may be regarded as the sum of the potential energy m_0c^2 and the kinetic energy $m_0c^2\{[1 - (v^2/c^2)]^{-1/2} - 1\} = \tfrac{1}{2}m_0v^2 + \cdots$. We might call $\tfrac{1}{2}m_0v^2$ the Newtonian kinetic energy. In many cases, e.g. in most of chemistry, the final mass is taken to be equal to the initial mass and so the m_0c^2 terms appear on both sides of the mass balance equation and are ignored. However, we shall see that this is not strictly correct. It should be noted that the relativistic expression for the kinetic energy is $(m - m_0)c^2$ which is *not* the same as $\tfrac{1}{2}mv^2$ (see Problem 8.6).

Since energy and mass appear to be related, it may be possible to observe the conversion of mass into energy and vice versa. It also raises doubts about two of our conservation laws, namely "conservation of mass" and "conservation of energy". If we can convert one into the other, neither need be conserved, but we might perhaps find conservation of "mass + energy". This is observed to be so experimentally in nuclear reactions where some mass may be considered to disappear and reappear as energy. Cockroft and Walton (1932) bombarded lithium with protons and produced α particles according to the reaction

$$^1_1\text{H} + {}^7_3\text{Li} \rightarrow 2\,{}^4_2\text{He}.$$

Rest masses (a.m.u. for $^{12}\text{C} = 12$) are as follows:

$$1.00782 + 7.01598 \rightarrow 2 \times 4.00259.$$

Kinetic energies (erg from $\tfrac{1}{2}m_0v^2$) are as follows:

$$4 \times 10^{-7} + 0 \rightarrow 2 \times 1.4 \times 10^{-5}.$$

Thus the kinetic energy is greater after the reaction than before but the mass is smaller. The decrease in mass is

$$(1.00782 + 7.01598) - 2 \times 4.00259 = 0.01862 \text{ a.m.u.}$$
$$= 0.01862 \times 1.67 \times 10^{-24} \text{ g}$$
$$= 3.1 \times 10^{-26} \text{ g}.$$

The mass equivalent of the kinetic energy produced, *if* $E_0 = m_0 c^2$, is

$$\frac{2.8 \times 10^{-5}}{c^2} = \frac{2.8 \times 10^{-5}}{(3 \times 10^{10})^2} = 3.1 \times 10^{-26} \text{ g.}$$

Hence, if it is true that $E_0 = m_0 c^2$, we have conversion of mass into energy. In this reaction, there is neither conservation of mass nor of kinetic energy, but there is conservation of (rest + kinetic energy), that is $m_0 c^2 + \frac{1}{2} m_0 v^2$, provided the rest energy is calculated as $m_0 c^2$. Since $v/c \ll 1$, $\frac{1}{2} m_0 v^2$ is practically the relativistic kinetic energy so we can say this is likely to correspond in general to conservation of total mass m *or* total energy mc^2. It is in this sense that the rest mass m_0 may be regarded as potential energy $m_0 c^2$, since part of this potential energy was released in the reaction.

We can also have the reverse process, conversion of energy into rest mass. For example, this happens in the photon production of an electron–positron pair $\gamma \rightarrow e^+ + e^-$. (N.B. This reaction must be "catalysed" by a nucleus so that momentum can also be conserved.) Clearly the energy of the photon $h\nu$ must be greater than $2m_e c^2$ for this reaction to occur, that is $\nu > 2.5 \times 10^{20}$ Hz or $\lambda < 10^{-2}$ Å. This can be done, in particular, with γ rays from nuclear reactions. This "threshold" is one of the striking and simple results of relativity. If the γ ray has not sufficient energy, the reaction does not occur and that is that, no more need be said. However, if the γ ray is energetic enough, the reaction can occur but when and how it occurs is a more complex matter to explain. As happens with many discontinuities in classical physics, the threshold is not so sharply defined when quantum mechanics is taken into account.

In these discussions, it is implicit that mass corresponds not only to kinetic but to potential energy and this is sometimes more difficult to imagine. We can get into difficulty, for instance, with the apparent arbitrariness of the zero for potential energy, or indeed for any energy. We can see that the potential energy of interaction of two particles corresponds to mass. Consider two identical particles approaching each other each with speed v. Their total mass is $2m_0 [1 - v^2/c^2]^{-1/2}$. Owing to repulsive forces between them, they come momentarily to rest at some moment during the collision. At this moment their total mass must still be $2m_0 [1 - v^2/c^2]^{-1/2}$ which is greater than $2m_0$. The mass difference is now associated with the potential energy of interaction of the particles so potential energy does have mass associated with it.

The reason why most nuclei are stable is that the mass of the nucleus is less than the sum of the masses of its constituent parts. For example, the mass of ^7_3Li is 7.01598 a.m.u.. It consists of four neutrons and three protons which when separate have a total mass $4 \times 1.00861 + 3 \times 1.00782 = 7.0579$ a.m.u., i.e. mass of ^7_3Li < mass of 3p + 4n. Hence the lithium nucleus is stable and does not break up spontaneously. Strictly speaking, we have only shown that ^7_3Li will not spontaneously break up into the separate fundamental particles of which it is composed. However, it might possibly be unstable to break up into three

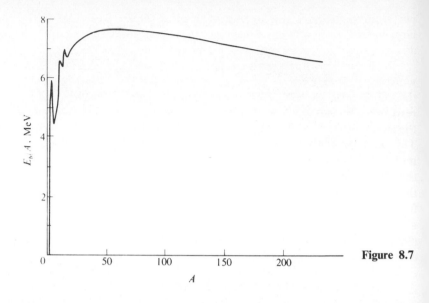

Figure 8.7

deuterons and one neutron and so on—it is actually stable. However, the $^7_3$Li nucleus might combine with another nucleus to form a more stable nucleus.

The mass defect ΔM, the difference between the mass of a nucleus of atomic number Z and mass number A and that of its constituent particles,

$$\Delta M = Zm_p + (A - Z)m_n - M_{Z,A}.$$

The corresponding energy is $E_b = 931\Delta M$ Mev, since 1 a.m.u. $\equiv$ 931 Mev, and so

$$\frac{E_b}{A} = 931[Zm_p + (A - Z)m_n - M_{Z,A}]A^{-1} \text{ Mev}.$$

The form of the curve of E_b/A versus A given in Fig. 8.7 shows that we can gain energy by splitting up heavy nuclei or by combining light ones. Thus the radio-active elements (large A) can break up spontaneously in various ways into two or more particles which are less massive than the parent. Hence the break-up is possible but the *rate* may vary enormously. If the same result is brought about at a controlled rate by bombardment with other particles, e.g. neutrons, we have nuclear fission. It is observed that heavy nuclei, $A \sim 240$, tend to break into two nuclei with A in the range 120 ± 40. Since E_b/A is about 6.6 Mev per nucleon at $A \sim 240$ and about 7.5 Mev per nucleon at $A \sim 120$ (see Fig. 8.7), the energy released is about $240(7.5 - 6.6) \approx 200$ Mev per atom (Problem 8.19). This is enormously larger than the few Mev of energy per atom released in other types of nuclear reaction.

The other way of gaining energy, by combination of light nuclei, is called nuclear fusion. For example, the fusion of two deuterons may give a helium three nucleus and a neutron and the release of 3.3 Mev of energy. The energy released per atom in fusion is similar to that in most nuclear reactions but is roughly as large as that for fission per unit mass, since the atoms involved are light ones. The advantages of fusion over fission for producing energy are of a technical nature.

It is useful to note that the value of E_b/A tends to be about 8 Mev. In other words, the binding energy per nucleon is about 8 Mev. The main contribution to the energy of a nucleus is the interaction between the nuclei in pairs and in this respect nuclear matter is rather like an atomic or molecular solid or liquid where the energy is also mainly due to short range pairwise attractions between particles. This contributes an energy to E_b which is proportional to the volume of nuclear matter, i.e. to A, and so E_b/A should be constant. However, the nucleons near the surface of the nucleus do not have as many other nucleons to interact with as those inside the nucleus and so the binding energy must be lower than expected from the volume effect just mentioned. This is analogous to the surface tension of a liquid. The effect is proportional to the area of the surface, i.e. to d_n^2 or to $A^{2/3}$ (Section 3.4). On the other hand, the energy of binding is also lower because of the electrostatic repulsion between the charges on the Z protons in the nucleus. Since every proton interacts with *every* other one and the typical distance between them is of order $d_n/2$, this energy is proportional to Z^2/d_n. But in Chapter 3 we saw that $Z \approx \frac{1}{2}A$ and we have that $d_n \propto A^{1/3}$ so that this negative contribution to the binding energy is proportional to $A^{5/3}$. Consequently, in this "liquid drop model" of the nucleus, which was introduced by Bohr in 1936, we have for the binding energy per nucleon

$$E_b/A = C_v + C_s A^{-1/3} + C_c A^{2/3}.$$

The constants C_v, C_s, and C_c can be chosen to fit the general form of the curve of Fig. 8.7 (Problem 8.25) and are simple characteristic parameters of nuclear matter.

We had, in Newton's scheme, energy = force × distance, or $E = \mathbf{F} \cdot \mathbf{s}$, or $dE/dt = \mathbf{F} \cdot \mathbf{v}$. The latter relation is still true relativistically if we use $\mathbf{F} = d\mathbf{p}/dt$, that is

$$\frac{dE}{dt} = \frac{d\mathbf{p}}{dt} \cdot \mathbf{v} = \frac{d}{dt}(p^2/2m),$$

where $\mathbf{p} = m\mathbf{v}$, $E = mc^2$, and $m = m_0(1 - v^2/c^2)^{-1/2}$ (see Problem 8.26).

We can postulate that *any* energy E has a mass E/c^2 associated with it. We see now in our conservation laws that, instead of energy and mass being conserved separately, we get conservation of mass–energy, mc^2. It is *this* which is related to time invariance (Table 5.3). It is usual to illustrate the mass–energy relation by reference to nuclear reactions. In fact, the relation holds in *any* situation where energy is released or absorbed, e.g. in chemical reactions, but there it is not feasible to measure the mass changes involved. A chemical explosion may be just as validly considered to be a mass to energy conversion as a nuclear explosion. You can convert mass into energy by lighting the gas!

All this is true for material particles. Does it apply to light? Light must be highly relativistic and very basic to relativity, since it travels at the limiting velocity c.

8.4 LIGHT HAS PARTICLES

It is thought that light consists of photons which behave in some ways like particles of energy hv, or in wave notation $\hbar\omega$ where v is the frequency of the light (the wavelength is $\lambda = c/v$). This is demonstrated by the photoelectric effect which is discussed below. Hence the mass of a photon is expected to be $m_{ph} = hv/c^2$. For visible light with, say, $\lambda = 5000$ Å, $m_{ph} \approx 4 \times 10^{-33}$ g, whereas the mass of the electron is about 10^{-27} g. Light is light! This of course corresponds to inertial mass. The gravitational mass of the photon is considered below.

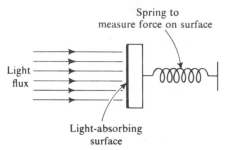

Figure 8.8

Since the photon travels at velocity c, its momentum is $p_{ph} = m_{ph}c = hv/c = h/v$ (or in wave notation $p_{ph} = (h/2\pi)(2\pi/\lambda) = \hbar k$), or $\lambda = h/$momentum, for light. This relation can be shown to be *consistent* with the relation $E = hv$ experimentally by experiments on radiation pressure. One such experiment is illustrated in Fig. 8.8. We can measure the wavelength of the light λ using a diffraction grating. We can measure the intensity I of the incident light in erg cm^{-2} s^{-1} using a bolometer, which just measures the heat produced. If each photon has an energy hv, the number of photons per cm^2 per second arriving at the plate is I/hv. If the momentum of each photon is h/λ, the momentum per cm^2 per second transferred to the plate is $(I/hv) \times (h/\lambda) = I/v\lambda = I/c$. Hence the force per cm^2 on the plate is I/c. This has been confirmed by experiment. Hence the two assumptions, $E_{ph} = hv$ and $p_{ph} = h/\lambda$, are consistent. The result is that also predicted by electromagnetic wave theory using the fact that for any wave $E/p = \omega/k$. It is again clear that this experiment can be explained classically, since Planck's constant h does not appear in the result. This is an example of transfer of momentum by particles having no rest mass.

In the photoelectric effect (laboratory Experiment 5), we use light to eject electrons from a surface (Fig. 8.9a). The energy required to remove an electron from the surface is $e\phi$ (see Problem 10.4 for an estimate of ϕ); therefore $hv = e\phi + \frac{1}{2}m_e v^2$. This relation is observed experimentally (Fig. 8.9b). We can show that the photoelectric effect depends on photons and not waves by considering what happens as we reduce the intensity of the light. Whatever the intensity of the light, photoelectrons may be ejected within about say 10^{-7} s. This happens even with light whose intensity is so low that it would take about one thousand times as long to accumulate sufficient energy from a wave. (The energy supplied by a light wave

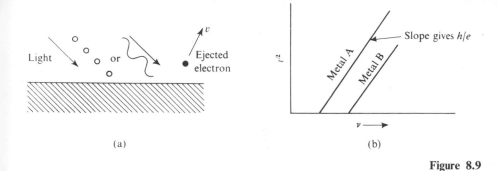

Figure 8.9

of electric field amplitude E_0 and cross-section A in a time t is $(E_0^2/8\pi)Act$.) More-over, the velocity of the ejected electrons does not depend on the intensity of the incident light; only their number depends on the intensity. Hence the effect does not depend on the electric field in the light wave and the effect cannot be a classical one. On the other hand, of course, the mean number of electrons ejected over a long period of time corresponds to the energy supplied by the wave. Although an electron *may* be ejected very promptly, it also may not and if we repeat the experiment we find a probability distribution in the time we have to wait for the ejection of an electron by a weak incident light flux. Hence a photocell is a photon detector rather than a wave detector.

Further evidence of the validity of the photon concept is given by the Compton effect discussed in Section 8.7.

8.5 PARTICLES HAVE WAVES

De Broglie* suggested that the relations $\lambda = h/p$ and $E = h\nu$ which we have found for light are also true for *material* particles, although it was not clear for some time what the λ and ν referred to. They are now regarded as the wavelength and frequency of *matter waves*. Let us calculate the values of λ associated with some objects.

$$\lambda \text{ for } \begin{cases} \text{a car moving at 60 m.p.h.} & \sim 10^{-29} \text{ Å} \\ \text{a bullet at 500 m.p.h.} & \sim 10^{-23} \text{ Å} \\ \text{the PVC sphere of Section 2.3} & \sim 10^{-14} \text{ Å} \\ \text{a molecule in a gas at room temperature} & \sim 10^{-1} \text{ Å} \\ \text{an electron at room temperature} & \sim 25 \text{ Å} \end{cases}$$

Clearly λ is minute for macroscopic objects and small even for atoms unless they are moving quite slowly. However, for electrons in atoms, m is small and at the same time the dimensions of the atom are small. For an electron in a hydrogen

---

* L. DE BROGLIE, *Compt. Rend.* **177,** 507 (1923).

atom we found $v \sim 2 \times 10^8$ cm s^{-1} (Section 8.2), so that

$$\lambda = \frac{h}{m_e v} \approx \frac{6.6 \times 10^{-27}}{9.1 \times 10^{-28} \times 2 \times 10^8} = 3.6 \times 10^{-8} = 3.6 \text{ Å}.$$

This wavelength is comparable with the diameter of the hydrogen atom. Indeed, it can be shown (see Problem 8.7) that, for the ground state of the hydrogen atom, $\lambda = 2\pi r_0$ where r_0 is the first Bohr radius. Thus one wavelength corresponds to the electron wave going round the nucleus once. This can hardly be an accident and in fact it is not. The wave mechanics of atoms follows very much from this.

The wavelength associated with an electron can be demonstrated directly by the observation of a diffraction pattern for the electrons scattered by a grating. If we use a stream of electrons all with the same energy, i.e. with the same velocity or momentum p, they can, according to the above analysis, be regarded as having an associated wavelength h/p. It so happens that, for electrons of convenient energy (a few tens of kev), the atoms in the surface of a crystal form a suitable grating. Since the atomic spacing is known, the diffraction pattern gives the wavelength, since the experiment is just the inverse of that for light discussed in Chapter 2. The observed wavelength is indeed found to be given by h/p. Since the electrons are usually accelerated by an electric potential difference, the calculation of p involves the assumption that the charge is independent of velocity. This is closely related to the problem of the gain of kinetic energy discussed in Section 8.1.

8.6   MASS–ENERGY–MOMENTUM

We have the relations $E = mc^2$, $p = mv$, and $m = m_0/(1 - v^2/c^2)^{1/2}$. We can eliminate m to get

$$E^2 = m_0^2 c^4 + p^2 c^2,$$

which is a relation between energy and momentum. This relation is extensively used for dealing with relativistic situations (e.g. Problem 8.22), since there we are seldom concerned with velocity as such. It is a convenient expression for use in calculations concerning conservation of energy and of momentum.

If we put $m_0 \to 0$ in the equation, we get $E^2 \to p^2 c^2$ or $p \to E/c$. For light, this means that $p = hv/c$, a result which we found in Section 8.4. Thus light consists of particles having zero rest mass. In fact, photons *always* travel at the velocity of light so the term "rest mass" is a considerable abstraction. Neutrinos (and gravitons, if they exist) are the only other particles which are known to have zero rest mass and they also always travel at the velocity of light.

The total energy of a particle is $E = mc^2 = m_0 c^2/(1 - v^2/c^2)^{1/2}$. We can let $m_0 \to 0$ and $v \to c$ at the same time so that E has *any* chosen value. Hence a zero rest mass particle may have *any* total energy, e.g. if it is a photon its energy is hv where v can take *any* value. The distinction between photons and neutrinos is, of course, in other properties.

8.7 THE COMPTON EFFECT*

Perhaps the best illustration of the particle nature of light is in the interaction of light and electrons. A good way of finding the properties of an unknown particle is to look at its collisions with a known particle. We shall use the known particle, the electron, to investigate the unknown one, the photon.

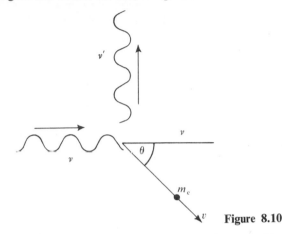

Figure 8.10

Consider light of frequency v incident on a stationary electron. For simplicity, consider only light scattered at right angles (for the general result, see Problem 8.17). Suppose the observed frequency of the scattered light is v' and the velocity of the scattered electron is v (Fig. 8.10). For conservation of momentum in the horizontal and vertical directions,

$$\frac{hv}{c} = m_e v \cos \theta \quad \text{and} \quad \frac{hv'}{c} = m_e v \sin \theta.$$

Adding the squares of these two equations, we get

$$\frac{h^2}{c^2}(v^2 + v'^2) = m_e^2 v^2 \quad \text{or} \quad v^2 = \frac{h^2}{m_e^2 c^2}(v^2 + v'^2).$$

For conservation of energy,

$$hv = hv' + \tfrac{1}{2}m_e v^2 \quad \therefore \quad (v - v') = m_e v^2/2h,$$

for non-relativistic electrons. Substituting this value of v^2 in the equation above, we get

$$v - v' = \left(\frac{m_e}{2h}\right)\left(\frac{h^2}{m_e^2 c^2}\right)(v^2 + v'^2) = \left(\frac{h}{2m_e c^2}\right)(v^2 + v'^2).$$

If v is small, very little energy is given up to the electron by the light—in any case v must be small for our calculation because we are assuming the kinetic energy of

---

* A. H. COMPTON, *Phys. Rev.* **22**, 411 (1923).

the electron is given by $\frac{1}{2}m_e v^2$; we have $v \approx v'$, so that

$$v - v' \approx \left(\frac{h}{2m_e c^2}\right) 2 \times v^2 \quad \text{or} \quad \frac{v - v'}{v^2} = \frac{h}{m_e c^2} \quad \text{or} \quad \Delta v/v^2 = h/m_e c^2,$$

where $\Delta v = v - v'$. But

$$v\lambda = c \qquad \therefore \quad \lambda = c/v \qquad \therefore \quad \Delta\lambda = -c\,\Delta v/v^2.$$

We therefore have for the change in the wavelength of the scattered light,

$$-\Delta\lambda = c\,\frac{h}{m_e c^2} = \frac{h}{m_e c} = 0.0242 \text{ Å},$$

independent of λ (actually this result is correct even for relativistic electrons). The observed change in wavelength has just this value.

This experiment cannot be explained on the wave theory of light. The electric vector of the light wave merely causes the electron to oscillate and it can only reradiate light at the *same* frequency as that of the incident light. (This is not strictly true because of the Doppler effect but the predicted classical effect does not agree with experiment.) Since the change of wavelength is fixed, it is relatively unimportant (and difficult to measure) for long wavelength electromagnetic radiation and so the classical (wave) picture works. For short wavelengths, the change in wavelength is important and the particle picture is required. Neither picture is entirely correct or entirely wrong. A more general theory, quantum electrodynamics, gives a unified explanation.

As in all scattering experiments, we can calculate the scattering cross-section; in this case of the electron for photons. It turns out to correspond to a radius for the scattering of the photon by the electron of $r_e = (\frac{8}{3})^{1/2} e^2/m_e c^2$ which is effectively the "classical" radius of the electron (Section 4.2). This last result can also be obtained, and was obtained, by a classical calculation (as might be expected, since the result does not contain h). The result is of some fundamental interest, since, if we measure the scattering cross-section A per unit volume for x rays by a material which contains N atoms per unit volume, then the cross-section per atom is A/N. For x rays with $\lambda < 1$ Å and for light elements, the electrons behave as effectively free particles with cross section πr_e^2. Hence $(A/N)/\pi r_e^2$ gives the number of electrons in the atom. For example, it has been shown in this way that the carbon atom (in graphite) has six electrons.* It is rather satisfactory to be able to count the electrons in an atom in this direct way. Incidently, since the atom is neutral, this means that the carbon nucleus carries a charge of six times the electronic charge. Other nuclear charge numbers Z can be determined as a check on the other methods described in Section 4.1.

---

* BARKLA and SADLER, *Phil. Mag.* **7**, 543 (1904); **17**, 739 (1909); **21**, 648 (1911).

8.8 THE GRAVITATIONAL MASS OF THE PHOTON

If light has mass, it ought to be affected by gravity like everything else which has mass, since, as we saw in Section 5.9, we have always found that inertial mass and gravitational mass are proportional to one another. The gravitational mass of the photon has been confirmed recently by terrestrial experiments. The result was foreseen by Einstein from a conceptual experiment which only assumed conservation of energy. The inertial mass of a photon was found in Section 8.4 to be $h\nu/c^2$; hence the force on a photon in a gravitational field g should be $(h\nu/c^2)g$. Therefore the increase in energy ΔE of a photon in falling through a height H is $(h\nu/c^2)gH$ (i.e. "mgH"). Therefore the increase in frequency is $\Delta\nu = \Delta E/h = \nu gH/c^2$. For $g = 981$ cm s^{-2} and $H = 100$ m $= 10^4$ cm, $\Delta E/E = \Delta\nu/\nu = gH/c^2 = 981 \times 10^4/(3 \times 10^{10})^2 \approx 10^{-14}$. This very small relative change in frequency, i.e. in mass, has actually been measured using the Mössbauer effect which involves a γ-ray photon of extremely well-defined energy and which we can use to measure relative energy changes of this order (Fig. 8.11). An alternative explanation of this experiment is to say that clocks go slower at lower gravitational potential so the frequency of the fallen photon had only appeared to have increased because we had not properly compared our high and low clocks. However, this gets us into so-called general relativity (Section 9.7) which we cannot pursue here.

The effect just discussed is clearly a relativistic rather than a quantum-mechanical effect, since Planck's constant h does not appear in the answer. The trick of regarding light as composed of photons of momentum $h\nu/c$ and mass $h\nu/c^2$ may be used to calculate the deflexion of light by the sun (Problem 8.8). The angular deflexion of light of grazing incidence is $2GM_S/R_Sc^2$ where G is the universal gravitational constant, M_S is the mass of the Sun, and R_S is the radius of the Sun. Inserting the approximate values, we find that this is one second of arc.

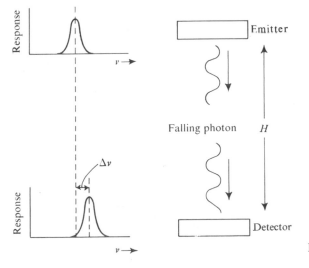

Figure 8.11

Einstein's general theory of relativity gives just *twice* this value and is confirmed by experiment so that in this more complex situation the ordinary photon mass idea is inadequate.

The photon turns out to be the particle associated with an electromagnetic field. This leads to speculation as to whether there is a particle associated with the gravitational field and whether this field is propagated with a finite velocity. Considerations similar to the above suggest that there is a particle, called a graviton, with zero rest mass which moves with velocity c but that it has a spin angular momentum $2\hbar$ rather than the $\hbar$ for the photon. It has not yet been observed. Zero rest mass is associated with an inverse square law of force, as for electricity and gravity. If the force between particles falls off faster than the inverse square law, a particle of finite mass is required to describe the interaction. Thus the short-range nuclear force field particle is the π meson which has a mass $273.1m_e$.

We have so far only looked at relativistic *mechanics*. This is in many respects the same as Newtonian mechanics provided we replace m_0 by m. In more complicated situations, in particular where light is involved, this is not sufficient and we are led into deeper waters.

PROBLEMS

8.1. If the angular momentum of the electron in the ground state of the hydrogen atom is $\hbar$, show that the velocity v of the electron is given by $v/c = e^2/\hbar c = \alpha \approx 1/137$ (α is the fine structure constant).

8.2. Show that the electrons in the beam of a TV set or a CRO with an accelerating potential of 5 kv have $v/c \sim 1/7$.

8.3. Show that 1 a.m.u. $\equiv$ 931 Mev (a.m.u. = atomic mass unit $\approx$ mass of the hydrogen atom).

8.4. Currently, the longest linear electron accelerator is two miles long. Calculate the minimal possible time for the electron to travel down it. If the electron starts from rest and gains 2 Mev per cm, calculate the final electron energy. What is the effective mass of the electron when it hits the target?

8.5. In the CERN proton synchrotron, the final energy of the protons is about 30 Gev. Were relativistic effects dominant in the design of this machine? (1 Gev $= 10^9$ ev).

8.6. The Newtonian kinetic energy is $\frac{1}{2}m_0v^2$. The relativistic kinetic energy is $(m - m_0)c^2$ but we might possibly have guessed that it would be $\frac{1}{2}mv^2$. Show that the guess is wrong by $\frac{1}{8}m_0c^2(v/c)^4 + 0(v/c)^6$. ($0(v/c)^6$ means the next term is proportional to $(v/c)^6$ in the power series expansion.)

8.7. Show that, if the angular momentum of the electron in the hydrogen atom in the nth level is $n\hbar$, then its de Broglie wavelength is $\lambda_n = 2\pi n r_0$ where r_0 is the first Bohr radius (≈ 0.53 Å). What is interesting about this result?

8.8. Regard a photon as a particle of momentum $h\nu/c$ and mass $h\nu/c^2$. Show that the angle of deflexion of light passing the Sun at grazing incidence is $2GM_S/R_Sc^2$ radians, independent of ν. Show that this angle is about one second of arc.

8.9. The original Compton scattering experiment was done with graphite and x rays. Show that the electrons involved may be regarded as effectively free, as required by the elementary theory.

8.10. The eye has a sensitivity to light of about 10^{-17} watt. What is the minimal number of photons per second (flux) needed for the eye to see something?

8.11. The minimal wavelength of x rays produced by bombardment of a target with 25 kv electrons is 0.5 Å. Find a value of Planck's constant from this.

8.12. Show that in Problem 7.5 it was a good approximation to use the Newtonian expression for the kinetic energy of the particles concerned.

8.13. If an electron is to be scattered in such a way as to indicate the structure of a nucleus, its wavelength must be short enough. Show that electrons with energy of greater than about 1000 Mev are required.

8.14. A typical energy of a chemical reaction is 2 or 3 ev. Show that this could explain why it is that we see with "visible" light.

8.15. An electron and a positron can suffer a head-on collision and be entirely converted into electromagnetic radiation (see Chapter 14). Show that, in order to conserve energy and linear momentum, at least two photons must result.

8.16. The intensity of solar radiation at the Earth's surface is about 8 J cm^{-2} min^{-1}. What is the force on the Earth due to radiation from the Sun if it is all absorbed?

8.17. Show that the electromagnetic radiation scattered by an angle ϕ in the Compton experiment (Section 8.7) is shifted in wavelength by $(h/m_e c)(1 - \cos \phi)$.

8.18. Show that the curve of v^2 versus kinetic energy T in Section 8.1 and Fig. 8.1 is given by $v^2 = c^2[1 - (1 + T/m_0 c^2)^{-2}]$.

8.19. In Section 8.3, it is stated that the fission of a nucleus of mass about 240 a.m.u. into two fragments of about 120 a.m.u. releases about 200 Mev per atom. Show that this corresponds to an energy yield of order 10^8 kwh per kg for complete conversion.

8.20. Use the masses given in Section 6.2 to show that the mass defect of $^4_2$He is 7.0 Mev per nucleon. What can we conclude from the fact that this is well above the average mass-defect curve in Section 8.3 for mass 4 a.m.u.?

8.21. Show that, for an electron starting from rest at time $t = 0$ in a constant electric field E along the x axis, the distance travelled in time t is given by

$$x = \frac{m_0 c^2}{eE}\left[1 - \left(1 + \frac{e^2 E^2 t^2}{m_0^2 c^2}\right)^{1/2}\right].$$

(Use the value of $v(t)$ in Section 8.3.)

8.22. In nuclear physics, we can usually only measure the kinetic energy T and the momentum p of a particle but the particle can often be identified from the value of its rest mass m_0. Show that $m_0 = (p^2 c^2 - T^2)/2Tc^2$. (HINT: Use result in Section 8.6.)

8.23. A particle with charge q and rest mass m_0 is accelerated from rest by falling through a potential difference V. Show that the de Broglie wavelength of the accelerated particle ($\lambda = h/p$) is given by

$$\lambda = h[(eV/c)^2 + 2eVm_0]^{-1/2}.$$

8.24. Sodium D lines (5893 Å) are emitted when sodium vapour is bombarded by electrons which have been accelerated by a potential difference of 2.11 v. Explain why this is so.

8.25. Find suitable constants for the nuclear binding energy on the liquid drop model, $E_b/A = C_v + C_s A^{-1/3} + C_c A^{2/3}$ (see Section 8.3).

8.26. It is asserted that $dE/dt = d\mathbf{p}/dt \cdot \mathbf{v}$ in Section 8.3. Show that the two sides of the equation are equal by substituting $E = mc^2$ on the left and $\mathbf{p} = m\mathbf{v}$ on the right where $m = m_0[1 - v^2/c^2]^{-1/2}$, bearing in mind that $\mathbf{v}$ is a function of t.

CHAPTER 9

The nature of space and time

*The views of space and time which I wish to lay before you have sprung
from the soil of experimental physics, and therein lies their
strength.* H. MINKOWSKI

Since the velocity of light c turned up in our *mechanical* experiments, there must
be something special about this particular velocity and probably about light
itself. Clearly, there must be some relation between mechanics and light, especially
when we consider physical objects moving at very high velocities. In fact, the
whole of the so-called theory of special relativity can be based on relativity (see
below) and on the idea that the velocity of light *in vacuo* is *always* the same,
provided we measure it in our own frame of reference (see Section 9.5 and Problem
9.2). Special relativity is the study of the dynamics of particles (or objects) in
frames of reference moving relative to one another with constant velocity. If the
frames of reference accelerate relative to each other, the matter is much more
complex and the field of study is called *general* relativity (Section 9.7). Even so,
the postulate of the constancy of the velocity of light as measured locally is still
a powerful one. Since light is an electromagnetic wave, we are essentially involved
in a study of electromagnetism. In fact, putting m for m_0 in Newtonian mechanics
makes it agree with the predictions of electromagnetic theory in most respects,
which it does not do otherwise, but we shall not be able to look into this question
formally here. The study of the propagation of light signals is relevant and important for the study of particles because it leads to important modifications in
our understanding of space and time—in which particles move. Apart from this,
the actual study of particles usually involves electromagnetic signals in the measuring process. We must therefore clearly understand many of the properties of
electromagnetic waves. We shall not go into the theory of relativity in any detail
and the reader is referred to elementary texts devoted to this subject (see "Further
Reading"). We shall use one well-known experiment to suggest some of the principal results which, together with the experiments described in Chapter 8, will
allow us to obtain a sufficient feeling for the subject for our purposes.

9.1 THE MICHELSON–MORLEY EXPERIMENT

A crucial experiment on light was carried out by Michelson and Morley in 1887.*
Note that this was long before Bucherer's and similar experiments on the variation

---

* A. A. MICHELSON and E. W. MORLEY, *Am. J. Sci.* **34**, 333 (1887); for a modern version, see
JASEJA, JAVAN, MURRAY, and TOWNES, *Phys. Rev.* **133**, A1221 (1964).

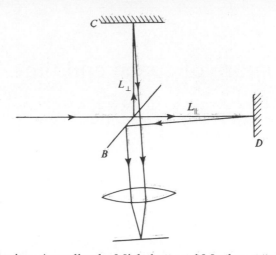

Figure 9.1

of mass with velocity. Actually, the Michelson and Morley experiment was under-
taken in connexion with a controversy about the "ether" but let us just regard it
simply as an experiment on light for the moment.

The experiment is shown diagrammatically in Fig. 9.1. The incident light
is split by a half-silvered mirror so that the two parts follow the paths as shown to
the mirrors C and D, return to the half-silvered mirror and finally come together
again at the photographic plate. If the paths are not too long, we expect constructive
interference at a particular line on the plate if $L_\perp = L_\parallel$ and any other slight path
differences are much smaller than λ, the wavelength of the light. In fact, a set of
interference fringes is formed and we only need $L_\perp = L_\parallel + n\lambda$, where n is an integer,
for constructive interference, but let us take $n = 0$ for simplicity. Now suppose
we do the experiment again when the whole apparatus is moving relative to some
supposed basically fixed system (the ether) with uniform velocity u to the right.
Then the light must be regarded as moving in the basic frame of coordinates rather
than in the frame moving with us and we must allow for this in the calculation.
In Fig. 9.2, C', B', and D' show the new positions of the mirrors when the appropriate
beam of light actually gets to them. The situation is now rather like the one in
which we consider the difference between rowing upstream and down again as
compared with rowing across the stream and back. It does not take the same time
to make the two different journeys and return to the same spot.

We might say that, if the velocity of light in the "absolute" system referred
to above is c, its velocity in our moving system is $(c - u)$ to the right and $(c + u)$
to the left. We then immediately expect trouble, since we already have evidence
that c is a limiting velocity at least for material particles, hence $(c + u)$ is suspect—
in fact so is $(c - u)$, but this is less obvious. However, light does not consist of
material particles in any obvious way so we ignore this possible difficulty for the
moment. Alternatively, we may say that the light has a speed c in the "absolute"
system but there it has to travel horizontally a distance $L_\parallel + ut_1$ to the right and
$L_\parallel - ut_2$ to the left where the times required to do this are t_1 and t_2, respectively.

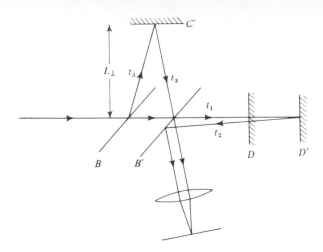

Figure 9.2

In both cases, the light travels a distance measured on the *apparatus* of $L_{\parallel}$. We have

$$ct_1 = L_{\parallel} + ut_1 \quad \text{and} \quad ct_2 = L_{\parallel} - ut_2.$$

Hence, solving for t_1 and for t_2, we get

$$t_1 + t_2 = L_{\parallel}/(c - u) + L_{\parallel}/(c + u) = 2L_{\parallel}c/(c^2 - u^2) = (2L_{\parallel}/c)/(1 - u^2/c^2).$$

The light going from B to C' and back to B' has a longer path to travel in the absolute system, in which it travels at velocity c, than it had before. During the time t_3, the light travels a distance ct_3 and the apparatus travels a distance ut_3 relative to the absolute frame in a direction perpendicular to $L_{\perp}$. For the right-angled triangle formed by ct_3, ut_3, and $L_{\perp}$, we have

$$(ct_3)^2 = L_{\perp}^2 + (ut_3)^2 \quad \text{or} \quad 2t_3 = 2L_{\perp}/(c^2 - u^2)^{1/2} = (2L_{\perp}/c)/(1 - u^2/c^2)^{1/2}.$$

We see, therefore, that the time for the light to travel perpendicular to the "stream" is different from that to travel parallel to the stream, since $t_1 + t_2 \neq 2t_3$ even if $L_{\parallel} = L_{\perp}$. Note, however, that an encouragingly familiar expression, $(1 - u^2/c^2)^{1/2}$, turns up. The surprising result of the Michelson–Morley experiment was that in fact there is *no shift* in the fringes due to motion. At least, the shift is not as large as that expected for the velocity of the Earth in its orbit. This could be tested by setting up the apparatus so that the incident light was first parallel to the motion of the Earth in its orbit and then turning the apparatus through 90°. The time difference for the two beams $(t_1 + t_2 - 2t_3)$ is changed by an amount $\Delta t = 4L/c\{(1 - u^2/c^2)^{-1} - (1 - u^2/c^2)^{-1/2}\}$ so that the fringes should shift by $c\,\Delta t/\lambda$ fringes (see Problem 9.5). The fringes should also move in an oscillatory manner with a period of six months if the solar system is moving relative to some absolute system of coordinates. The fringes do not move. The experiment has been repeated many times and the result is certainly correct.

Some basic assumption must be wrong. The assumption that is wrong is that there is a unique absolute system in which the velocity of light is c. We cannot find any experimental reason to consider any one inertial frame as more absolute than any other.

Notice that we are now trying to do quite different things from those discussed in Chapter 8 where we studied the mechanics of particles. We are now discussing lengths and times and light in *moving* systems and this is a very different and more difficult matter. Notice also that u is the relative velocity of two coordinate systems not the velocity of some material particle relative to one coordinate system, for which we usually use the different symbol v. Nevertheless, there is surely a connexion between the expression $(1 - v^2/c^2)^{1/2}$ of Chapter 8 and the expression $(1 - u^2/c^2)^{1/2}$ we have found here.

9.2 LENGTH CONTRACTION

One way out of the difficulty of the null result of the Michelson–Morley experiment was suggested by Lorentz. He said, experiment gives $t_1 + t_2 = 2t_3$; this is true if

$$(2L_{\parallel}/c)/(1 - u^2/c^2) = (2L_{\perp}/c)/(1 - u^2/c^2)^{1/2},$$

or

$$L_{\parallel} = L_{\perp}(1 - u^2/c^2)^{1/2}, \quad \text{that is} \quad L_{\parallel} < L_{\perp}.$$

Hence there is a *contraction* of lengths in the direction of motion, or an elongation at right angles to the motion, or a bit of both! In fact, it can be shown (see below) that $L_{\perp}$ must be unchanged and so this experiment suggests that $L_{\parallel}$ contracts. In fact, this is not the correct explanation, since if the two arms of the interferometer have different lengths—apart from the Lorentz contraction—then the null result of the experiment is not explained. It is in fact true, however, that there is a measurable Lorentz contraction of the amount given above for two frames of reference actually moving relative to one another at velocity u. There is no measurable contraction for motion relative to the ether. We therefore only use the Michelson–Morley experiment to suggest how the idea of length contraction may arise when we consider systems moving relative to one another.

Perpendicular lengths do not change because they can be compared first when they are both at rest and then also when they are in motion at the instant that they pass each other. If the length did change (Fig. 9.3), then we would have the situation that A says B's rod has shortened but B says A's rod has lengthened

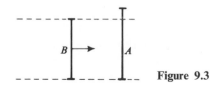

Figure 9.3

(or the same argument inverted if B got longer). Therefore, A's view of B is different from B's view of A and there is an asymmetry. This asymmetry is denied by relativity theory and is not observed experimentally but we are not able to go into the matter here. It arises again briefly in Section 9.5. A quite different situation exists for rods parallel to the direction of motion, since we cannot in this case *simultaneously* compare the two ends.

It is a valid idea that if we measure a body moving relative to us at velocity v its *measured* length is contracted to $(1 - v^2/c^2)^{1/2}$ of the value if it is stationary, i.e. the *relative* motion is to be allowed for. This is symmetrical in the sense that A says B's rod is contracted *and* B says A's is contracted because $(1 - v^2/c^2)^{1/2}$ is unchanged if we replace v by $-v$.

One important application of the Lorentz contraction is to explain the magnetic part of the Lorentz force $q\mathbf{v}/c \times \mathbf{B}$ as a motional effect of the electrostatic interaction. This force is easy to measure, even for quite small velocities but nevertheless it is relativistic in origin.

It should be noted that the length contraction we have deduced for an object moving relative to us is a *measured* length contraction and that we would not actually *see* the contraction as such even if we could see directly objects moving at velocities comparable with that of light. This is because what we see corresponds to the situation when the light was emitted from the object and if the object is moving with velocity comparable with the velocity of light the time differences for light from different parts of the object to reach our eyes are significant. It can be shown that an object moving at right angles to our line of sight at velocity v appears to be rotated about an axis perpendicular to the plane containing the eye and the trajectory of the object by an angle $\sin^{-1} v/c$.* In particular, a spherical object still appears spherical. For a cube whose side is actually facing us we can see part of the leading face and the side. It is perhaps comforting to note that we can never actually see the back side of the cube, since the angle of rotation has a maximum of $90°$ for $v \to c$. This somewhat hypothetical experiment serves a useful purpose in emphasizing the care which must be taken, particularly in relativistic considerations, to define clearly how we actually carry out an experiment and what constitutes a measurement as opposed to an observation.

9.3 TIME DILATION

However, time and space are always mixed up as we have already seen in a rather general way and the same is true here. If we explain the Michelson–Morley experiment in terms of a length contraction in the direction of motion, we get into trouble with time. The value of t_3 clearly depends on whether the person measuring the length is moving relative to it or not. We have $t_3 = (L_\perp/c)/(1 - u^2/c^2)^{1/2}$. $L_\perp$ is independent of the relative velocity u, since it is perpendicular to u, so we have to conclude that t_3 increases with u—a velocity-dependent time measurement!

---

* V. F. WEISSKOPF, *Phys. Today* **13**, 24 (1960).

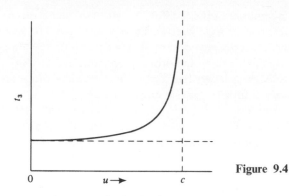

Figure 9.4

Again the relation is correct for actual physical systems moving relative to one another and is not strictly deducible from the Michelson–Morley experiment alone. The time dilation, as seen from Fig. 9.4 is, like the length contraction, only appreciable for velocities approaching that of light.

We ought to observe that things happen more slowly in the system moving relative to us. This is *time dilation*. Things happen more slowly if we give them more time in which to happen. This can in fact be observed *experimentally*. One of the most striking manifestations of this concerns the decay of the μ meson.* In the upper atmosphere, cosmic ray particles produce π mesons (they can also be produced by accelerating machines). These π mesons decay rapidly into μ mesons and neutrinos,

$$\pi^\pm \to \mu^\pm + \nu, \quad \text{with half-life} \quad 2.54 \times 10^{-8} \text{ s.}$$

The μ meson formed decays more slowly into an electron and two different neutrinos, ν and ν'.

$$\mu^\pm \to e^\pm + \nu + \nu', \quad \text{with half-life} \quad 2.22 \times 10^{-6} \text{ s.}$$

This half-life τ for a μ meson of 2.22 $\times$ 10^{-6} s is the value measured in the laboratory for stationary μ mesons whether produced in the atmosphere or by a machine. However, it is known that μ mesons from cosmic rays are formed in the upper atmosphere and a far larger proportion get to ground level than would be expected from this value of its half-life. However, even if μ mesons travel at the velocity of light c, they can only travel in their average lifetime τ a distance τc which is 2.2 $\times$ $10^{-6} \times 3 \times 10^{10}$ cm $\sim 10^5$ cm, i.e. 1 km. Hence how can a large fraction possibly get down from a height of about 50 km in the upper atmosphere where they are formed? The answer is that time in their system is dilated as far as we are concerned by the factor $1/(1 - v^2/c^2)^{1/2}$. If v approaches c, this factor can easily be 50. They therefore have sufficient time to make the 50 km journey. Since we can only conveniently measure the flux of mesons at ground level and not at the top of the atmosphere, the experiment is actually to measure the flux of mesons as a function of height and to show that the flux of particles does not fall off as rapidly with

* D. H. FRISCH and J. H. SMITH, *Am. J. Phys.* **31,** 342 (1963).

decreasing height as expected for Newtonian space–time. In fact, therefore, the measured time dilation is given by $1/(1 - v^2/c^2)^{1/2}$.

In the meson's own rest system, that is if we were travelling with the meson and observing it, its lifetime would still on average be 2.2×10^{-6} s. However, if we are travelling with the particle then we measure the distance from the top of the atmosphere to the ground, or indeed any distance, as being contracted (Section 9.2) and so we have plenty of time to travel the distance which is foreshortened by the *same* factor $1/(1 - v^2/c^2)^{1/2}$. It is clear, therefore, that time dilation and length contraction are really only two different ways of looking at the same thing and we could not possibly have the one without the other. In relativity, therefore, the connexion between space and time is a very close one. This is expressed more explicitly in Section 9.5. Although space and time are closely connected and interdependent, it is misleading to suggest that they are so very similar as might be understood by such expressions as "four-dimensional space–time". Time and space are still distinct but not as different as in Newtonian mechanics. The greater flexibility in relativistic mechanics is still restricted by the requirement that effect must follow a cause and not vice versa. Common sense must not be abandoned entirely!

9.4 MOVING CLOCKS GO SLOW

Ives and Stillwell* showed time dilation more directly by using rapidly moving excited hydrogen atoms which emit light as they move.

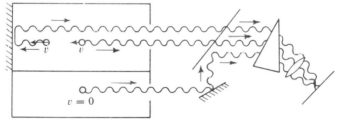

Figure 9.5

In the experiment, shown diagrammatically in Fig. 9.5, atoms moving with velocity v are selected and excited. They can emit radiation both backwards and forwards. The forward radiation is returned by a mirror and both the backward and forward beams are selected by a slit. The light is analysed by a spectrograph. Light from similar but effectively stationary atoms is also provided and is fed into the spectrograph. The spectrum has a line from each of the three different components of light emitted by the three differently moving types of atoms as shown diagrammatically in Fig. 9.6. The lower spectrum shows the additional shift $\delta\lambda$ of the mean wavelength of the two outer Doppler lines exaggerated to show on this figure (see Fig. 9.6). The relative Doppler wavelength shift for an emitter moving at velocity $\pm v$ in the line of sight is $\Delta\lambda/\lambda = \pm(v/c)$ and so the Doppler lines from the moving atoms should be symmetrical about the line for

* *J. Opt. Soc. Am.* **28**, 215 (1938).

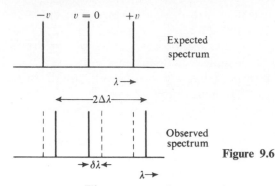

Figure 9.6

$v = 0$ from the stationary atoms. They are not because the atoms moving at velocity v have in the laboratory frame a time dilation by the factor $(1 - v^2/c^2)^{-1/2}$ and so to us the moving atoms oscillate more slowly. Their frequency is lower and so, since $v\lambda = c$, the wavelength of the emitted light is longer than it would otherwise be. Hence the mean wavelength of the Doppler shifted lines is longer than that of the wavelength for the unshifted lines, i.e. for $v = 0$. The time dilation can be measured from the "discrepancy". The experimental result is shown in Fig. 9.7. The measured value does indicate a time dilation by the factor $(1 - v^2/c^2)^{-1/2}$ (see Problem 9.6). This corresponds to the full line in Fig. 9.7. We can say, alternatively, that the Doppler shift for velocities in the line of sight is $\pm(v/c) \times (1 - v^2/c^2)^{\mp 1/2}$ which is its relativistic value. It may be noted that the optical experiment just described shows a positive measurable effect which is more satisfactory than a null experiment like that of Michelson and Morley.

Again, consider an atom which is known to radiate electromagnetic energy of wavelength λ when it is not moving relative to the spectrometer. Now suppose it is moving at velocity v relative to the spectrometer *perpendicular* to the line of sight (Fig. 9.8). The atomic clock must again appear to be running slow by the factor $(1 - v^2/c^2)^{1/2}$ and so the wavelength λ' of the light received by the spectrometer should now be longer and $\lambda' = \lambda(1 - v^2/c^2)^{-1/2}$. There is therefore a transverse Doppler effect. The effect is quite small compared with the longitudinal

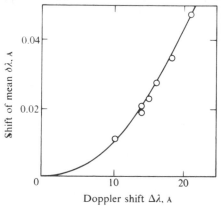

Figure 9.7. Adapted from IVES and STILL-WELL, *J. Opt. Soc. Am.* **28**, 215 (1938).

Figure 9.8

Doppler effect unless v is comparable with c. It is difficult to observe because, unless the atom is moving precisely transverse to the observer, a small fraction of the much larger longitudinal Doppler effect will obscure it. In non-relativistic mechanics, there is no transverse Doppler effect.

9.5 FRAMES OF REFERENCE

There is, of course, a much more fundamental aspect to relativity theory than the concepts of mass–energy, time dilation, and so on, which we have dealt with in a rather empirical manner. Relativity is really concerned with the validity of physical laws in moving frames of reference. In special relativity, the moving frames are inertial frames and in general relativity the frames of reference may move in any way.

Newton recognized the importance of the relativity concept and stated, in our language, that the dynamics of particles has the same form in any uniformly moving system. (In spite of this, he also believed in an absolute space and time.) It is interesting and useful to try to describe the motion of the particles for two different systems of coordinates moving relative to each other. We have to express the behaviour of a particle in terms of coordinates x, y, z, t in one system and x', y', z', t' in the other and to relate the two descriptions of the motion.

If the dashed system is moving at constant velocity u relative to the undashed system in the x (or x') direction, we expect to have

$$
\begin{aligned}
x' &= x - ut & \qquad x &= x' + ut \\
y' &= y & \qquad y &= y' \\
z' &= z & \qquad z &= z' \\
t' &= t & \qquad t &= t'.
\end{aligned}
$$

or

We can see that these relations are correct by calculating the coordinates of the general point P in Fig. 9.9 for each coordinate system (x, y) and (x', y'). It can be shown that the relations above give the desired result of relative motion at velocity u by formal differentiation. Differentiating the first equation with respect to t', we

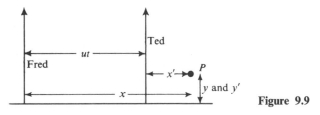

Figure 9.9

have

$$\frac{dx'}{dt'} = \frac{dx}{dt'} - u\frac{dt}{dt'}$$

but $t' = t$ so that $dt' = dt$,

$$\therefore \quad \frac{dx'}{dt'} = \frac{dx}{dt} - u.$$

In other words, $v'_x = v_x - u$. Similarly $v'_y = v_y$ and $v'_z = v_z$. Hence the two systems of coordinates *are* moving relative to one another at velocity u as required.

It is important to note that the two sets of transformation equations have the same *form* except for the sign of u.

Newton's laws of motion are invariant for this transformation of coordinates. Consider the second law, in the unprimed reference frame, $F = m(d^2x/dt^2)$.

ce $x = x' + ut$, we have

$$\frac{dx}{dt} = \frac{dx'}{dt} + u = \frac{dx'}{dt'} + u.$$

Therefore

$$\frac{d^2x}{dt^2} = \frac{d}{dt}\left(\frac{dx'}{dt'} + u\right) = \frac{d^2x'}{dt\,dt'} = \frac{d^2x'}{dt'^2},$$

since $t = t'$. We might expect that forces are not affected, since they are physical and ought not to depend on the description of the phenomenon and so we expect that $F = F'$. We therefore expect to have $F' = m\,d^2x'/dt'^2$, which is of same form as $F = m(d^2x/dt^2)$ with the same m. This is found to be so for small velocities, namely that mechanical experiments behave in the same way in any frame of reference moving with constant velocity relative to a frame in which it is known that Newton's laws of motion are obeyed, i.e. in inertial frames. More explicitly, all mechanical systems behave in the same way independently of u. The set of equations is called a Galilean transformation.

However, this transformation is not true for relativistic velocities or for electromagnetism. It is found here that the transformation needed to give agreement with the experimental results is that given by Lorentz, which is as follows

$$x' = \frac{x - ut}{(1 - u^2/c^2)^{1/2}} \qquad x = \frac{x' + ut'}{(1 - u^2/c^2)^{1/2}}$$

$$y' = y \qquad \text{or} \quad y = y'$$

$$z' = z \qquad z = z'$$

$$t' = \frac{t - ux/c^2}{(1 - u^2/c^2)^{1/2}} \qquad t = \frac{t' + ux'/c^2}{(1 - u^2/c^2)^{1/2}}$$

Note that, here again, the forward and reverse transformations have the same *form* and only differ in the sign of u.

For $u \ll c$, the Lorentz transformation reduces to the Galilean transformation given above. The Lorentz transformation must clearly contain the length contraction and time dilation discussed in Sections 9.2, 9.3, and 9.4.

The length contraction is easy to see. Ted* uses a rule and measures a length which is fixed in his (primed) system. Suppose that he chooses a length which is at the origin at $t = t' = 0$ and finds the other end is at x'. However, Fred (who is in the unprimed system) says Ted is using a rule foreshortened by the factor $(1 - u^2/c^2)^{1/2}$. Hence to Fred the length which Ted measures is shorter; it is $x'(1 - u^2/c^2)^{1/2}$. However, Fred is of the opinion that Ted measures the other end at a time t later when Ted has moved away a distance ut. Hence Fred says that the coordinate of the other end of Ted's length is at $x = x'(1 - u^2/c^2)^{1/2} + ut$, that is $x' = (x - ut)/(1 - u^2/c^2)^{1/2}$ as in the first Lorentz equation.†

Time measurement is more subtle. Fred says that Ted's clocks all go slow. Therefore any time interval Ted measures, say t', is actually longer for Fred. The hands on Ted's clock do not move fast enough and so the indicated time interval is too small. Hence $t > t'$. If Ted's clock remains at his origin of coordinates, that is $x' = 0$, this is the whole story and we have the time dilation already discussed, that is $t = t'/(1 - u^2/c^2)^{1/2}$. However, if the space origins were not coincident at the beginning of the time measurement, then the time coordinate must be corrected for this, which leads to $t = (t' + ux'/c^2)/(1 - u^2/c^2)^{1/2}$, the fourth Lorentz equation.

9.6 RELATIVISTIC ADDITION OF VELOCITIES

Comparison of velocities in different frames of reference is much more complicated than for the Galilean transformation.

We write $\beta = (1 - u^2/c^2)^{1/2}$. Then the first Lorentz equation is

$$x' = (x - ut)/\beta$$

and so

$$dx' = (dx - u\, dt)/\beta.$$

Therefore

$$\frac{dx'}{dt'} = \left(\frac{dx}{dt'} - u\frac{dt}{dt'}\right)\bigg/\beta = \left(\frac{dx}{dt} - u\right)\frac{dt}{dt'}\frac{1}{\beta}.$$

Also, we have

$$t' = (t - ux/c^2)/\beta,$$

so that

$$dt' = [dt - (u/c^2)\, dx]/\beta$$

---

* We use British observers, Ted and Fred, but they are blood brothers of Feynman's Joe and Moe.

† A good example of how much more difficult is a verbal argument than a mathematical analysis!

and therefore

$$\frac{dt'}{dt} = \left[1 - (u/c^2)\frac{dx}{dt}\right]\bigg/\beta.$$

Substituting for dt/dt' in the expression for dx'/dt' gives

$$\frac{dx'}{dt'} = \left(\frac{dx}{dt} - u\right)\left\{\beta\bigg/\left[1 - (u/c^2)\frac{dx}{dt}\right]\right\}1/\beta.$$

In other words,

$$v'_x = (v_x - u)/[1 - (u/c^2)v_x].$$

In particular, if $v_x \to c$,

$$v'_x \to \frac{c - u}{1 - (u/c^2)c} = \frac{c - u}{1/c(c - u)} = c,$$

i.e. adding *any* velocity u to c gives c. If the velocity is c in one coordinate system, it is c in *any* coordinate system. This is true of light in particular. Hence the Lorentz transformations are equivalent to Einstein's postulate that the velocity of light is the same in all systems moving uniformly relative to one another, that is, in all inertial frames.

Consider a reference frame B moving relative to A with velocity u and then a reference frame C moving relative to B in the same direction with velocity w. For a Galilean transformation, the motion of C relative to A corresponds to a relative velocity $(u + w)$. This cannot be true relativistically, since frames cannot move relative to one another with a velocity greater than c and clearly $(u + w)$ can exceed c even though u and w themselves do not exceed c. Applying two successive Lorentz transformations, we find that the velocity v of C relative to A is given by $v = (u + w)/(1 + uw/c^2)$ (see Problem 9.7). This has the expected properties. For instance, if w (or u) $= c$, $v = c$ for any u (or w). If $w = c$ *and* $u = c$, we have $v = c$. This is just not common sense, but in everyday life we do not often encounter objects moving with velocities approaching that of light.

We can relate these results back once more to our physical observations about particles in time and space. As we saw with the meson lifetime problem, time and space must be connected for reasons of consistency. The time dilation for one observer (in this case on the ground) corresponds to a length contraction for the other observer (on the meson). This is expressed in the Lorentz relations in which, for instance, x' depends on x *and* t.

We can see that all inertial frames are equivalent as far as any experiments we can do are concerned, including the determination of the velocity of light. However, there *is* a special frame for a given observer. This is the one in which he and his instruments are at rest. In particular, his clock registers a smaller interval for a physical event in this frame than for the same clock in any other inertial frame. This interval is called the proper time. It has a similar status to rest mass.

9.7 GENERAL RELATIVITY

It is known from experiment that the *form* of physical laws is the same in any inertial frame and that this fact is embodied in the Lorentz relation of Section 9.5 between the coordinates of the same event as measured in different inertial frames. This, together with the constancy of the velocity of light, whatever the velocity of its source and whatever inertial frame it is measured in, is the basis of special relativity. Considerably greater difficulties arise when we consider frames of reference accelerated relative to one another and we are familiar with the elementary form of those in rotatory motion at low velocities where we find centrifugal and Coriolis forces. The difficulties are much greater when we have velocities comparable with the velocity of light *and* accelerated frames of reference. The solution of these problems is the field of general relativity which may be regarded as the desire to express the physical laws in such a way that their form is invariant in all frames of reference, even accelerated ones.

PROBLEMS

9.1. Show explicitly that both the Galilean and the Lorentz transformations are inverted (i.e. instead of x in terms of x', etc., get x' in terms of x, etc.) simply by exchanging primes and reversing the sign of u, the relative velocity of the two frames.

9.2. According to Einstein, the velocity of light is always c in all inertial frames (moving at uniform velocity relative to each other). Two frames are coincident at $t = t' = 0$ and move at relative velocity u along the x (or x') direction. Because of Einstein's hypothesis, a pulse of light generated at the origin at the moment the origins of the two frames are coincident spreads spherically in *both* frames. Show that this implies the Lorentz transformation, $x = (x' + ut')/\beta$, $y = y'$, $z = z'$, $t = (t' + ux'/c^2)/\beta$ where $\beta = (1 - u^2/c^2)^{+1/2}$. (HINT: Put $x = (x' + ut')/\beta$ and $t = (t' + \gamma x')/\alpha$ and find α, β, and γ.)

9.3. Show that the Lorentz transformation for two systems moving relative to each other along the x axis at velocity u which were coincident at $t = t' = 0$ correspond to a rotation about an axis perpendicular to the (x, ict) or (x', ict') plane by an angle $\theta = \cos^{-1}(1 - u^2/c^2)^{-1/2}$. Hence or otherwise show that two simultaneous spacially separate events in one system are not simultaneous in the other. (This is Einstein's classic refutation of simultaneity.)

9.4. For the conditions of Problem 9.3, show that two events which are coincident but not simultaneous in one system need not be coincident in the other system.

9.5. Show that in Michelson and Morley's experiment, the fringe pattern for visible light and $L = 3$ metres should move by about one-tenth of a fringe if u is the velocity of the Earth in its orbit. This shift would be easy to see.

9.6. Show that the result of the Ives and Stillwell experiment given in Fig. 9.7 *does* correspond to time dilation by a factor $(1 - v^2/c^2)^{-1/2}$.

9.7. Show by two successive applications of the Lorentz transformation equations that, if frame B moves at u relative to A and frame C moves at w relative to B, then C moves relative to A at $(u + w)/(1 + uw/c^2)$.

9.8. Show that the generalization of the Lorentz transformation equations given in Section 9.5 for relative motion of two frames at velocity u along the x axis, to the case of relative motion at velocity $\mathbf{u}$ may be written

$$\mathbf{r}' = \mathbf{r} + \frac{\mathbf{u}}{u^2}\,(\mathbf{r} \cdot \mathbf{u})(\beta^{-1} - 1) - \beta^{-1}\mathbf{u}t, \qquad t' = \beta^{-1}(t - \mathbf{u} \cdot \mathbf{r}/c^2).$$

(It is helpful to obtain the relation for a Galilean transformation first and also to write the equations of Section 9.5 in vector notation.)

9.9. In some circumstances, an electromagnetic field can be obtained from a scalar potential $\varphi(x, y, z, t)$ which obeys the relation

$$\frac{\partial^2 \varphi}{\partial x^2} + \frac{\partial^2 \varphi}{\partial y^2} + \frac{\partial^2 \varphi}{\partial z^2} = \frac{1}{c^2}\frac{\partial^2 \varphi}{\partial t^2}$$

in free space. Show that the form of this equation is invariant under a Lorentz transformation but not under a Galilean transformation.

CHAPTER 10

Many particles—
probability and statistics

La théorie des Probabilités n'est au fond que le bon sens reduit au calcul. LAPLACE

10.1 A COMPLETE SOLUTION IS IMPOSSIBLE—AVERAGES

We often have to deal with many particles at once. For instance, we have say one cubic centimetre of copper which contains some 8×10^{22} atoms and we ask what is happening inside it. In principle, we could answer this question if we knew the position and momentum, $\mathbf{r}$ and $\mathbf{p}$, for every atom at some initial time and all the forces acting on each atom. We could then predict precisely all that would happen to the body at any time later since, as we have seen in Section 5.2, the momentum and position of any particular particle i at a time t later are given by

$$\mathbf{p}_i(t) = \mathbf{p}_i(0) + \int_0^t \mathbf{F}_i(t') \, \mathrm{d}t',$$

and

$$\mathbf{r}_i(t) = \mathbf{r}_i(0) + \frac{1}{m} \, \mathbf{p}_i(0)t + \frac{1}{m} \int_0^t \mathrm{d}t' \int_0^{t'} \mathbf{F}_i(t'') \, \mathrm{d}t''.$$

This would need the solution of $6 \times 8 \times 10^{22}$ simultaneous equations! Some other way of solving the problem must be found. The actual situation is even more complex than it appears, since the $\mathbf{F}_i(t)$ depend on the $\mathbf{r}_i(t)$, or at least on the distances between particles, $|\mathbf{r}_i(t) - \mathbf{r}_j(t)|$ in the simplest cases. The $\mathbf{F}_i(t)$ might be due, for instance, to our typical interaction force between atoms discussed in Section 4.1. Moreover, in general, we may have "particles" such as molecules which have moments of inertia and whose orientation in space is relevant. For example, the force between molecules depends on their orientations relative to one another as we saw, for instance, in the discussion of van der Waals forces in Chapter 4. Again, molecules may have internal vibrations and their electrons can be excited. The latter is so even for atoms. All these possibilities need time-dependent sets of coordinates to describe them. The basic expressions for $\mathbf{p}_i$ and $\mathbf{r}_i$ given above refer basically to particles and in this sense the complications just mentioned are already implicit in them.

Nevertheless, it is often found that large numbers of particles as a whole quite often behave quite simply—if we measure the right things. The translational motion of the cubic centimetre of copper under external forces is quite well described by three equations rather than 10^{23}. For a cubic centimetre of gas of low density having, say, 10^{19} particles, we have the very simple relation $PV = nRT$ with only *three* variables, P, V, and T, for the given quantity, n moles, of gas. The reason for these simple results is quite clear. For the copper block, all the atoms move together and so most of the 10^{23} equations are irrelevant. The distances between the particles are effectively fixed so that all the $\mathbf{r}_i$ vary in the same way with time and similarly for the momenta $\mathbf{p}_i$. For the gas, P, V, and T are properties of the gas as a whole. P is the mean or *average* force per unit area due to the molecules striking the wall. T is proportional to the *mean* energy of a molecule. V is the space that *all* the molecules are in. It is clear from this that, if we look at *averaged* properties, we would expect in general to get simpler results. Of course the force on the wall of the container actually varies with time in a very complicated way, as is suggested by Fig. 10.1, but the fluctuations are usually very small compared with the mean value and they are extremely rapid. If this were not so, the concept of pressure would not be a very useful one. The fluctuations arise because the actual force is the resultant of a large number of collisions of the molecules with the wall of the container. The actual force on the wall is due to the repulsive force between the molecules of the gas and the molecules of the wall at short distances. The details of the interaction do not affect the pressure, provided the dimensions of the container are larger than the mean free path. This is very adequately so at low enough densities. The lower the density, the more precisely does the gas obey the equation of state $PV = nRT$. The deviations from this equation depend on the properties of the molecules as discussed in Section 7.2.

We therefore often measure only the properties of the *object* and we are frequently not interested in what is actually happening to the particles of which it is composed, except in so far as these determine the properties of the object. A somewhat analogous situation was encountered when we considered the dynamics of a rigid body consisting of particles. We said that, as far as translational motion was considered, the system of particles in which a typical one is of mass m_i at the point $\mathbf{r}_i$ behaves as an object of total mass $M = \sum_i m_i$ at the point $\mathbf{R} = \sum m_i\mathbf{r}_i / \sum m_i$. Notice that the centre of mass is an *averaged* position within the object. For the movement of the object as a whole, we are not much interested in the individual particles, except in so far as these determine M and $\mathbf{R}$.

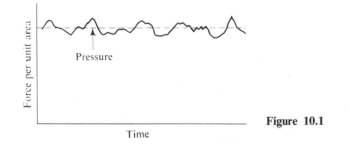

Figure 10.1

Other properties of macroscopic objects which we will want to look at, some of which we have treated briefly already, are specific heats, thermal expansion, electric and magnetic susceptibilities, compressibility and other elastic moduli, and so on. Furthermore, we want to know what is really meant by temperature, entropy, free energy, and other thermodynamic properties in terms of physical ideas and to be able to deduce these properties from the properties of the particles alone. Eventually, we would also want to explain non-equilibrium, but still averaged quantities, such as viscosity, self-diffusion, and so on! All these properties are properties of the collection of particles and *even if* we could solve the actual equations of motion of the particles, we would still need a theory to relate that solution to these observable properties which we actually measure.

10.2 THE PERFECT GAS LAWS

We illustrate the importance of averages more explicitly by calculating the pressure of a perfect gas (Fig. 10.2). For an elastic collision of an atom or molecule of velocity $\mathbf{v}$ and of mass m with the wall at an angle θ, the momentum transfer is $2mv \cos \theta = 2mv_x$. If there are N molecules in the volume V, there are $n = N/V$ per unit volume. In a time t, half as many molecules as are in a volume of cross-section A and length $v_x t$ hit the piece of wall of area A, that is to say $\frac{1}{2}nv_x tA$ atoms. The factor $\frac{1}{2}$ is there because half the molecules are travelling away from the wall and we are only counting those travelling towards the wall. The actual molecules which were in this column of gas will mostly not hit the wall unless t is very small but the same *number* will. This is because any molecule which moves out of the column, by reason of its transverse velocity or because of collisions, will on average be replaced by another at effectively the same place in the column and having effectively the same velocity component v_x. The same is true for any change in the velocity component v_x of any particular molecule in the column. If the velocity of the particular molecule we are observing is changed to some other value by a collision with another molecule, then somewhere in the close vicinity another molecule will acquire the velocity of the original one and so we can transfer our attention to the second one. The velocity distribution of the molecules in the gas is constant. In this way, we can readily take account of the collisions in the gas and the effect of the velocity components parallel to the plane of the wall. Hence the transfer of momentum in time t is given by the transfer per particle multiplied

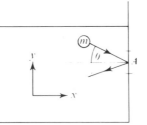

Figure 10.2

by the number of particles colliding with the wall in time t, that is $(2mv_x)(\frac{1}{2}nv_x tA) = nmv_x^2 At$. This is resisted by a force F provided by the wall acting for the time t and so, balancing momenta since the wall is stationary,

$$Ft = nmv_x^2 At, \quad \text{that is} \quad \frac{F}{A} = nmv_x^2.$$

Of course, all the molecules do not have the same x component of velocity v_x and so actually the force F varies with time, for instance as in Fig. 10.1. If we consider F over a long enough period of time, molecules with a whole range of velocities will have struck the wall and it will make sense to speak of the mean force. It is clear then that $P = nm\overline{v_x^2}$ where $\overline{v_x^2}$ is the mean value of v_x^2, since the pressure P is the mean force per unit area $(\overline{F}/A)$. To be consistent, if we consider the molecules of the gas, we ought to consider the molecules of the wall of the container. We then clearly have a situation which is very different from the simple "reflection" of the gas molecules as in Fig. 10.2 and in fact it is usually more true to assume that the molecules rebound from the wall randomly in all directions. Nevertheless, on average a molecule approaching the wall with a velocity v_x perpendicular to it rebounds with a velocity v_x and the result obtained above is still correct. Of course, the molecules have the whole range of v_x values. As we show later, the probability of finding a molecule having a velocity near v_x, $p(v_x)$, has the form shown in Fig. 10.8. But the gas is isotropic, in other words any property must be independent of the direction in space associated with it. We cannot distinguish by physical measurements any difference between the x, y, and z axes—indeed these axes are applied arbitrarily to the gas and we clearly do not change the properties of the gas by *thinking* of a set of axes set up to describe it. In this particular case, we therefore have $\overline{v_x^2} = \overline{v_y^2} = \overline{v_z^2}$. Also the actual velocity is given by $v^2 = v_x^2 + v_y^2 + v_z^2$ so that $\overline{v^2} = 3\overline{v_x^2} = 3\overline{v_y^2} = 3\overline{v_z^2}$. But we had $P = nm\overline{v_x^2}$, so that

$$P = \tfrac{1}{3}nm\overline{v^2} = \tfrac{2}{3}n(\tfrac{1}{2}m\overline{v^2}) = (N/V)\tfrac{2}{3}(\tfrac{1}{2}m\overline{v^2}).$$

That is to say,

$$PV = N\tfrac{2}{3}(\tfrac{1}{2}m\overline{v^2}).$$

But for N molecules in volume V we know by experiment that $PV = (N/N_0)RT$ where N_0 is Avogadro's number or $PV = NkT$. Therefore $kT = \tfrac{2}{3}(\tfrac{1}{2}m\overline{v^2})$ or $\tfrac{1}{2}m\overline{v^2} = \tfrac{3}{2}kT$ or $\tfrac{1}{2}m\overline{v_x^2} = \tfrac{1}{2}kT$, a result we have used in Section 4.2. Alternatively, we may use the experimental result of Section 10.4 that $\tfrac{1}{2}m\overline{v_x^2} = \tfrac{1}{2}kT$ to show that $R = kN_0$, a result that was used in Section 2.2.

Hence, in this simplest case, *temperature* is directly related to kinetic *energy*. This idea can be generalized. The relations between the averaged quantities such as P, T, energy, and so on, is thermodynamics. If we look more closely at the situation, for example if we ask what is the meaning of $\tfrac{1}{2}m\overline{v^2}$ or $p(v_x)$, and so on, we have statistical mechanics.

Thermodynamics gives very generally valid but restricted results. Thermo-dynamic results are something like the conservation laws in mechanics which involve total properties of the system, for example Kepler's second law of planetary motion.

Statistical mechanics gives more detailed information than thermodynamics but requires detailed knowledge of what is in the problem. Statistical mechanical results are something like following, in Newtonian mechanics, the actual paths of particles, for example the detailed form of the orbit of a planet.

10.3 PROBABILITY

We have introduced averages such as $\overline{v_x^2}$ and probability distributions such as $p(v_x)$. In order to understand the meaning of these more precisely, we must first study a few basic ideas about probability. The probability is a measure of the anticipated result of some action (an event) in certain well defined circumstances. If we toss a coin once and it is a "good" coin, we are just as likely to get heads (H) as tails (T). The probability of getting heads is the same as the probability of getting tails. Therefore, the *numbers representing* the two probabilities, $P(H)$ and $P(T)$, should be made equal to one another so that $P(H) = P(T)$. The probability of getting heads *or* tails in one toss is higher, since we have extended the possibilities and this result is more likely to be found. It is $[P(H) + P(T)]$. Indeed, we are certain to get heads or tails as the result of tossing a coin. We cannot get both heads and tails, and no other result is possible. The two results H and T are mutually exclusive. (If the results of a trial are not mutually exclusive, the matter is a little more complicated.) We put $P(H) + P(T) = 1$. This is the convention that certainty has associated the numerical value one—we *must* get heads or tails. Clearly then, in this example, the numerical expression of the probability of getting heads (tails) in one toss is $P(H) (= P(T)) = \frac{1}{2}$. Another way of looking at this is to say that when we toss a coin there are two possibilities. However, there is only one way of getting heads, i.e. 1 in 2 or $\frac{1}{2}$. More generally then, we can define the probability of something happening as

$$\frac{\text{(the number of ways the desired result can happen)}}{\text{(the total number of possible results)}}.$$

This definition is quite adequate for all physical applications and is in agreement with the results just given for the coins.

Suppose we toss a coin N times. We can ask how many heads we *expect*. Clearly, we are most likely to get $N/2$ heads but we *could* get any integral number from 0 to N. Hence we ought to be able to associate a number with the probability of getting any particular number N_H of heads after N tosses and we would expect this set of numbers to have a peak in value at or nearest to $N_H = N/2$. It is surely unlikely to get N heads in a row or N tails in a row, particularly if N is large, and so we expect to associate a much smaller number with these results.

If we consider two successive events I and II which are mutually exclusive, like successive tosses of a coin, and which have separate probabilities P_1 and P_2, then the probability of each happening in two trials in this order is P_1P_2. We are restricting the possibilities if we want both events in a given order and so the resultant probability is smaller (P_1P_2 is smaller than P_1 and P_2, since both P_1 and P_2 are less than unity). If we want the probability of getting I and II in any order, i.e. I and then II *or* II and then I, we are extending the possibilities again and the probability increases and we have to sum the separate probabilities. We have for this probability ($P_1P_2 + P_2P_1$) or $2P_1P_2$. On the other hand, if we want the probability of getting I (or II) in both trials, the probability is P_1^2 (or P_2^2) and the question of their order does not arise. In the simple case of the coin, the possible events (heads or tails) have equal probability and are the only possible ones, that is $P_1 = P_2 = \frac{1}{2}$. (We called these probabilities $P(H)$ and $P(T)$ above.) In simple problems, it is often more straightforward to enumerate all the possible results and simply pick out the ones satisfying the conditions laid down. The ratio of the latter number to the former is then the probability as defined earlier. We now do this for two successive tosses of a coin but also point out the relation to the more general case where P_1 and P_2 are not necessarily equal to $\frac{1}{2}$.

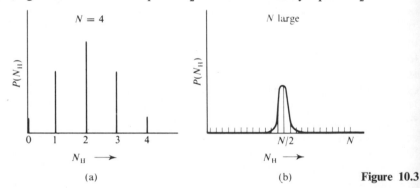

(a)   (b)   **Figure 10.3**

If we toss a coin twice we have the four possible results HH, HT, TH, and TT. Two heads appears once in four so that $P(2H) = \frac{1}{4} = (\frac{1}{2})^2$, that is P_1^2. A head and a tail appear twice so that $P(H \text{ and } T) = \frac{2}{4} = 2(\frac{1}{2})^2$, that is $2P_1P_2$. Two tails appear once, so that $P(2T) = \frac{1}{4} = (\frac{1}{2})^2$, that is P_2^2. Note that the 2 in the exponent is the number of tosses. In the same way, for 4 tosses, we have the following values for the probability $P(N_H)$ of getting N_H heads, $P(0) = P(4) = (\frac{1}{2})^4$, $P(1) = P(3) = 4(\frac{1}{2})^4$, and $P(2) = 6(\frac{1}{2})^4$. This is the result given in Fig. 10.3(a). The probability of getting *any* number of heads in the four tosses is

$$P(0) + P(1) + P(2) + P(3) + P(4)$$

which is

$$(\tfrac{1}{2})^4[1 + 4 + 6 + 4 + 1] = 1.$$

This is the expected result, since we are certain to get *any* number of heads. In general, for N throws

$$P(N_H) = C_{N_H}^N (\tfrac{1}{2})^N,$$

where $C_{N_H}^N$ is the binomial coefficient $N!/(N - N_H)!N_H!$. The plot of $P(N_H)$ versus N_H is more peaked at $N/2$ the greater the value of N (see Problem 10.7). Notice that even for small N the $P(N_H)$ curve, e.g. Fig. 10.3(a), has a lot of the properties of the curve for large N, e.g. Fig. 10.3(b). In Fig. 10.3(b), the different values of N are so close together that we can join the set of points giving the values of $P(N_H)$ into a smooth curve. The curve of $P(N_H)$ as a function of N_H is then rather similar to an analytical relation between the two quantities $P(N_H)$ and N_H much as we might write $y = ax^2$ as an analytical relation between y and x. However, it must always be borne in mind that $P(N_H)$ and quantities like it are not continuous functions. It should also be noted that the actual value of $P(N_H)$ is generally speaking smaller the larger is N because the sum of all the $P(N_H)$ is fixed at unity. For a very large number of tosses, the probability of any particular number of heads is very small, even the probability of getting $N/2$ (if N is even). It is the relative probabilities which are of more interest; for example, how much more probable is it to get $N/2$ heads than $N/3$ heads (if N is divisible by six). We shall make extensive use in later calculations of the sort of result which we have obtained here. We have noted that even for $N = 4$ the peaking of $P(N_H)$ near the value for $N_H = N/2$ is already obvious and that this effect becomes more marked on increasing N. There is some hope, therefore, that we may be able to deduce something about what happens when N is so large that the calculation is difficult from the result when N is small and exact computation is easy.

There is a most probable value of N_H: it is the value of N_H for the maximal value of $P(N_H)$. In this case it is $N/2$.

We can also get a mean value or expectation value defined as

$$\bar{N}_H = \sum_{N_H} N_H P(N_H).$$

In our example of four tosses of a coin, we get by substituting the values of $P(N_H)$ given above, that

$$\bar{N}_H = (\tfrac{1}{2})^4[(0 \times 1) + (1 \times 4) + (2 \times 6) + (3 \times 4) + (4 \times 1)]$$
$$= 2 = \tfrac{4}{2} = N/2.$$

The mean value is the most probable value. It is not true in general that the mean and the most probable values are the same. For the distribution shown in Fig. 10.4, the most probable value of N_H is zero with $P(0) = 2/N$ but the mean value of N_H is $N/3$.

These averages as defined above are quite familiar. If we have N_A objects of type A and N_B objects of type B and we take any object at random, we have by our definition that the probabilities of getting A, or B, are

$$P(A) = \frac{N_A}{N_A + N_B} \quad \text{and} \quad P(B) = \frac{N_B}{N_A + N_B}, \text{ respectively.}$$

Of course, $P(A) + P(B) = 1$; we are certain to get either A or B. If A are weights

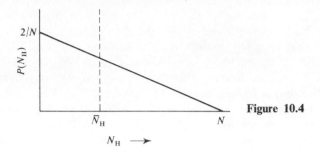

Figure 10.4

m_A and B are weights m_B then the mean weight m is given by,

$$\bar{m} \equiv \sum_i m_i P(m_i) = m_A P(A) + m_B P(B) = m_A \frac{N_A}{N_A + N_B} + m_B \frac{N_B}{N_A + N_B},$$

$$= \frac{m_A N_A + m_B N_B}{N_A + N_B},$$

the familiar expression for a mean. For any property x which has a probability $P(x)$, the mean value of x is $\bar{x} = \sum xP(x)$. Similarly, for the mean square, $\overline{x^2} = \sum x^2 P(x)$. For example, suppose x has probability of $\frac{1}{2}$ of being $+1$ and of $\frac{1}{2}$ of being -1 (like the coins), then $\bar{x} = (+1) \times \frac{1}{2} + (-1) \times \frac{1}{2} = 0$ and $\overline{x^2} = (+1)^2 \times \frac{1}{2} + (-1) \times \frac{1}{2} = 1$. Also $\overline{x^0}$ is unity, as it must be, since $\sum_{\text{all } x} P(x)$ is unity. More generally, $\overline{f(x)} = \sum f(x)P(x)$ where $f(x)$ is any function of x.

If x is effectively a continuous variable, we say there is a probability $p(x) \Delta x$ of x lying in the range Δx near x, where Δx is "small". Then $p(x)$ must be normalized so that

$$\int_{-\infty}^{\infty} p(x) \, dx = 1.$$

Clearly, the mean of $f(x)$ for a continuous distribution is

$$\overline{f(x)} = \int_{-\infty}^{\infty} f(x)p(x) \, dx.$$

Notice that $p(x)$ is rather different from $P(x)$ and so we use a different but similar symbol. For obvious reasons, $p(x)$ is called a probability density. It often happens that $P(x)$ and $p(x)$ are proportional to one another, but this is not necessarily so.

10.4 THE VELOCITY DISTRIBUTION IN A GAS

We have had a case of a probability distribution, that of v_x, that is $p(v_x)$, for the translational velocity of atoms or molecules in a gas. Here the most probable value of v_x is zero and the mean value $\bar{v}_x$ is zero, but the mean value of the square of the velocity $\overline{v_x^2}$ is not zero. We can ask what is the actual probability distribution

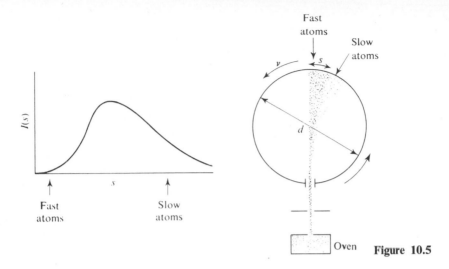

Figure 10.5

of v_x. It can be measured experimentally and it can be calculated using statistical mechanics.

The experiment was done in various ways over a long period of years from 1908 onwards. The experiment is difficult to do directly but all experiments depend on some method of velocity selection. We consider first an experiment in which atoms or molecules emerge from a collimated slit and enter a rotating drum. In Fig. 10.5, the drum is shown in a position to momentarily accept atoms from the oven. Effectively, the same experiment can be performed using discs as shown in Fig. 10.6 where again the rotor is shown in a position to momentarily accept the beam of molecules.

The velocity selection is by the time of flight of the molecules across the drum (or between the discs). For the drum experiment, atoms with velocity v will land a distance s from the other end of the diameter containing the inlet slit given by $s = \pi d^2 v / v$ where v is the speed of rotation of the drum in revolutions per second. We have to find the relative number of atoms in the oven which emerge from the slit with a range of velocities Δv about v. This is not $p(v_x)\,\Delta v_x$ since this only selects those atoms which have a certain range of velocity in a particular direction and *any* velocity in the other directions y and z. It can be shown (see below) that

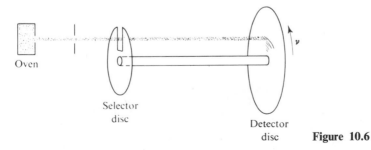

Figure 10.6

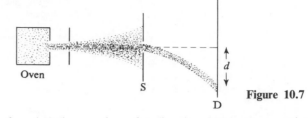

Oven

d

S

D

Figure 10.7

from the expression for $p(v_x)$ the number of molecules, ΔN in the speed range Δv at v, is proportional to $v^2 \exp(-\frac{1}{2}mv^2/kT)\,\Delta v$. However, the number of molecules per unit time in the beam emerging from the hole with velocity v is not only proportional to this number but has an additional factor v, since the molecules come out at a rate proportional to v. (It is the same factor that arose in the calculation of the gas pressure in Section 10.2.) Hence the number of molecules, $\Delta N'$, entering the drum in the range Δv is proportional to $v^3 \exp(-\frac{1}{2}mv^2/kT)\,\Delta v$. Since $s \propto 1/v$, we have $\Delta s \propto (-1/v^2)\,\Delta v$. Consequently, the number of molecules per unit length falling at a distance s from the zero position is proportional to $\Delta N'/\Delta s$, i.e. the density of the deposit is expected to be proportional to $v^5 \exp(-\frac{1}{2}mv^2/kT)$ or, in terms of s, $s^{-5}\exp(-a^2s^{-2})$ where a is a constant. Various experimental difficulties were encountered but this formula was confirmed for various values of m and T and we can say that the relation $p(v_x) \propto \exp(-\frac{1}{2}mv_x^2/kT)$ has been confirmed experimentally. (Strictly speaking, we have only found the distribution for the speed v.) An attractively simple idea but one which involves very great experimental difficulties is to use gravity as a velocity selector, since then the apparatus has no moving parts. In this experiment,[*] a beam of caesium atoms emerges from an oven in a roughly horizontal path and must pass through a slit S in order to fall on a detector screen D (Fig. 10.7). Clearly, the smaller the velocity of the atom, the lower it has fallen before it hits the screen (Problem 10.11). The density distribution on the screen as a function of the fall d therefore determines the velocity distribution of the atoms emerging from the oven. We therefore have from experiment the relation

$$p(v_x) = C \exp(-\frac{1}{2}mv_x^2/kT),$$

where C is a constant. We require that

$$\int_{-\infty}^{\infty} p(v_x)\,dv_x = 1$$

so that

$$C\int_{-\infty}^{\infty} \exp(-\frac{1}{2}mv_x^2/kT)\,dv_x = 1.$$

Put $\frac{1}{2}mv_x^2/kT = y^2$, so that

$$C\int_{-\infty}^{\infty} \exp(-y^2)\left(\frac{2kT}{m}\right)^{1/2} dy = 1$$

---

[*] ESTERMANN, SIMPSON, and STERN, *Phys. Rev.* **71**, 238 (1947).

and therefore

$$C = \left(\frac{m}{2kT}\right)^{1/2} \Big/ \int_{-\infty}^{\infty} \exp\left(-y^2\right) dy = \left(\frac{m}{2\pi kT}\right)^{1/2}.$$

Hence,

$$p(v_x) = \left(\frac{m}{2\pi kT}\right)^{1/2} \exp\left(-\tfrac{1}{2}mv_x^2/kT\right).$$

This is called the Maxwell–Boltzmann distribution for a perfect gas. Clearly, $\bar{v}_x = 0$, but

$$\overline{v_x^2} = \int_{-\infty}^{\infty} v_x^2 p(v_x)\, dv_x = \left(\frac{m}{2\pi kT}\right)^{1/2}\left(\frac{2kT}{m}\right)^{3/2} \int_{-\infty}^{\infty} y^2 \exp\left(-y^2\right) dy$$

$$= \left(\frac{m}{2\pi kT}\right)^{1/2} \frac{1}{2}\left(\frac{2\pi kT}{m}\right)^{1/2}\left(\frac{2kT}{m}\right)$$

$$= \frac{kT}{m}.$$

$$\therefore \quad \tfrac{1}{2}m\overline{v_x^2} = \tfrac{1}{2}kT \quad \text{or} \quad \tfrac{1}{2}m\overline{v^2} = \tfrac{3}{2}kT.$$

Hence this particular result, which is derived from our experimentally determined $p(v_x)$, is in agreement with that derived from the gas laws, as of course it must be. Note, however, that we have obtained much more than the gas laws alone when we have $p(v_x)$. From $p(v_x)$, we can obtain all statistical properties which involve v_x.

Another simple example of the use of the probability density $p(v_x)$ is the following. Suppose, in the problem of Section 10.2, the area A of wall is actually a small area of the wall which is missing but A is so small that it does not much affect the way in which the molecules approach the wall in this region. It must be so small that the gas does not simply flow out. For this to be so the linear dimensions of A must be smaller than the mean free path (Section 7.1). We found that the number of molecules approaching the wall in time t was $\frac{1}{2}nv_x tA$. Hence the number passing through a hole per unit area of the hole per unit time is $\frac{1}{2}n\,\overline{|v_x|}$, where $\overline{|v_x|}$ is the average over molecules travelling in *one* direction. (This is usually written in the equivalent but less interesting form $\frac{1}{4}n\bar{v}$, since $\overline{|v_x|} = \frac{1}{2}\bar{v}$ (see Problems 10.9 and 10.10). Using the expression for $p(v_x)$, we find that $\overline{|v_x|} = (2kT/\pi m)^{1/2}$ and so we can calculate the total number of molecules passing through a hole. This would be useful, for instance, in the design of the experiment just discussed to determine $p(v_x)$ itself. It is also a vital result in the theory of the production of high vacua.

It is sometimes of interest to know the probability distribution of the *speed* of the molecules in a gas. For instance, it was for the drum experiment. The probability of finding a molecule with velocity components in Δv_x at v_x is $p(v_x)\,\Delta v_x$, in Δv_y at v_y is $p(v_y)\,\Delta v_y$, and in Δv_z at v_z is $p(v_z)\,\Delta v_z$. The probability of finding a molecule with all three restrictions is

$$p(v_x)p(v_y)p(v_z)\,\Delta v_x\,\Delta v_y\,\Delta v_z = \left(\frac{m}{2\pi kT}\right)^{3/2} \exp\left(-\tfrac{1}{2}mv^2/kT\right)\Delta v_x\,\Delta v_y\,\Delta v_z.$$

Notice that there are three restrictions applied here and so the three probabilities must be multiplied together. However, this is the distribution function for the velocity **v**. For the speed v, we must integrate over all directions of **v**, since speed means velocity in any direction. We put $\Delta v_x\,\Delta v_y\,\Delta v_z = v^2\,\Delta v\,\sin\theta\,\Delta\theta\,\Delta\phi$ where θ and ϕ are the polar coordinates of the vector **v**. Adding the probabilities for all directions means replacing $\sin\theta\,\Delta\theta\,\Delta\phi$ by

$$\int_0^\pi \sin\theta\,d\theta \int_0^{2\pi} d\phi = 4\pi.$$

These integrations can be carried out independently of the factor $\exp\left(-\tfrac{1}{2}mv^2/kT\right)$, since this is independent of θ and ϕ. Hence

$$p(v)\,\Delta v = 4\pi\left(\frac{m}{2\pi kT}\right)^{3/2} v^2 \exp\left(-\tfrac{1}{2}mv^2/kT\right)\Delta v.$$

The mean speed of a molecule is therefore

$$\bar{v} = \int_0^\infty v \times 4\pi\left(\frac{m}{2\pi kT}\right)^{3/2} v^2 \exp\left(-\tfrac{1}{2}mv^2/kT\right)dv = \left(\frac{8kT}{\pi m}\right)^{1/2}.$$

It should be noted that this is different from the root mean square (r.m.s.) velocity of a molecule which is $(\overline{v^2})^{1/2} = (3kT/m)^{1/2}$. It is also different from the mean value of the velocity of a molecule in one direction which is $\overline{|v_x|} = (2kT/\pi m)^{1/2}$. The probability distribution curves $p(v_x)$ and $p(v)$, although referring to the same distribution of velocities, have very different forms as shown in Fig. 10.8. Some care must be taken to use the appropriate form.

We can look at our probability distribution in another way. We have $p(v_x) \propto \exp\left(-\tfrac{1}{2}mv_x^2/kT\right)$. But $\tfrac{1}{2}mv_x^2$ is the energy associated with v_x and so we call

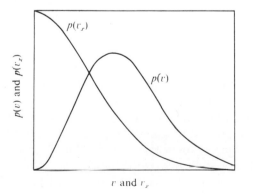

Figure 10.8

it $\varepsilon(v_x)$, then

$$p(v_x) \propto \exp\left[-\varepsilon(v_x)/kT\right],$$

and this is what really determines the properties of an ideal monatomic gas.

There are many ways of deriving the Boltzmann distribution for a gas from theoretical considerations and this can be a very complex and difficult matter. We shall give a general derivation of the distribution in Section 11.4, which can be applied to a gas in particular, but in view of the importance of this distribution we also give another rather superficial, derivation for a gas which will suffice for the moment.

Consider a collision of two gas molecules such that the velocities before collision are $\mathbf{v}_1$ and $\mathbf{v}_2$ and after collision are $\mathbf{v}'_1$ and $\mathbf{v}'_2$. Because of conservation of energy, we have

$$v_1^2 + v_2^2 = v_1'^2 + v_2'^2.$$

If the number of molecules in the gas with speeds in the range dv at v is $f(v)\,dv$, then the probability of the collision described is proportional to $f(v_1)f(v_2)$. On the other hand, if we consider the inverse collision, which is obtained by reversing all the velocities, we see that the probability of this collision is proportional to $f(v'_1)f(v'_2)$. Since we see no reason to regard the one collision as more probable than the other—here is the subtlety—we can say that

$$f(v_1)f(v_2) = f(v'_1)f(v'_2).$$

This relation and the energy conservation relation can only both be satisfied for any otherwise arbitrary set of velocities if,

$$f(v) \propto \exp\left(-\alpha v^2\right),$$

where α is a constant. This is the Maxwell–Boltzmann distribution obtained above if $\alpha = -\frac{1}{2}m/kT$.

10.5 THE BOLTZMANN DISTRIBUTION

The expression $\exp\left[-\varepsilon(v_x)/kT\right]$ given in Section 10.4 is a special case of the *Boltzmann distribution*. If we have a body in equilibrium at temperature T and we have an energy $\varepsilon(q)$ associated with the coordinate q, then the probability distribution of the coordinate q is given by

$$p(q) \propto \exp\left[-\varepsilon(q)/kT\right],$$

where k is Boltzmann's constant, T is the temperature as measured using an ideal gas thermometer, and q can be any "coordinate". The most interesting cases are where q determines an energy, as in the example in Section 10.4 when q was v_x. The expression is still true even if q does not determine an energy. For example, in a perfect gas the energy of a molecule is independent of its position in the gas so that $\varepsilon(x)$ is a constant independent of x. We can ask what is the probability distribution, $p(x)$, of x. $p(x)\,\Delta x$ is the probability of finding a molecule in a position such that its x coordinate is in the range Δx at x. Using the general formula with q replaced by x we have $p(x) \propto \exp\left[-\varepsilon(x)/kT\right]$ = a constant = C, say. Let us assume the gas is in a container with plane ends, two of which are the planes $x = 0$ and $x = L$. If we look outside the box there are no molecules so that $p(x) = 0$, that is $p(x) = 0$ for $x > L$ or $x < 0$. The integral over all values of x,

$$\int_{-\infty}^{\infty}, \quad \text{therefore reduces to} \quad \int_{0}^{L}.$$

But

$$\int_{0}^{L} p(x)\,dx = CL$$

which must equal 1, since the particle is certainly somewhere in the box. $\therefore C = L^{-1}$, that is $p(x) = L^{-1}$ and is independent of x. Hence the molecule is just as likely to be found *anywhere* within the volume, which is the result to be expected for any gas and in particular for a perfect gas.

The Boltzmann distribution is the most important result of statistical mechanics and many thermodynamic results can be deduced from it. Since it is so important, we shall give another illustration, the density of a gas in a uniform gravitational field. Consider a column of gas at temperature T in, say, the Earth's gravitational field g. Consider a section of gas at height h above an arbitrary zero of height. Let there be $n(h)$ molecules per unit volume at height h. The gas pressure is $P = nkT$.* Hence,

$$P(h) = n(h)kT \quad \text{and} \quad P(h + \Delta h) = n(h + \Delta h)kT \approx \left[n(h) + \frac{dn}{dh}\Delta h\right]kT$$

for small Δh. The upward force on the section of area A and of height Δh is

$$P(h)A - P(h + \Delta h)A = A\{P(h) - P(h + \Delta h)\} \approx -A\frac{dn}{dh}\Delta h kT.$$

This force must be balanced by the downward force due to the weight of the gas in the section of height Δh at equilibrium which is $nmgA\,\Delta h$. We therefore have

$$-A\frac{dn}{dh}\Delta h kT = nmgA\,\Delta h \quad \text{or} \quad \frac{dn}{n} = -\left(\frac{mg}{kT}\right)dh.$$

This equation is readily integrated to give

$$n(h) = n(0)\exp\left(-mgh/kT\right).$$

But $n(h)$ is proportional to the probability of finding particles at height h, that is $p(h) \propto n(h)$. $n(h)$, and therefore $p(h)$, clearly depend on the energy associated with this height, since $\varepsilon(h) = mgh$. We can write

$$p(h) = p(0)\exp\left[-\varepsilon(h)/kT\right],$$

---

* $PV = (N/N_0)RT = NkT \quad \therefore \quad P = (N/V)kT = nkT.$

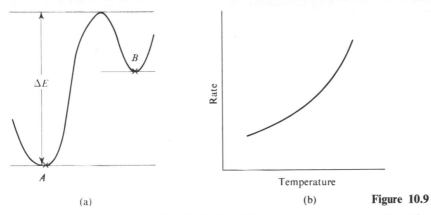

(a)   (b)   **Figure 10.9**

which is of the form $p(q) \propto \exp\left[-\varepsilon(q)/kT\right]$. This of course also describes the pressure of the gas as a function of height since $P(h) \propto n(h)$ for constant temperature.

The Boltzmann distribution turns up very frequently and we shall have many more occasions to use it. One important case is in the analysis of the dependence of the rate of chemical and physical reactions on temperature. Suppose that in order for a particle to go from A to B it must pass over the energy barrier of height ΔE (Fig. 10.9a). The probability of the reactants acquiring an energy ΔE is, by the Boltzmann distribution, proportional to $\exp(-\Delta E/kT)$ at temperature T. (But see Problem 11.11.) Therefore, the rate of reaction is proportional to $\exp(-\Delta E/kT)$ and this usually is the most important term involving the temperature. This effect of temperature on the rate of a reaction is observed in that many reactions have a rate which increases very rapidly with temperature (Fig. 10.9b). For instance, if the activation energy ΔE is 10 kcal mol^{-1} and T is about room temperature, the rate of the process about doubles for a 10°C change of temperature. The size of ΔE may determine, in practical terms, whether something does or does not happen. Since the rate of the change is proportional to $\exp(-\Delta E/kT)$, the time τ for a significant change to occur is proportional to $\exp(\Delta E/kT)$ and we may write

$$\tau = \tau_0 \exp(\Delta E/kT).$$

There is some theoretical justification* for choosing $\tau_0 \approx h/kT \approx 10^{-13}$ s as an order of magnitude. In that special case and for room temperature ($T \approx 300°$K), we find the values of τ given in Table 10.1. 10^{20} seconds is greater than the age of the universe so this corresponds to no observable change. 10^{-11} second is instantaneous for most purposes. Such vast changes in rate correspond to quite small changes in activation energy. A rather similar situation is found for radioactive α-decay times which depend exponentially on the energy of the emitted α particles. This is statistical also but in a rather different sense.

---

* GLASSTONE, LAIDLER, and EYRING, *The Theory of the Rate Process*, McGraw-Hill, New York (1941).

Table 10.1

ΔE, ev	2	1	0.1
τ, s	10^{20}	10^2	10^{-11}

Another application of the Boltzmann distribution law, which is rather closely connected with the one just given, is the calculation of the vapour pressure, which is the pressure of the vapour in equilibrium with a solid or liquid at a given temperature. Let ε_v be the heat of vaporization of a molecule, that is the energy required to move it from inside the condensed phase into the gas. If n_c and n_v are the number densities of the condensed and vapour phases, respectively, we have from the Boltzmann distribution law that

$$n_v/n_c \propto \exp\left(-\varepsilon_v/kT\right).$$

If, as is usually true, the vapour density is low we may put $P_v = n_v kT$ where P_v is the vapour pressure. Hence,

$$P_v \propto T \exp\left(-\varepsilon_v/kT\right).$$

We can evaluate ε_v from the change of P_v with temperature, since the exponential varies rapidly with temperature but the other parameters in practice vary rather slowly with temperature. We see from this that the pressure of the vapour, which is relatively easy to measure, tells us something about the corresponding liquid or solid. This is particularly valuable in chemistry where we often have to deal with quite complex liquids and the energy of interaction of a molecule inside the liquid is a useful quantity to know.

We have so far considered that the temperature determines the distribution. Looking at it the other way round, we see that a measure of the distribution gives the temperature. This is used, for instance, in measuring the temperature of hot gases and plasmas. The distribution of velocities of the molecules or ions $p(v_x)$ gives a distribution of Doppler shifts to the frequency or wavelength of the light emitted by the molecules or ions, proportional to v_x/c. The spectral line shape of any emitted light therefore corresponds directly to a Boltzmann distribution for the temperature of the emitting material and the temperature of the emitting medium can be deduced from it.

PROBLEMS

10.1. A plasma consists of a gas of electrons and positive ions in proportions such that the gas is neutral. Show that, in a hydrogen plasma in thermal equilibrium (assume the ions are all protons), the root mean square velocity of the electrons is about 40 times that of the protons.

10.2. The collision of two deuterons can produce neutrons (and energy!) by the reaction ${}_1^2H + {}_1^2H \rightarrow {}_2^3He + {}_0^1n + 3.3$ Mev. The cross-section for the reaction is substantial for collisions of energy about 0.1 Mev. Estimate the order of magnitude of the temperature required in a fusion reactor for this DD reaction to be useful.

10.3. Actual results, in arbitrary units, for the drum experiment in Section 10.4 were found as follows

Density of deposit	0.4	1.2	3.4	6.8	8.8	9.3	8.5	6.0	3.3	2.0	1.2	0.5
Distance s	0.5	0.8	1.0	1.2	1.5	1.7	2.0	2.5	3.0	3.5	4.0	5.0

Investigate whether this result is consistent with the Maxwell–Boltzmann distribution law.

10.4. Assume that the electrons in a metal behave like free classical particles at temperature T. In order to escape from the metal surface, an electron must overcome the electrostatic interaction with the body of the metal. Suppose this corresponds to an energy $e\varphi$. Thus only electrons approaching the surface of the metal with a kinetic energy greater than $e\varphi$ can escape. Hence show that the thermionic emission current of a metal with work function φ is proportional to $T^{1/2} \exp(-e\varphi/kT)$. Show that $e\varphi$ is of order 3 ev if the electron is subject only to the electrostatic image force from a distance of about 1 Å from outside the surface (this is plausible because the surface cannot be regarded as plane to better than an atomic radius).

10.5. In a perfect atomic gas in thermal equilibrium at temperature T, the mean energy of an atom is $\frac{3}{2}kT$. If a very small hole is made in the container, atoms escape. Show that the mean energy of *these* atoms is $2kT$. (HINT: The mean energy for directions transverse to the hole is unchanged so $\frac{1}{2}kT + \frac{1}{2}kT = kT$ of the $2kT$ is easily accounted for.)

10.6. Calculate the root mean square velocity of a molecule of H_2, He, N_2, and O_2, respectively, at 300°K and compare with the terrestrial escape velocity (Problem 5.16). What conclusion might be drawn from this?

10.7. Show the peaking referred to in Section 10.3 explicitly for the binomial distribution by calculating $N!/[(N - m)!m!]$ for $N = 2, 4, 8$, and 16 and plotting on an abscissae scale of m/N (which is the same for all N). Show that the curve is approximately gaussian for $N = 16$, i.e. it is of the form $b \exp[-a(x - \bar{x})^2]$ where a and b are constants and $\bar{x}$ is the mean value of x.

10.8. Explain physically why it is that, in the "exponential atmosphere" (Section 10.5) at constant temperature, the velocity distribution is the same at all heights in spite of the density change.

10.9. Show that, for a Maxwell–Boltzmann distribution of velocities, $\overline{|v_x|} = \frac{1}{2}\bar{v}$.

10.10. Show directly (i.e. without using the result of Problem 10.9 or using a Maxwell–Boltzmann distribution) that the rate of effusion of gas molecules through a small hole is $\frac{1}{4}n\bar{v}$ per unit area per unit time.

10.11. In the falling atom experiment for the determination of the velocity distribution of atoms in a gas described in Section 10.4, show that a typical distance of fall is given approximately by $gS^2m/6kT$ where g is the acceleration due to gravity, S is the horizontal distance travelled, m is the mass of the atom, and T is the temperature of the oven.

10.12. The Clausius–Clapeyron equation relating the change in vapour pressure ΔP for a change in temperature ΔT of a vapour in contact with the corresponding pure liquid to the latent heat per mole L and the difference in volume ΔV as between one mole of vapour and one mole of liquid is $dP/dT = L/(T \Delta V)$. Show that this result is equivalent to the result $P_v \propto \exp(-\varepsilon_v/kT)$ obtained in Section 10.5.

CHAPTER 11

The distribution of particles on energy levels

The Boltzmann distribution is more true than any proof of it. ANON

In this chapter, we shall get the Boltzmann distribution in a more general way using a little very elementary quantum mechanics. We shall also try to get a clear idea of what is meant by temperature, entropy, and the second law of thermodynamics.

11.1 ENERGY LEVELS

First of all, notice that *energy* appears again in statistical mechanics as a most important concept, as it does in ordinary mechanics. Energy also plays a dominant role in the quantum mechanics of atomic systems. In atomic systems, the most striking result which has to be incorporated is that bodies can only have discrete values of energy. For example, the electrons in an atom can only be in certain orbitals which have corresponding energy levels. Often the energy levels are drawn for convenience as lines as in Fig. 11.1. Hence we can describe the state of an electron in an atom simply by the energy level it is in. This is not the whole story since, for example, for small atoms the states $2s$ and $2p_x$ have almost the same

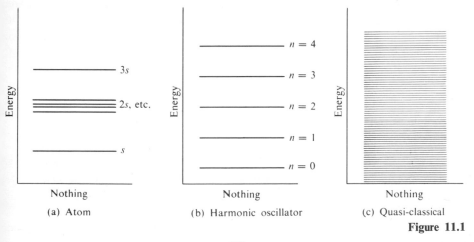

(a) Atom   (b) Harmonic oscillator   (c) Quasi-classical

Figure 11.1

167

energy. They differ in that they have different angular momentum. If different states have the same energy, the energy levels are said to be degenerate—we shall ignore this complication for the time being. However, it turns out that many important properties are determined mainly by the energy. For instance, in the case of the atom, the absorption and emission of electromagnetic radiation (e.g. light) corresponds to the atom moving from one energy level to another. This dominance of the role of energy is found for every system whose properties do not change with time. One of the most important problems in quantum mechanics is simply to find these energy levels. For the simplest atom, the hydrogen atom, the energy levels are given to a good approximation by

$$E = -\frac{m_e e^4}{2\hbar^2}\frac{1}{n^2},$$

in cgs units; $n = 1$ for the state $1s$, $n = 2$ for $2s$, $2p_x$, $2p_y$, and $2p_z$, $n = 3$ for $3s$, and so on.

There are very many demonstrations of the discreteness of energies of atoms and other objects but it is outside the scope of this book to discuss these matters. It may be worth reminding the reader, however, that line spectra imply discrete energy levels. In the visible region, the discrete energy levels are mostly those for the electrons in atoms. In the infrared, they correspond usually to the energies of vibration and rotation of molecules. Further, the specific heat of solids and of gases can only be explained by invoking discrete energy levels (see Section 11.3). The energy levels of electrons in an atom can be directly seen from collisions of electrons with atoms (the Franck–Hertz experiment). Many other experiments point to the existence of discrete energy levels in stationary systems. Indeed, it is true that for any object the energy can have only discrete values and is not continuous. This may seem strange in many circumstances but it is certainly true.

For any harmonic oscillator, the possible energies are restricted to the values $(n + \frac{1}{2})h\nu$ where ν is the classical vibration frequency and n is any positive integer including zero. The harmonic oscillator can have *only* these energies. This is the simplest energy level system (see Fig. 11.16) and we shall make considerable use of it.

In many cases, the energy levels are close together and then it may not make much difference that the energy is discrete rather than continuous. In fact, "classical" physics is correct when the energy levels are "close" together (see Section 11.3). Since energy is always quantized and it is possible to go over from discrete to continuous energy but not *vice versa* and because it is easier to deal mathematically with discrete systems, we tackle the problem from that point of view.

We shall proceed by taking situations which are rather simple for which we can do the calculation exactly. We shall then try to generalize these results to more complex and more realistic cases and try to derive some general results.

Take the special case in which the energy levels are equally spaced—this is actually so for a harmonic oscillator as we saw above but is not true in general. However, our results will not be restricted to harmonic oscillators, important as

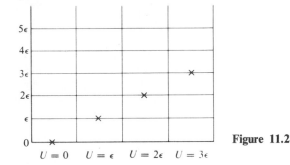

Figure 11.2

these are. They will be quite general, since most of the results will be true for *any* system of energy levels. We assume that the energy levels are ϵ or 2ϵ, etc. Thus the energy of a particle may take any particular value, $n\epsilon$, where $n = 0, 1, 2, \ldots$ and its lowest energy is 0 (the case of non-zero lowest energy involves a simple modification as we show later). The energy of a particle may be represented diagrammatically as in Fig. 11.2. If the particle is isolated from all outside influences, it of course stays indefinitely in its energy level. By acting on it from outside, we could either decrease or increase its energy (Fig. 11.3), e.g. by a collision with another particle, by using electromagnetic radiation, etc. Now suppose we have more than one particle in an isolated system. Suppose first that we have *two*. Since the system is isolated, its energy is fixed. The lowest possible energy is zero. We shall suppose we can distinguish the particles and we name them A and B (the important modifications which are required if we cannot distinguish particles will be mentioned later). The energy level diagram is given in Fig. 11.4(a). If we now add one unit ϵ of energy we have *two* possibilities, 1 and 2, which are shown in Figs. 11.4(b) and (c). For example, suppose we had two equally massive perfectly elastic particles in line in a box with perfectly elastic walls and initially one is at rest near the centre and one is moving. Then we have the possibilities (i) to (iv) shown in Fig. 11.5 and they correspond to the energy state 1 or 2 of Fig. 11.4. Notice that, as time goes on, the motion in this rather idealized system causes the balls to have the motions shown in each of the four diagrams in turn for equal lengths of time. Hence, if we looked at the system at any particular time, we are just as likely to find it in any one of the four states (i) to (iv). Since states (i) and

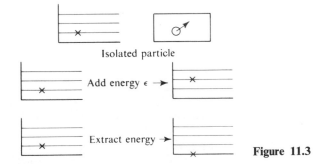

Isolated particle

Add energy ϵ →

Extract energy →

Figure 11.3

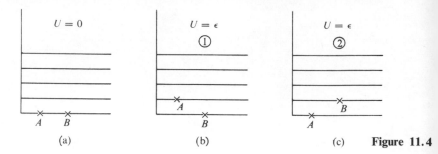

Figure 11.4

(iv) correspond to the energy state 1 and (ii) and (iii) to the energy state 2, it is also equally probable to find state 1 or 2 if we look at the system at any time. Hence the two energy diagrams 1 and 2 have "equal *a priori* probability". The reason there are four diagrams (i) to (iv) and only two energy states 1 and 2 is that the states are distinguished not only by the energy a ball has but also by its momentum. If we agree to ignore momentum differences, the pairs of states (i) and (iv), (ii) and (iii) are identical. It will be recalled that, in the hydrogen atom, the energies of the states $2s$, $2p_x$, $2p_y$, and $2p_z$ were the same to a good approximation, but that they could be distinguished by the different angular momenta of the different states. Our simple mechanical system has two doubly degenerate energy levels.

It should be understood that, in general, the energy need not be kinetic. The diagrams (Figs. 11.4b and c), or states 1 and 2, are referred to as two *complexions*. If we only specify the energy as being ϵ, then we must conclude that either of these two complexions is equally probable, i.e. they each have a probability $\frac{1}{2}$ of having energy ϵ.

Now increase the energy to 2ϵ and we have the three possibilities shown in Fig. 11.6. Each of these complexions has a probability $\frac{1}{3}$. It is more difficult to give a mechanical example of this. Thus, the number of possible complexions increases with the energy. This statement is true in general and is closely related

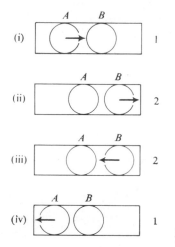

Figure 11.5

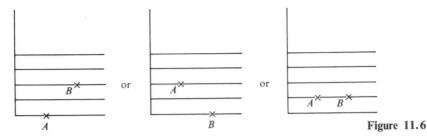

Figure 11.6

to the thermodynamic statements, "the temperature (T) of a body increases on heating" and "the entropy ($\int dq/T$) increases on heating", as we shall see soon.

In this simple case for two particles and for an energy $n\epsilon$, we have ($n + 1$) complexions. If only the *total* energy is stated, we have to assume that each complexion has equal *a priori* probability. There is no reason to think that any one complexion is more probable than any other (Problem 11.1).

11.2 PROBABILITY OF OCCUPATION OF LEVELS

We can now look at some other probabilities. Let us ask, what is the probability of any particle being found on any particular energy level? Call this $P(\varepsilon)$. Of course ε can only have the values $0, \epsilon, 2\epsilon, 3\epsilon, \dots$, and so we get a histogram. Clearly $P(\varepsilon)$ depends on the total energy U. For $U = 0$, the result is obvious. $P(0) = 1$ and $P(n\epsilon) = 0$ for $n \geq 1$, *whatever the number of particles* (Fig. 11.7). We now consider a particular number of particles N and a series of values of total energy U for each N. We calculate the probability of finding any particular particle in a given energy level, that is $P(\varepsilon)$. We begin with two particles and work our way up to numbers corresponding to macroscopic amounts of matter (of order 10^{23} particles).

(i) 2 Particles

For $U = \epsilon$, we have the two complexions of Fig. 11.4(b) and (c) and for the probabilities of finding particles on the various levels we have $P(0) \propto 1 + 1 = 2$, $P(\epsilon) \propto 1 + 1 = 2$, and $P(2\epsilon) \propto 0 + 0 = 0$. But we must have

$$P(0) + P(\epsilon) + P(2\epsilon) + \cdots = \sum_0^\infty P(n\epsilon) = 1.$$

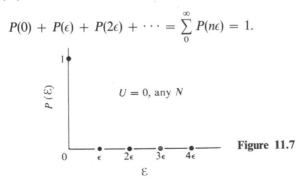

Figure 11.7

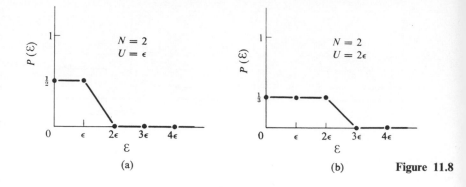

(a)   (b)   **Figure 11.8**

∴ $P(0) = \frac{2}{4} = \frac{1}{2}$, $P(\epsilon) = \frac{1}{2}$, and $P(n\epsilon) = 0$ for $n \geq 2$, and this is shown in Fig. 11.8(a).

For $U = 2\epsilon$, we have the three possible complexions of Fig. 11.6 and so $P(0) \propto 1 + 1 + 0 = 2$, $P(\epsilon) \propto 0 + 0 + 2 = 2$, $P(2\epsilon) \propto 1 + 1 + 0 = 2$, and $P(3\epsilon) \propto 0 + 0 + 0 = 0$. Hence again, since the sum of the probabilities for all levels must be unity, we have

$$P(0) = \tfrac{2}{6} = \tfrac{1}{3}, \qquad P(\epsilon) = \tfrac{1}{3}, \qquad P(2\epsilon) = \tfrac{1}{3},$$

and

$$P(n\epsilon) = 0 \quad \text{for} \quad n \geq 3.$$

It is now obvious what happens for higher energies: $P(\mathcal{E})$ just gets smeared out and we can see this effect in Fig. 11.8.

Clearly, only two particles is not very "statistical". Let us therefore increase the number of particles to three and then to more and see if we can see any pattern which will allow us to guess what will happen for large numbers of particles.

(ii) 3 Particles

$U = 0$. All three particles A, B, and C are in the lowest level; there is only one energy level diagram and the probability distribution is as in Fig. 11.7.

$U = \epsilon$ (see Fig. 11.9a). We have $P(0) \propto 2 + 2 + 2 = 6$, $P(\epsilon) \propto 1 + 1 + 1 = 3$, and $P(2\epsilon) \propto 0 + 0 + 0 = 0$. Therefore $P(0) = \frac{2}{3}$, $P(\epsilon) = \frac{1}{3}$, and $P(2\epsilon) = 0$. The plot of $P(\mathcal{E})$ against ϵ is linear in this case (Fig. 11.11a).

$U = 2\epsilon$. The diagrams for the various possible complexions are shown in Fig. 11.9(b) and the corresponding probabilities of occupation of levels are $P(0) = \frac{1}{2}$, $P(\epsilon) = \frac{1}{3}$, $P(2\epsilon) = \frac{1}{6}$, and $P(3\epsilon) = 0$.

We can now see that $P(\mathcal{E})$ is going to be linear in ϵ for all U but shows the same trends as for two particles and the results are plotted in Fig. 11.11(a). We note also that the number of complexions increases more rapidly with the energy than it did for $N = 2$ (Fig. 11.11a).

In order to illustrate a further point, we look more closely at what we get for $N = 3$ and $U = 4\epsilon$. We find using the diagram of Fig. 11.10 that $P(0) = \frac{5}{15}$, $P(\epsilon) = \frac{4}{15}$, $P(2\epsilon) = \frac{3}{15}$, $P(3\epsilon) = \frac{2}{15}$, and $P(4\epsilon) = \frac{1}{15}$. This is again a linear plot of

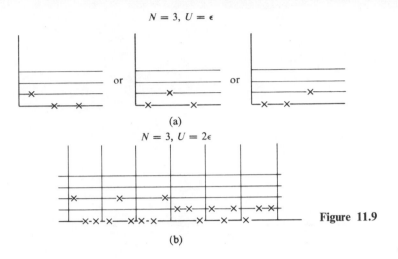

(a)

(b)

Figure 11.9

$P(\varepsilon)$ against ε, as we expected (see Fig. 11.11a), but we have drawn the diagram of Fig. 11.10 in a special form. The complexions are grouped together in *arrangements*. Within each arrangement, the different complexions only differ in the identity of a particle(s) on a given level and make the same contribution to $P(\varepsilon)$. In evaluating $P(\varepsilon)$, therefore, we do not need to enumerate each complexion; we can merely enumerate each arrangment and the number of times each arrangement arises. The numbers 3, 6, 3, and 3 in Fig. 11.10 are the numbers of complexions in a given arrangement for this particular case $N = 3$ and $U = 4\epsilon$. From now on, then, we shall concentrate on the arrangement rather than the complexions.

We notice that one particular *arrangement* is more common than the others, e.g. for $N = 3$ and $U = 4\epsilon$ one arrangement occurs twice as often as any other. We take up this important observation again later. This is an effect which becomes more marked as N increases and is of both physical and computational significance.

In going from $N = 2$ to $N = 3$, there has been a substantial change in the form of $P(\varepsilon)$. Compare Fig. 11.8 and 11.11(a). We must clearly have still more particles in order to get a more realistic picture.

$N = 3, \ U = 4\epsilon$

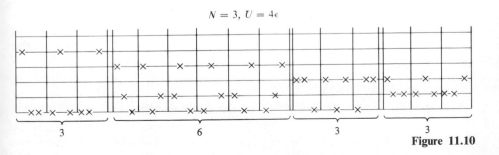

Figure 11.10

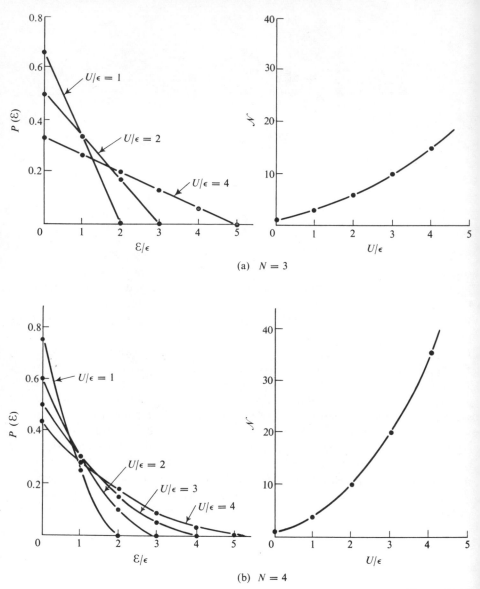

(a) $N = 3$

(b) $N = 4$

Figure 11.11

(iii) 4 Particles

$U = 0$. Number of complexions $\mathcal{N}_4(0) = 1$.

$U = \epsilon$. Number of complexions $\mathcal{N}_4(\epsilon) = 4$ and $P(0) = \frac{3}{4}$, $P(\epsilon) = \frac{1}{4}$, $P(2\epsilon) = 0$, etc.

$U = 2\epsilon$. $\mathcal{N}_4(2\epsilon) = 10$. The *arrangements* are as in Fig. 11.12. The horizontal position of a particle on a level is not now significant. We have $P(0) \propto 3 \times 4 +$

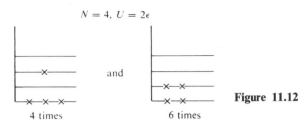

Figure 11.12

$2 \times 6 = 24$, $P(\epsilon) \propto 0 \times 4 + 2 \times 6 = 12$, and $P(2\epsilon) \propto 1 \times 4 + 0 \times 6 = 4$. Hence, $P(0) = 0.6$, $P(\epsilon) = 0.3$, and $P(2\epsilon) = 0.1$.

$U = 3\epsilon$, $\mathcal{N}_4(3\epsilon) = 20$. We find using Fig. 11.13 that $P(0) = 0.50$, $P(\epsilon) = 0.30$, $P(2\epsilon) = 0.15$, and $P(3\epsilon) = 0.05$.

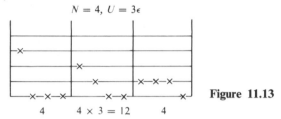

Figure 11.13

$U = 4\epsilon$, $\mathcal{N}_4(4\epsilon) = 34$. The distribution is $P(0) = 0.43$, $P(\epsilon) = 0.29$, $P(2\epsilon) = 0.17$, $P(3\epsilon) = 0.09$, and $P(4\epsilon) = 0.03$. The results for $N = 4$ are plotted in Fig. 11.11(b) and we see that $P(\mathcal{E})$ is now a curve and that $\mathcal{N}$ increases very rapidly with U. (Strictly speaking, the result is a histogram but we have joined the points into smooth curves to make it easier to see the general behaviour of $P(\mathcal{E})$.)

(iv) 5 Particles

Finally, let us take five particles, $N = 5$. Fortunately, this will be sufficient, since clearly it is getting impossibly tedious to calculate for any larger number of particles exactly.

$U = 0$, $\mathcal{N}_5(0) = 1$; $P(0) = 1.0$.

$U = \epsilon$, $\mathcal{N}_5(\epsilon) = 5$; $P(0) = 0.8$ and $P(\epsilon) = 0.2$.

$U = 2\epsilon$, $\mathcal{N}_5(2\epsilon) = 15$; $P(0) = 0.67$, $P(\epsilon) = 0.27$, and $P(2\epsilon) = 0.06$.

$U = 3\epsilon$, $\mathcal{N}_5(3\epsilon) = 35$; $P(0) = 0.57$, $P(\epsilon) = 0.29$, $P(2\epsilon) = 0.11$, and $P(3\epsilon) = 0.03$.

$U = 4\epsilon$, $\mathcal{N}_5(4\epsilon) = 70$.

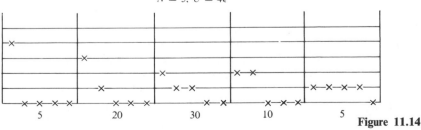

Figure 11.14

The diagram for $N = 5$, $U = 4\epsilon$ is shown in Fig. 11.14 and, in order to make the method of calculation quite clear, we give the details once again.

$$P(0) \propto 4 \cdot 5 + 3 \cdot 20 + 2 \cdot 30 + 3 \cdot 10 + 1 \cdot 5 = 175 \quad P(0) = 0.50$$

$$P(\epsilon) \propto \ \ 0 \ + 1 \cdot 20 + 2 \cdot 30 + \ \ 0 \ \ + 4 \cdot 5 = 100 \quad P(\epsilon) = 0.29$$

$$P(2\epsilon) \propto \ \ 0 \ + \ \ 0 \ \ + 1 \cdot 30 + 2 \cdot 10 + \ \ 0 \ \ = 50 \quad P(2\epsilon) = 0.14$$

$$P(3\epsilon) \propto \ \ 0 \ + 1 \cdot 20 + \ \ 0 \ \ + \ \ 0 \ \ + \ \ 0 \ \ = 20 \quad P(3\epsilon) = 0.06$$

$$P(4\epsilon) \propto 1 \cdot 5 + \ \ 0 \ \ + \ \ 0 \ \ + \ \ 0 \ \ + \ \ 0 \ \ = \underline{5} \quad P(4\epsilon) = \underline{0.01}$$

$$ 350 1.00$$

For $N = 5$ and $U = 5\epsilon$, we find $\mathcal{N}_5(5\epsilon) = 126$; $P(0) = 0.44$, $P(\epsilon) = 0.28$, $P(2\epsilon) = 0.16$, $P(3\epsilon) = 0.08$, $P(4\epsilon) = 0.03$, $P(5\epsilon) = 0.01$. The distributions $P(\varepsilon)$ for $N = 5$ and for several values of U are shown in Fig. 11.15(a).

We note again, in passing, that for $N = 5$ and $U = 4\epsilon$ there is a most probable arrangement (see the middle diagram of Fig. 11.14) which includes 30 out of a total possible number of 70 complexions. The probability distribution for *this* particular arrangement is

$$P^*(0) = 0.4, \qquad P^*(\epsilon) = 0.4, \qquad P^*(2\epsilon) = 0.2, \quad \text{and} \quad P^*(3\epsilon) = 0.$$

This distribution $P^*(\varepsilon)$ is not very different from the actual distribution $P(\varepsilon)$ given above. On the other hand, the less probable arrangements give distributions which are very different from $P(\varepsilon)$. The less probable the arrangement, the less like $P(\varepsilon)$ it is. For example, the first arrangement of Fig. 11.14 has $P(0) = 0.8$, $P(\epsilon) = P(2\epsilon) = P(3\epsilon) = 0$, and $P(4\epsilon) = 0.2$. As the number of particles is increased but comparing the situation for the same mean energy per particle, these two effects become more marked. The most probable arrangement and ones similar to it become overwhelmingly more probable than arrangements which differ significantly from it. Moreover, the most probable distribution becomes more nearly the actual distribution, $P^*(\varepsilon) \to P(\varepsilon)$. This property is explored further in Sections 11.4 and 12.5.

The $P(\varepsilon)$ curves for $N = 5$ are given in Fig. 11.15(a) (strictly speaking, the result is a histogram) and they are not very different from those for $N = 4$ in Fig. 11.11(b) and so we can guess that the form of the curves will not change much for larger N and that we have probably now reached a large enough number of particles to draw some general conclusions with reasonable reliability. We may now summarize the various results and point out some aspects of the behaviour which are important and which become accentuated as the number of particles increases.

For a given N, the distribution function $P(\varepsilon)$ is a particular type of curve as shown, for instance, in Fig. 11.15(a). For any given total energy U, it is always

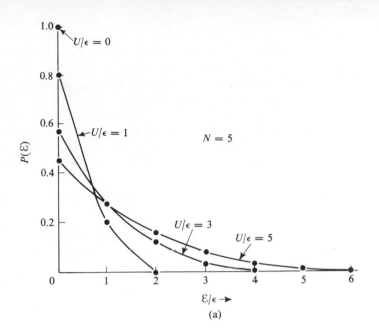

(a)

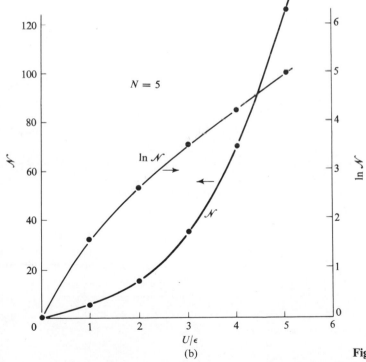

(b)

Figure 11.15

most likely that we shall find particles in the *lowest* energy level and the probability falls steadily with increasing energy ε of the particle. In other words, the higher the energy, the less likely are we to find a particle with that energy. This corresponds very well with our expectations for a perfect gas. We have already noted that a very fast molecule is likely to be slowed down because in a binary collision with a slower molecule it almost always loses energy.

As the total energy U is increased for a given number of particles, of course, the probability of finding a particle in a higher level tends to increase and consequently the probability of finding a particle in the lowest levels decreases. Thus $P(\varepsilon)$ gets flatter and more stretched out as U increases. This effect can be seen explicitly from the $P(\varepsilon)$ curves. It should be noted though that it is still true that $P(\varepsilon)$ is largest for smallest ε whatever the value of U. The actual form of the curves of $P(\varepsilon)$ is discussed in Section 11.3.

11.3 TEMPERATURE

We now appeal to intuition and experience and we recall that, as we add energy (heat) to a sample, its temperature increases. We also have reason to expect that we should have a Boltzmann distribution (see Chapter 10) so that the temperature might be expected to appear in the form $P(q) \propto \exp[-\varepsilon(q)/kT]$. This function behaves with increasing temperature in much the same way as our $P(\varepsilon)$ curves do with increasing U. Hence it might be possible to identify the temperature from the $P(\varepsilon)$ curves.

First of all, suppose the temperature approaches the absolute zero. Then $P(q)$ becomes a delta function $\delta(q)$ for which $\delta(q) = 0$ if $q \neq 0$, but $\int \delta(q)\,dq = 1$ as shown in Fig. 11.16(a). This is the distribution we got for $U = 0$ and any N (Fig. 11.7). For example, for $N = 5$ and $U = 0$, the distribution diagram is as shown in Fig. 11.16(b) and for this $\mathcal{N} = 1$. Hence the absolute zero, $T = 0$, corresponds to $U = 0$, i.e. the lowest possible energy (not necessarily zero energy) and also the number of possible arrangements is at the minimal value of 1, *for all N*.

Now, for $N = 5$, let us find the best fitting curve in the form $A_n \exp[-a_n(\varepsilon/\epsilon)]$, where A_n and a_n are functions of U/ϵ and $n = U/\epsilon$, to $P_U(\varepsilon)$ for $U = (1, 2, \ldots, 5)\epsilon$ without worrying too much about what exactly we mean by "best fit". The result is given in Table 11.1. We expect $\exp[-a_n(\varepsilon/\epsilon)]$ to correspond to

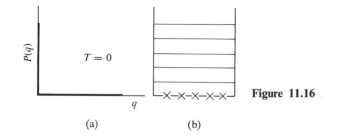

Figure 11.16

(a)   (b)

Table 11.1

$U = 0$	—	$a_0 \to \infty$	$1/a_0 = 0$
$U = \epsilon$	$A_1 = 0.8$	$a_1 = 1.39$	$1/a_1 = 0.72$
2ϵ	$A_2 = 0.67$	$a_2 = 0.92$	$1/a_2 = 1.08$
3ϵ	$A_3 = 0.57$	$a_3 = 0.69$	$1/a_3 = 1.44$
4ϵ	$A_4 = 0.50$	$a_4 = 0.56$	$1/a_4 = 1.78$
5ϵ	$A_5 = 0.45$	$a_5 = 0.47$	$1/a_5 = 2.1$

Boltzmann's distribution $\exp(-\varepsilon/kT)$. They indeed have the same functional form to a good approximation for $N = 5$ and for the two cases $U = \epsilon$ and $U = 5\epsilon$, as shown in Fig. 11.17(a). We therefore have $a(\varepsilon/\epsilon) = \varepsilon/kT$. Therefore $T = (\epsilon/k)(1/a)$, that is $1/a$ is the temperature in units of ϵ/k. Note that the dimensions of ϵ/k are correct, energy/(energy deg^{-1}) = deg. Strictly speaking, the physical argument only gives that a is a *function* of the temperature. We shall shortly confirm it is proportional to T^{-1} by comparison with the gas equation. The plot of $1/a$ versus U in Fig. 11.17(b) shows how the "temperature" rises as heat is added to the five-particle system.

We could even find the specific heat of our five-particle body. In general, this is given by $c = (1/M)(\Delta q/\Delta T)$, where Δq is the heat added which causes a temperature rise ΔT in a sample of mass M. Also in general, from the first law of thermodynamics (which is, of course, just conservation of energy), $\Delta q = \Delta U - \Delta w$ where ΔU is the increase in internal energy and Δw is any work done on the body, such as $-P\,\Delta V$, corresponding to a change in volume ΔV, which occurs on adding the heat Δq. In our example, we have assumed that the energy levels are fixed. Hence the volume is constant* and so $\Delta w = 0$. Thus $\Delta q = \Delta U$. Further, in our case, $M = 5m$ where m is the mass of a particle. Thus we have $c_v = [1/(5m)]\,dU/dT \propto 1/(dT/dU)$. Since the graph of $1/a$ versus U/ϵ is a straight line, except for small values of $1/a$, dT/dU is a constant. Hence the specific heat is a constant independent of temperature except at very low temperatures; the actual result is shown is Fig. 11.17(c). This behaviour is what we expect for a monatomic gas. The internal energy U in this case is the kinetic energy of motion. We have therefore, for N molecules, $U = N(\frac{1}{2}mv^2) = N(\frac{3}{2}kT)$ (see Section 10.4). Therefore $dU/dT = \frac{3}{2}Nk$ so that c_v is independent of T. The fall in c_v at low temperatures is observed experimentally in solids—but not in gases. We can compare Figs. 11.18 and 11.17(c). This is an essentially quantum-mechanical effect. It arose in our calculations (Fig. 11.17c) because we based them on a quantum-mechanical effect, the discreteness of energy levels. We shall return to this point later. It is worth noting, however, that we can see that the fall off in c_v occurs when the temperature is such that kT is comparable with the spacing of the lowest energy levels ϵ. As we have seen, one unit of temperature $1/a$ is ϵ/k. The fall off in c_v in Fig. 11.17(c) starts when $1/a$ is approximately unity so that the temperature

---

* This statement is justified in Section 13.4.

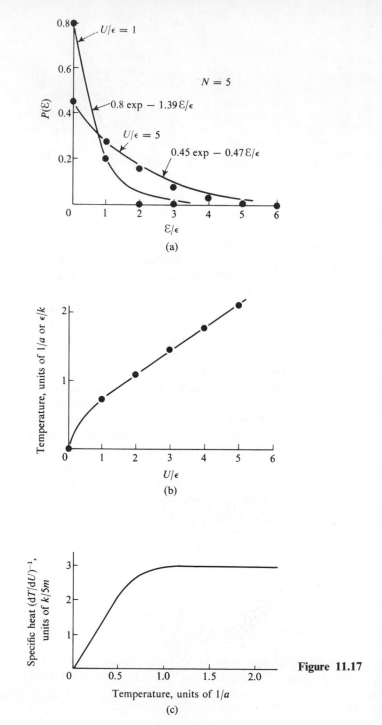

Figure 11.17

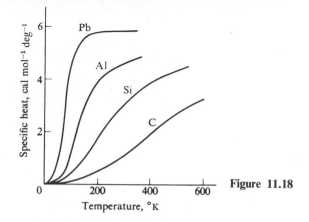

Figure 11.18

sought is that for which $T \sim \epsilon/k$, that is when $kT \sim \epsilon$, as stated above. This result is also true in general. Hence, conversely, we can estimate the spacing of energy levels from the temperature at which the specific heat falls off. Thus the classic and elementary measurement of the specific heat of a solid is evidence of quantization, and immediately gives us an estimate of the spacing of the energy levels.

11.4 THE BOLTZMANN DISTRIBUTION FOR LARGE NUMBERS OF PARTICLES AND ANY SYSTEM OF ENERGY LEVELS

It is actually not very difficult to deduce the Boltzmann distribution for large numbers of particles and for any system of energy levels. The reason for giving the analysis of Section 11.3 was that this gave a much better physical picture of how the Boltzmann distribution arises and it did not involve any mathematical analysis.

Suppose the energy levels are ϵ_1, ϵ_2, ... , which are not necessarily evenly spaced. Suppose we have N particles altogether. One possible arrangement is to have

n_1 particles with energy ϵ_1,

n_2 particles with energy ϵ_2,

. . . .

n_s particles with energy ϵ_s

. . . .

Obviously, we must have also

$$n_1 + n_2 + \cdots n_s + \cdots = N,$$

because the total number of particles is fixed. This last requirement is a *restrictive* condition on the populations of the levels which we can write more concisely as

$\sum\limits_s n_s = N$. Again, we take a fixed total energy U and so, clearly,

$$n_1\epsilon_1 + n_2\epsilon_2 + \cdots n_s\epsilon_s + \cdots = U,$$

or $\sum\limits_s n_s\epsilon_s = U$. This is a second restrictive condition on the values of the numbers n_s.

The number of ways in which the N particles can be arranged so that there are n_1 on level ϵ_1, n_2 on ϵ_2, and so on, if the way they are arranged on the level is not important, is

$$\frac{N!}{n_1!n_2!\ldots n_s!\ldots}$$

The product in the denominator is continued until all the particles are accounted for. If a level happens to have no particles on it, the corresponding factorial does not appear, since $0! = 1$. We can easily see that this formula is correct by taking some of the cases which we have dealt with already, e.g. for 5 particles with energy $U = 5\epsilon$, we have the arrangements shown in Fig. 11.19. The formula for the number of complexions in a given arrangement can be understood as follows. Set out the N objects in an ordered sequence. The choice for the first object is N leaving $N - 1$ objects. The choice is then of $N - 1$ objects and so the number of ways of choosing the first two objects is $N(N - 1)$. Continue this process and we get $N(N - 1)(N - 2)\cdots 3\cdot 2\cdot 1$ which is $N!$ Now we regard the sequence as divided into groups.

$$a, b, c, \qquad d, e, f, g, \ldots$$

If we decide that the first group is to have, say, three objects in it, then, like the particles on the first level, we do not care in which order we put them, that is whether they are abc, acb, bac, bca, cab, or cba, which is 6, or 3!, ways. Hence the number of distinct ways of doing this is $N!/3!$. More generally, if the first group contains n objects, the number of ways is $N!/n!$. Similarly for any further groups and so we get $\mathscr{N}_a = N!/n_1!n_2!\ldots n_s!\ldots$. The question we have to answer is,

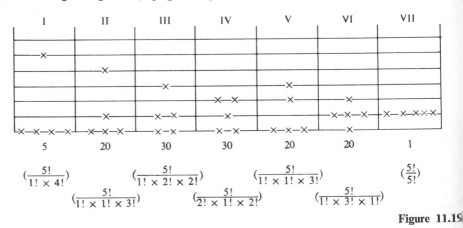

Figure 11.19

what are the most probable values of $n_1, n_2, \ldots n_3, \ldots$? The answer is, the particular distribution or arrangement which can be set out in the most ways, i.e. which has the most complexions. We call this $\mathcal{N}^*$ ways. This is the most probable arrangement, which we have already mentioned. For a large number of particles, the total number of complexions $\mathcal{N}$ is of order $\mathcal{N}^*$ and in fact, for all practical purposes, we may take $\mathcal{N}^*$ to be $\mathcal{N}$, since only $\ln \mathcal{N}$ arises in comparisons with observable quantities (see Problem 11.3 and Section 12.3). For large N, the most probable arrangement and arrangements similar to it become overwhelmingly more probable than other arrangements which are significantly different. The question of what is meant by "significantly different" is taken up in Section 12.5. This also corresponds to our assertion in Section 11.2 that $P^*(\varepsilon) \approx P(\varepsilon)$, which we could only establish rather approximately for small N. However, we have already noted this tendency (Section 11.2) even for $N = 4$. For $N = 5$, it is quite obvious that $P^*(\varepsilon)$ for arrangement III or IV (Fig. 11.19) fits $P(\varepsilon)$ much better than $P^*(\varepsilon)$ for arrangement I or VII.

Our problem is therefore a purely mathematical one to find the maximal value of $\mathcal{N}_a = N!/n_1! n_2! \ldots n_s! \ldots$, subject to $\sum n_s = N$ and $\sum n_s \varepsilon_s = U$.

If there are small changes in $n_1, n_2, \ldots$ of $\Delta n_1, \Delta n_2, \ldots$, then the change in $\mathcal{N}_a$ is

$$\Delta \mathcal{N}_a = \frac{\partial \mathcal{N}_a}{\partial n_1} \Delta n_1 + \frac{\partial \mathcal{N}_a}{\partial n_2} \Delta n_2 + \cdots \frac{\partial \mathcal{N}_a}{\partial n_s} \Delta n_s + \cdots$$

$$= \sum_s \frac{\partial \mathcal{N}_a}{\partial n_s} \Delta n_s.$$

Actually, since we are only going to find the maximum of $\mathcal{N}_a$, we can equally well look for the maximum of $\ln \mathcal{N}_a$ (this will appear more physically plausible when we come to discuss entropy (Section 12.3) but in any case it is mathematically quite valid). We have, for the change in $\ln \mathcal{N}_a$ which results from changes in the n_s,

$$\Delta(\ln \mathcal{N}_a) = \sum_s \frac{\partial(\ln \mathcal{N}_a)}{\partial n_s} \Delta n_s.$$

But we must also have

$$\Delta n_1 + \Delta n_2 + \cdots \Delta n_s + \cdots = \sum_s \Delta n_s = \Delta(N) = 0$$

and

$$\epsilon_1 \Delta n_1 + \epsilon_2 \Delta n_2 + \cdots \epsilon_s \Delta n_s + \cdots = \sum_s \epsilon_s \Delta n_s = \Delta(U) = 0.$$

Since adding zero does not change anything, we can combine the three relations and get

$$\Delta(\ln \mathcal{N}_a) = \sum_s \frac{\partial(\ln \mathcal{N}_a)}{\partial n_s} \Delta n_s + \alpha \sum_s \Delta n_s + \beta \sum_s \epsilon_s \Delta n_s,$$

where α and β are constants which do not depend on the n_s. They are called "Lagrange's undetermined multipliers", since their value at this stage is not fixed.

Table 11.2

n	5	10	25
$n!$	120	$3.7 \cdots \times 10^6$	$1.6 \cdots \times 10^{22}$
$\ln n!$	4.8	15.1	58
$n \ln n - n$	3.0	13.0	55.5

This relation may be written

$$\Delta(\ln \mathcal{N}_a) = \sum_s \left[\frac{\partial(\ln \mathcal{N}_a)}{\partial n_s} + \alpha + \beta\epsilon_s \right] \Delta n_s.$$

But, if $\mathcal{N}_a$ is a maximum, $\Delta(\ln \mathcal{N}_a)$ must be zero for any small change Δn_s in any n_s. This is true if

$$\frac{\partial(\ln \mathcal{N}_a)}{\partial n_s} + \alpha + \beta\epsilon_s = 0 \qquad \text{for all } s.$$

But

$$\ln \mathcal{N}_a = \ln \frac{N!}{n_1! n_2! \ldots n_s! \ldots} = \ln N! - \ln n_1! - \ln n_2! - \cdots \ln n_s! - \cdots$$

$$\therefore \quad \frac{\partial}{\partial n_s}(\ln \mathcal{N}_a) = -\frac{\partial}{\partial n_s}(\ln n_s!),$$

all the other terms being zero, since they do not depend on the variable n_s. The right-hand side is very difficult to evaluate exactly but it can be done by a trick. If n is a large number, Stirling's theorem (see Problem 11.3c) states that

$$n! \approx n^n \exp(-n), \quad \text{or} \quad \ln n! \approx n \ln n - n.$$

We can confirm this for moderately large numbers by direct calculation (compare Rows 3 and 4 of Table 11.2). Using Stirling's formula, we have

$$\frac{\partial(\ln n!)}{\partial n} = \frac{\partial}{\partial n}(n \ln n - n) = n \cdot \frac{1}{n} + \ln n - 1 = \ln n.$$

But

$$\frac{\partial(\ln \mathcal{N}_a)}{\partial n} \quad \text{is} \quad -\frac{\partial}{\partial n_s}(\ln n_s!), \quad \text{and so is} \quad -\ln n_s.$$

Hence, the relation

$$\frac{\partial}{\partial n_s}(\ln \mathcal{N}_a) + \alpha + \beta\epsilon_s = 0$$

becomes

$$-\ln n_s + \alpha + \beta\epsilon_s = 0, \qquad \text{for a maximum† of } \ln \mathcal{N}_a$$

$$\therefore \quad n_s^* = \exp(\alpha + \beta\epsilon_s) = \exp(\alpha)\exp(\beta\epsilon_s).$$

† Strictly speaking, for a stationary value of $\ln \mathcal{N}_a$, but it *is* actually a maximum (see Problem 11.10).

The numbers n_s^* are the most probable values of the numbers n_s, which is why we use the special notation n_s^*. Since, as we have already noted, the most probable arrangements are overwhelmingly more probable than any others, then these values of n_s^* are overwhelmingly more likely to be observed than any other. We may compare this result with the Boltzmann distribution,

$$n_s/N = \exp\left(-\epsilon_s/kT\right)/\sum_t \exp\left(-\epsilon_t/kT\right).$$

We conclude that $\beta = -(1/kT)$ and $e^\alpha = N/\sum_t \exp\left(-\epsilon_t/kT\right)$. This is the same exponential dependence of the probability of occupation of an energy level on the energy that we found when we were dealing with small numbers. For reasons which we cannot go into here, α is often written as μ/kT where μ is an important quantity called the chemical potential. In spite of its name, it is also of great importance in physics.

The fact that we already get proper statistical behaviour, to a good approximation, even for very moderate numbers of particles can be turned to advantage. There are, in fact, bodies which consist of a limited number of particles which are not connected in any fixed pattern. If this is so, it can be useful to use statistical methods even if the uncertainties and fluctuations (see Section 12.5) are quite large. It is thus not a bad approximation to treat a nucleus containing only between 20 and 300 nucleons in this way. In this sense, we speak of nuclear matter as a nuclear liquid and the energy of a given nucleon is given in principle by a Boltzmann distribution.

The simplest example of a Boltzmann distribution is for the molecular kinetic energy of a perfect gas, the Maxwell–Boltzmann distribution, as we have already seen in Section 10.4. We have also seen how the distribution can be used to obtain averages of dynamic variables, for example $\overline{v_x^2}$, and so on.

Usually, the energy is expressed in terms of a coordinate, say q, i.e. ε is $\varepsilon(q)$. An example of this is the kinetic energy of a molecule in a perfect gas $\frac{1}{2}mv_x^2$ when q is v_x. Then $P(\varepsilon) \propto \exp\left[-\varepsilon(q)/kT\right]$. In many cases, the energy levels are close enough together so that $\varepsilon(q)$ may be regarded as a continuous function of q (this is true if $\Delta\varepsilon(q) = \varepsilon(q_{r+1}) - \varepsilon(q_r) \ll kT$ for all r; it is therefore more likely to be true the higher the temperature). We then find it useful to consider the probability of the coordinate q lying in a small but finite range Δq near q. Δq must contain a large number of energy levels but $\Delta q \ll q$. We then have that this probability is proportional to $\exp\left[-\varepsilon(q)/kT\right]\Delta q$, since to get into the region q we need the factor $\exp\left[-\varepsilon(q)/kT\right]$ and the probability must also be proportional to the number of energy levels included, which is proportional to Δq. We can write $p(q)\Delta q \propto \exp\left[-\varepsilon(q)/kT\right]\Delta q$. The probability $p(q)$ is the probability per unit range of q at q and this is different from $P(q)$ which is the probability of finding precisely the value q. Since the energy levels now do not appear explicitly, this relation corresponds to the classical case. Including the normalization, we now have

$$p(q)\,dq = \exp\left[-\varepsilon(q)/kT\right]dq \Big/ \int_{\text{all } q} \exp\left[-\varepsilon(q')/kT\right]dq'.$$

This is the formula which we used in connexion with the distribution of the velocities of molecules in a gas. We showed in Section 10.4 that $\frac{1}{2}m\overline{v_x^2} = \frac{1}{2}kT$. We can show that *any* coordinate q which leads to a term in the energy proportional to q^2 leads to a contribution $\frac{1}{2}kT$ to the mean energy. Put $\varepsilon(q) = Cq^2$, where C is an arbitrary constant, then

$$\overline{\varepsilon(q)} = C\overline{q^2} = C\int_{-\infty}^{\infty} q^2 \exp\left(-Cq^2/kT\right)dq \Big/ \int_{-\infty}^{\infty} \exp\left(-Cq^2/kT\right)dq = \tfrac{1}{2}kT,$$

independent of C. Further, if $\varepsilon(q_1, q_2, \ldots, q_n) = C_1 q_2^2 + C_2 q_2^2 + \cdots + C_n q_n^2$, then $\bar{\varepsilon}(q_1, q_2, \ldots, q_n) = \frac{1}{2}nkT$. Every squared term in the energy gives a contribution $\frac{1}{2}kT$ to the mean energy. This is an important result and is called equipartition of energy. For example, for a harmonic oscillator of mass m and force constant κ,

$$\varepsilon = \text{kinetic energy} + \text{potential energy} = \tfrac{1}{2}mv^2 + \tfrac{1}{2}\kappa x^2.$$

Therefore, the mean energy of a harmonic oscillator is $\frac{1}{2}kT + \frac{1}{2}kT = kT$. We used this result in Section 4.2. At room temperature, the energy kT is about 10^{-13} erg and so is difficult to observe for macroscopic objects (e.g. the pendulum of a clock!). However, the smaller the object, the more important is the thermal energy kT and for molecules it is usually vital.

Although it is rather difficult to do, we could measure the mean square velocity of the particles in the Brownian motion experiment (Problem 2.10). We expect to find $\frac{1}{2}m\overline{v^2} = \frac{3}{2}kT$ (as assumed in Section 2.3) and so k could be determined in this way. On the other hand, we could also vary the temperature of the solution and plot $\overline{v^2}$ as a function of the temperature in °C (Fig. 11.20). We would find a linear relation which extrapolates back to -273°C for $\overline{v^2} = 0$. This in principle is just as good a way of determining the absolute scale of temperature as by the use of a "perfect" gas. Just as for a perfect gas, this thermometer breaks down at low temperatures. At low enough temperatures, the gap between the lowest and lowest but one energy levels must finally become comparable with kT and then the classical equipartition result no longer holds, because the integration we have used is no longer valid (see Section 13.3 and Problem 11.3d). The fall off

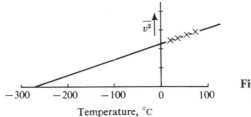

Figure 11.20

in specific heat at low temperatues shown in Figs. 11.17(c) and 11.18 is also due to the onset of invalidity of the equipartition principle.

As a second example of equipartition of energy, consider a mixture of two gases whose molecules have masses m_A and m_B. By the equipartition principle, we have $\frac{1}{2}m_A\overline{v_A^2} = \frac{1}{2}m_B\overline{v_B^2} = \frac{3}{2}kT$. Hence $(\overline{v_A^2}/\overline{v_B^2})^{1/2} = (m_B/m_A)^{1/2}$. On average, the lighter molecules travel faster. (Another example is that of a plasma, see Problem 10.1.)

11.5 ELECTRIC AND MAGNETIC SUSCEPTIBILITIES

One important application of the Boltzmann distribution is the calculation of susceptibilities. If we have a substance containing permanent dipoles (electric or magnetic) which can orientate in any direction, it will not be polarized in the absence of a field (except in the very unusual case that it is ferromagnetic or ferroelectric).

If we put on a field, there is a tendency for the dipoles to point in the direction of the field but this is opposed by the thermal agitation. If the field is strong enough, we expect to get to the limiting case where all the dipoles are lined up. The polarization is defined as the dipole moment per unit volume. Dipole moments can be added vectorially.

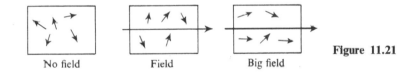

No field   Field   Big field   **Figure 11.21**

The polarization in the field direction has a contribution $\mu \cos \theta$ from a dipole of moment μ at an angle θ to the field. We write the average value of this over all the similar dipoles in the sample as $\mu \overline{\cos \theta}$. Then, if there are n dipoles per unit volume, we have for the polarization

$$P = n\mu \overline{\cos \theta}.$$

$\overline{\cos \theta}$ depends on the electric field $\mathbf{E}$. If $\mathbf{E} = 0$, the dipoles are not aligned in any particular direction so that $\overline{\cos \theta} = 0$ and $P = 0$. We shall show that, for small $\mathbf{E}$, $\overline{\cos \theta}$ is proportional to $\mathbf{E}$ and so $P \propto \mathbf{E}$. In this case, we can define a susceptibility $\kappa = P/E$ which is related to the dielectric constant ε, the quantity measured experimentally, by $\varepsilon = 1 + 4\pi\kappa$ (in cgs electrostatic units).

If all the dipoles are lined up, $\overline{\cos \theta} = 1$, since $\theta = 0$ for every one of them and so $P = n\mu$. Hence the general behaviour to be expected is as shown in Fig. 11.22. Thus for large E, P increases less rapidly with E and κ (and ε) fall. This is called saturation.

The energy of a dipole of moment $\mathbf{\mu}$ in a field $\mathbf{E}$ is $-\mathbf{\mu} \cdot \mathbf{E} = -\mu E \cos \theta$. Hence, in the Boltzmann distribution expression, $\exp(-\varepsilon/kT)$ is $\exp[+(\mu E/kT) \cos \theta]$. The coordinate in question here is the solid angle Ω. The probability $p(\Omega) \, d\Omega$

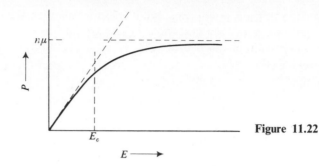

Figure 11.22

of being in dΩ at Ω is proportional to $\exp\left[+(\mu E/kT)\cos\theta\right]$ dΩ and dΩ = $\sin\theta$ dθ dϕ (the element of area on a unit sphere), therefore

$$p(\Omega)\,\mathrm{d}\Omega = \exp\left(+\frac{\mu E}{kT}\cos\theta\right)\mathrm{d}\Omega\bigg/\!\!\int\exp\left(+\frac{\mu E}{kT}\cos\theta\right)\mathrm{d}\Omega,$$

where the integral is over all values of Ω, i.e. over a unit sphere. The mean value of $\cos\theta$ is therefore

$$\overline{\cos\theta} = \int\cos\theta\,p(\Omega)\,\mathrm{d}\Omega = \int\cos\theta\exp\left(\frac{\mu E}{kT}\cos\theta\right)\mathrm{d}\Omega\bigg/\!\!\int\exp\left(\frac{\mu E}{kT}\cos\theta\right)\mathrm{d}\Omega$$

$$= \iint\cos\theta\exp\left(\frac{\mu E}{kT}\cos\theta\right)\sin\theta\,\mathrm{d}\theta\,\mathrm{d}\phi\bigg/\!\!\iint\exp\left(\frac{\mu E}{kT}\cos\theta\right)\sin\theta\,\mathrm{d}\theta\,\mathrm{d}\phi$$

$$= \int_0^{2\pi}\mathrm{d}\phi\int_0^{\pi}\cos\theta\exp\left(\frac{\mu E}{kT}\cos\theta\right)\sin\theta\,\mathrm{d}\theta\bigg/\!\!\int_0^{2\pi}\mathrm{d}\phi\int_0^{\pi}\exp\left(\frac{\mu E}{kT}\cos\theta\right)\sin\theta\,\mathrm{d}\theta.$$

Putting $x = \cos\theta$, this can be written more simply, and we have

$$\overline{\cos\theta} = \int_{-1}^{1} x\exp\left(\frac{\mu E}{kT}x\right)\mathrm{d}x\bigg/\!\!\int_{-1}^{1}\exp\left(\frac{\mu E}{kT}x\right)\mathrm{d}x \equiv L\left(\frac{\mu E}{kT}\right).$$

Hence $\overline{\cos\theta}$ depends only on one parameter, the combination $\mu E/kT$. $L(\mu E/kT)$ is called the Langevin function. If $\mu E/kT$ is very much less than unity, we can put $\exp\left[(\mu E/kT)x\right] \approx 1 + (\mu E/kT)x$ in the integrals (since $|x| \leq 1$), so that

$$\overline{\cos\theta} \equiv L(\mu E/kT) \approx \int_{-1}^{1} x\left[1 + \frac{\mu E}{kT}x\right]\mathrm{d}x\bigg/\!\!\int_{-1}^{1}\left[1 + \frac{\mu E}{kT}x\right]\mathrm{d}x$$

$$= \int_{-1}^{1}\left(\frac{\mu E}{kT}\right)x^2\,\mathrm{d}x*\bigg/\!\!\int_{-1}^{1}\mathrm{d}x = \frac{1}{3}\frac{\mu E}{kT}.$$

Hence, for $\mu E/kT$ is very much less than unity, $P = n\mu\,\overline{\cos\theta} = n\mu(\mu E/3kT)$ and so $\kappa \equiv P/E = n\mu^2/3kT$ and $\varepsilon = 1 + 4\pi n\mu^2/3kT$. Hence in particular for a gas,

---

* Since $\displaystyle\int_{-1}^{1} x\,\mathrm{d}x = 0.$

where the appropriate conditions hold, measurement of the variation of the dielectric constant with temperature, $\varepsilon(T)$, can be used to obtain the value of the molecular electric dipole moment μ. The values used in Section 4.5 and elsewhere were obtained in this way.

In general, we can show that

$$\overline{\cos \theta} \equiv L\left(\frac{\mu E}{kT}\right) = \coth\left(\frac{\mu E}{kT}\right) - \left(\frac{\mu E}{kT}\right)^{-1},$$

by exact evaluation of the integrals arising above (Problem 11.13). If $\mu E/kT \ll 1$, $L(\mu E/kT) \to \frac{1}{3}(\mu E/kT)$, as found above. If $\mu E/kT \gg 1$, $L(\mu E/kT) \to 1$ so that $P \to n\mu$ as expected. The plot of $L(\mu E/kT)$ versus $(\mu E/kT)$ bends over appreciably for $\mu E/kT \approx 1$, so that E_c of Fig. 11.22 is the field for which $\mu E_c/kT \approx 1$.

The effect of the field E on the dipoles depends on the relative magnitudes of the energy of the dipole in the field μE and the thermal energy kT, i.e. on the ratio $(\mu E)/(kT)$. The same analysis is true for magnetic dipoles $\boldsymbol{\mu}_m$ in a magnetic field $\mathbf{B}$, except for some quantum-mechanical corrections which are discussed below. In this case, we would write for the magnetization M, i.e. the magnetic dipole moment per unit volume, $M = \mu_m L(\mu_m B/kT)$. The magnetic susceptibility is given by M/H and the permeability by $1 + 4\pi(M/H)$ (in cgs electromagnetic units).

For a molecular electric dipole of 1 debye unit (10^{-18} e.s.u. cm) in a field of 3000 v cm^{-1} at room temperature, $\mu E/kT \approx 10^{-4}$. It is therefore difficult to observe electrical saturation. We need much bigger fields to increase $\mu E/kT$ to values of order unity and most material would suffer dielectric breakdown. Again, the value of $\mu E/kT$ cannot be substantially increased by lowering the temperature, since this usually invalidates our basic assumption that the only effective orientating couple on the dipole is that due to the field E. If other torques were present, they would have to be included in the expression for the probability density $p(\Omega)$. Put in simpler words, the orientation of the dipoles tend to get fixed at low temperatures and they then do not contribute to the field dependent polarization.

In the magnetic case, we have typically a Bohr magneton in 20,000 gauss at room temperature for which $\mu_B B/kT \approx 10^{-2}$. It should be possible, therefore, to observe saturation in the magnetic case at low temperatures if the dipoles are free to reorientate. Examples of this are given in Fig. 11.23. The actual measurements were made for temperatures of a few degrees Kelvin and magnetic fields of a few thousand gauss. The results in terms of the magnetic moment per ion in units of the Bohr magneton are plotted versus B/T. This is expected from the Langevin formula for M given above to be the appropriate parameter. The Bohr magneton, the atomic unit of magnetic moment, has already been mentioned in Sections 4.5(vi) and 5.7. In terms of the fundamental constants, it is $eh/4\pi m_e c$ (Experiments 9 and 17). We expect from the experimental results given in Fig. 11.23 that the ions in the crystals are such that Cr^{3+} has three unpaired electrons, Fe^{3+} has five, and Gd^{3+} has seven. This is in accordance with the well-known Hund's rules for building up atoms and from the structure of the ions. The Gd^{3+} ion referred to in Fig. 11.23 is in a crystal of gadolinium sulphate octahydrate and the ion has the electronic structure $(Xe)4f^7 5s^2 5p^6$.* The "magnetic" electrons are the seven $4f$ ones. The Fe^{3+} ion is in ferric ammonium alum and the electronic structure is $(Ar)3d^5$ which has five magnetic $3d$ electrons. The Cr^{3+} ion is in potassium chrome alum and the electronic structure is $(Ne)3s^2 3p^6 3d^3$ which has three magnetic $3d$ electrons. It appears, therefore, that each magnetic electron has a magnetic moment of one Bohr magneton associated with it and that the electronic moments are able to orientate freely in the applied magnetic field.

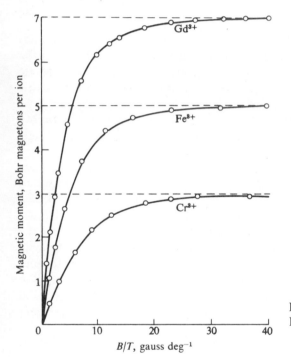

Figure 11.23. Adapted from W. E. HENRY, *Phys. Rev.* **88**, 561 (1952).

For the case of magnetic susceptibility due to the magnetism of fundamental particles, we have to bear in mind that such magnets can only take up a few restricted orientations in a magnetic field as first shown by the Stern–Gerlach experiment (Section 6.3). Our expression for $p(\Omega)$ must therefore be modified. However, the general result is very similar to the one we have obtained. The Langevin function is replaced by a similar one, the Brillouin function (see Problem 11.16). The full lines in Fig. 11.23 are actually for the Brillouin function.

---

* (Xe) refers to the inner group of electrons and is not of course, a xenon atom.

PROBLEMS

11.1.   In Section 11.1, it is stated that, for two distinguishable particles A and B with a total energy 2ϵ, there are three complexions with equal *a priori* probability. We might think that a possible model for this would be to toss two coins with one side of each marked A and the other side of each marked B. However, the three complexions do not then have equal probability; the probabilities are $\frac{1}{4}$, $\frac{1}{4}$, and $\frac{1}{2}$. What is wrong with this model?

11.2.   Consider the case of 6 independent localized particles isolated from their surroundings and having equally spaced available energy levels with separation ϵ units of energy. Enumerate explicitly all the complexions for internal energies $U = \epsilon$, 2ϵ, and 3ϵ, respectively. Calculate the probability distribution $P(\mathcal{E})$ for finding a particle on an energy level $\mathcal{E}$ for each case. Show that the distribution curves for $U = 3\epsilon$ is well represented by a curve of the form $A \exp(-a\mathcal{E}/\epsilon)$ and find A and a. In the case of $U = 3\epsilon$, show that the most probable distribution is a fair approximation to the same exponential as the actual distribution. Explain how the above simple model has many of the characteristics of the behaviour of large numbers of particles.

11.3.   In statistical mechanics, a number of simple mathematical results are needed. Verify the following statements by *numerical evaluation* of a sufficient number of explicit cases.

a) If the evaluation of a large number n is in error by the factor f, the relative error in $\ln n$ is much smaller ($\ln$ is the natural logarithm).

b) The number of ways in which N distinguishable particles can be arranged in three groups of particles containing n_1, n_2, and n_3 particles, respectively, is $N!/n_1!n_2!n_3!$ if the arrangement within the groups is immaterial (N.B. $n_1 + n_2 + n_3 = N$). If the particles are indistinguishable, the number of arrangements is 1.

c) $\ln n! \approx n \ln n - n$, if n is large (Stirling's formula).

d) $\displaystyle\sum_{s=0}^{\infty} \exp[-s(\epsilon_0/kT)] \propto \int_0^{\infty} \exp[-s(\epsilon_0/kT)]\, ds$

provided $\epsilon_0/kT \ll 1$.

11.4.   Show that the *ratio* of the populations of any two energy levels in a system in equilibrium depends only on the energy *difference* between the levels.

11.5.   Show that the Boltzmann probability distribution is independent of the choice of zero for the particle energy.

11.6.   Show that, if the energy level system is "degenerate", i.e. there are g_s levels corresponding to the energy ϵ_s, then the Boltzmann distribution is given by

$$P(\epsilon_s) = g_s \exp(-\epsilon_s/kT)/\sum_i g_i \exp(-\epsilon_i/kT).$$

11.7.   Show, by using the equipartition theorem, that the mean energy at temperature T (a) of a free atom is $\frac{3}{2}kT$, (b) of a rigid linear molecule is $\frac{5}{2}kT$, and (c) of a hydrogen chloride molecule is $\frac{7}{2}kT$, if T is high enough.

Show using (a) that the specific heat per mole at constant volume of a gas composed of atoms should be about 3 cal deg^{-1}. (One calorie is 4.2 joules.)

11.8. The viscosity of sulphuric acid varies with temperature as given in the table (Kaye and Laby, p. 36). Explain why this might be taken as evidence that the molecular process (or reaction) controlling viscosity in this liquid involves an energy barrier of 0.25 ev or 6 kcal mol^{-1}.

Temperature, °C	0	10	20	30	40	50
Viscosity, cp	56	49	27	20	14.5	11.0

Note: Take the probability of a particle having an energy ε as proportional to $\exp(-\varepsilon/kT)$.

11.9. Measurements indicate that the rate of a certain chemical reaction increases about ten-fold per 10°C rise in temperature at room temperature. What tentative conclusion would you draw about the energetics of the reaction?

Note: See note to Problem 11.8.

11.10. Show explicitly, for the uniformly spaced energy level system, that the Boltzmann distribution corresponds to a maximum in the number of configurations against variation in the populations of the levels, by moving one particle up from the ith to the $(i + 1)$th level and one down from the ith to the $(i - 1)$th level.

11.11. A system has uniformly spaced non-degenerate energy levels. Show that the probability of a particle having an energy *greater than* ΔE is equal to $\exp(-\Delta E/kT)$. Show that it may well be a good approximation to take the probability as proportional to $\exp(-\Delta E/kT)$, even if the energy levels are not uniformly spaced.

11.12. Particles have available two energy levels only, of energy $\pm\epsilon$ (e.g. a spin $\frac{1}{2}$ in a magnetic field). Show that, for N particles, the internal energy at temperature T is given by $U = N\epsilon \tanh(-\epsilon/kT)$.

11.13. Show that $L(\mu E/kT) = \coth(\mu E/kT) - (\mu E/kT)^{-1}$ (see Section 11.5).

11.14. For a system of electrons (magnetic moment one Bohr magneton) in a field of 10,000 gauss (1 wb m^{-2}), find the temperature at which the intrinsic electronic moments are appreciably aligned.

11.15. Show that, for an electric dipole moment 1 debye unit in an electric field of 3000 v cm^{-1} at room temperature, $\mu E/kT \approx 10^{-4}$.

11.16. For a spin one-half particle, it may be assumed that, in a magnetic field, the magnetic moment in the field direction is either $+\mu$ or $-\mu$. Show that, for such particles which are otherwise free to orientate in a magnetic field B in an environment at temperature T,

$$\overline{\cos\theta} = [\exp(\mu B/kT) - \exp(-\mu B/kT)]/[\exp(\mu B/kT) + \exp(-\mu B/kT)]$$

$$= \tanh(\mu B/kT).$$

This is the Brillouin function (Section 11.5) for spin one-half. Show that it is similar to the Langevin function.

CHAPTER 12

The second law of thermodynamics

That's Entropy, man! FLANDERS and SWANN (*At the Drop of a Second Hat*)

12.1 HEAT FLOWS FROM A HOT BODY TO A COLD BODY

The most characteristic thing about temperature is that heat flows from a body at a higher temperature to one at a lower temperature, never the other way. The meaning of the words hotter and colder is defined by the direction of flow of heat. The important part of this statement is that the heat *always* flows the same way if we start from the same initial conditions. We shall try to show how this comes about by our now familiar technique of doing exact calculations for small numbers of particles and extrapolating the results to large numbers of particles, that is to macroscopic bodies. We could see if this works by putting one of our "cold" systems of Chapter 11 in contact with a "hot" one. In order to reduce the complexity of the calculations, we consider a cold body A consisting of five particles and with one unit of energy, and a hot body B containing five particles and with five units of energy (Fig. 12.1a and b). We shall again assume that the energy levels are uniformly spaced and that the lowest possible energy is zero.

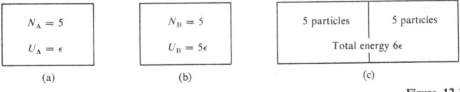

$N_A = 5$	$N_B = 5$	5 particles	5 particles
$U_A = \epsilon$	$U_B = 5\epsilon$	Total energy 6ϵ	
(a)	(b)	(c)	

Figure 12.1

We found in Chapter 11 that the distribution of particles over the energy levels for A is given by $P(\varepsilon) = 0.80 \exp(-1.39\varepsilon/\epsilon)$, that is the temperature "T" $= 1/1.39 = 0.7$ units. Body B has $P(\varepsilon) = 0.43 \exp(-0.47\varepsilon/\epsilon)$, that is "$T$" $= 1/0.47 = 2.1$ units. Now put bodies A and B together so that energy can flow, but not the particles, and so we have 5 particles in each body and a total energy of six units (Fig. 12.1c). We cannot say how the energy divides itself between the two bodies. We expect that, when the two bodies have come to thermal equilibrium, heat will have flowed from B to A.

Table 12.1

U_A/ϵ	U_B/ϵ	$\mathcal{N}_A$	$\mathcal{N}_B$	$\mathcal{N}_{AB} = \mathcal{N}_A\mathcal{N}_B$	$\mathcal{N}_{AB}/\mathcal{N} = P_{AB}$
0	6	1	210	210	0.04
1	5	5	126	630	0.13
2	4	15	70	1050	0.21
3	3	35	35	1225	0.25
4	2	70	15	1050	0.21
5	1	126	5	630	0.13
6	0	210	1	210	0.04
				$\mathcal{N} = 5005$	

We now consider all possible arrangements. First, all the energy might be shared in various ways and all these seven possibilities are given in the first two columns of Table 12.1. We note that, if two objects A and B have $\mathcal{N}_A$ and $\mathcal{N}_B$ equally likely complexions, respectively, independent of one another, then the number of complexions of A and B together is $\mathcal{N}_A\mathcal{N}_B$. This can be seen, for example, for two coins when $\mathcal{N}_A = 2$ (H and T), $\mathcal{N}_B = 2$ (H and T), and $\mathcal{N}_{AB} = \mathcal{N}_A\mathcal{N}_B = 4$ (HH, HT, TH, TT), or for a coin and a die* when $\mathcal{N}_A = 2$ (H and T), $\mathcal{N}_B = 6$ (1, 2, 3, 4, 5, 6), and $\mathcal{N}_{AB} = \mathcal{N}_A\mathcal{N}_B = 12$ (H and 1, H and 2, . . . , H and 6; T and 1, T and 2, . . . , T and 6). Hence we get the number of complexions $\mathcal{N}_{AB}$ of the two bodies A and B together is $\mathcal{N}_A\mathcal{N}_B$ as given in Table 12.1. The total number of complexions $\mathcal{N}$ is the sum of all these possibilities. The probability of any particular distribution of energy is $\mathcal{N}_{AB}/\mathcal{N}$, which we call P_{AB}. P_{AB} is the probability of finding the energy divided between the two bodies in a particular way. For only two bodies, if the energy of one is chosen, then that of the other is fixed and so P_{AB} may be considered a function of U_A or U_B only. From Table 12.1 or from the plot of $P_{AB}(U_A/\epsilon)$ of Fig. 12.2(a), we see that the most probable result is that for which $U_A = U_B = 3\epsilon$. This is yet another tendency which gets more marked with increasing numbers of particles and increasing energy. If we plot $P_{AB}(U_A)$ versus the fraction of the total energy

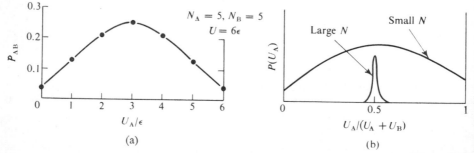

(a)

(b)

Figure 12.2

* The singular of dice!

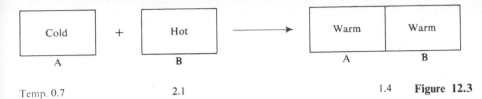

| Cold | + | Hot | $\longrightarrow$ | Warm | Warm |

| A | | B | | A | B |

in body A, that is $U_A/(U_A + U_B)$, we can show the effect on $P_{AB}(U_A)$ of increasing the number of particles. The effect is shown diagrammatically in Fig. 12.2(b). For large numbers of particles, it becomes overwhelmingly more probable for two similar bodies to share the total available energy equally than for any other distribution of energy.

This peaking of the curve of $P_{AB}(U_A)$ is similar in origin to that encountered in Section 10.3 for the peaking of the binomial distribution for increasing number of trials (see Problem 10.7). The most probable result in this particular example is that the two bodies A and B have the same internal energy U. Therefore, in this particular example, it is obvious they are most likely to be at the same temperature. We can see how the temperatures have changed explicitly. For $N = 5$ and $U = 3\epsilon$, we have from Section 11.3 that $P(\varepsilon) = 0.57 \exp\left[-0.69(\varepsilon/\epsilon)\right]$. The "temperature" corresponding to this distribution is $1/0.69 = 1.4$ units. This temperature (1.4 units) is intermediate between the temperature of the original cold body A which was 0.7 units and that of the hot body B which was 2.1 units (Fig. 12.3). Hence the heat has flowed from the hot to the cold body when they were put in contact. This is just what we expect heat to do. This is not a very decisive test of the way heat flows, except that the answer is known, since it is a rather special case to put two identical bodies together. A better test, because it is more general, is to consider two dissimilar bodies at different temperatures. We shall now investigate what happens when a big cold body A is put in thermal contact with a small hot one B. Let the body A have five particles and one unit of energy, $N_A = 5$ and $U = \epsilon$. A has a mass $5m$ and an initial temperature $T_{A,i} = 0.7$ unit. Let the body B have three particles and five units of energy, $N_B = 3$ and $U = 5\epsilon$. B has a mass $3m$ and an initial temperature $T_{B,i} = 4.9$ units. The temperature of B is very approximate because the $P(\varepsilon)$ versus ε curve is actually a straight line (see Fig. 11.11a). We construct a table just as before and find the probability P_{AB} of each possible way in which the two bodies can share the total energy (Table 12.2). The curve of P_{AB} in Fig. 12.4 is now asymmetric, because the two bodies are dissimilar. The most probable result, corresponding to the maximal value of P_{AB}, is $U_A = 4\epsilon$ and $U_B = 2\epsilon$, which, since $N_A = 5$ and $N_B = 3$, corresponds to final temperatures of $T_{A,f} = 1.78$ units and $T_{B,f} = 1.80$ units. Referring back to Section 11.3 and Figs. 11.11(a) and 11.15(a), it is clear again that fitting exponentials to the appropriate curves does not determine the temperature very accurately—the $P(\varepsilon)$ versus ε curve for $N = 3$ and $U = 2\epsilon$ is a straight line. Therefore the difference in temperature as between $T_{A,f}$ and $T_{B,f}$ is not significant. The most probable final state after the two bodies have

Table 12.2

U_A/ϵ	U_B/ϵ	$\mathcal{N}_A$	$\mathcal{N}_B$	$\mathcal{N}_{AB}$	P_{AB}
0	6	1	28	28	0.02
1	5	5	21	105	0.06
2	4	15	15	225	0.13
3	3	35	10	350	0.20
4	2	70	6	420	0.25
5	1	126	3	378	0.22
6	0	210	1	210	0.12
				$\mathcal{N} = 1716$	

been put in thermal contact is that they have the same *temperature*. Hence the heat has again flowed from the hot to the cold body, A has warmed up and B has cooled down (Fig. 12.5). In this case, the large body has been heated by the small one. Naturally, the smaller body has suffered the greatest change in temperature (Fig. 12.5) as the result of the flow of heat, since it has the smaller heat capacity. We notice once more that in this example, where we have only small numbers of particles, there is almost as high a probability of observing the adjacent distributions of the energy, $U_A = 3\epsilon$ and $U_A = 5\epsilon$ as $U_A = 4\epsilon$. It is, however, very unlikely that we should find body A with no energy. As the number of particles in each body is increased keeping N_A/N_B constant, and the total energy is increased in proportion, the peak in P_{AB} becomes more marked, much as in Fig. 12.2(b), but the peak remains at essentially the same value of $U_A/(U_A + U_B)$. To be exact, the peak will be at $U_A/(U_A + U_B) = 5/8 = 0.625$.

We can easily do another "experiment" to confirm that the direction of flow of heat is determined only by the *direction* of the temperature gradient and not by the size, or thermal capacity, of the two bodies by taking the *same* two bodies A and B as above but with the larger one A now the hotter one (Fig. 12.6). Let the body A have five particles and five units of energy, $N_A = 5$ and $U_A = 5\epsilon$. A has mass $5m$ and $T_{A,i} = 2.1$ units. Let the body B have three particles and one unit of energy, $N_B = 3$ and $U_B = \epsilon$. B has mass $3m$ and $T_{B,i} = 1.4$ units. The table for this case is *exactly the same* as Table 12.2 for the previous case, since the total energy $(U_A + U_B)$ is again 6ϵ and we have the same bodies. We

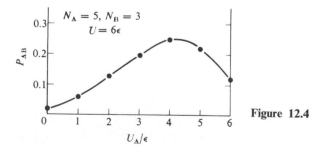

Figure 12.4

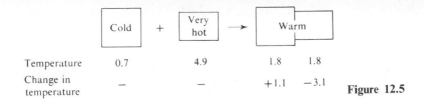

Temperature	0.7	4.9	1.8	1.8
Change in temperature	—	—	+1.1	−3.1

Figure 12.5

have no need, therefore, to carry out any further calculations. Hence again we have $T_{A,f} \approx T_{B,f} \approx 1.8$. When the two bodies are put in thermal contact, the heat again flows from the hot body to the cold one and the heat flow is as expected, in the opposite direction from the previous case (Fig. 12.6). It is perhaps obvious, but interesting to note explicitly, that once the two bodies have been brought together and are in thermal equilibrium all knowledge of their initial states when separate has been lost. It makes no difference whatever whether initially it was the body A or the body B which was the hotter. This is clearly in agreement with observation on large bodies; indeed, we can show that all these properties carry over to large bodies too.

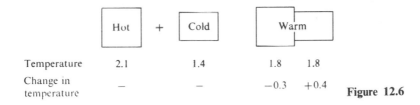

Temperature	2.1	1.4	1.8	1.8
Change in temperature	—	—	−0.3	+0.4

Figure 12.6

12.2 THERMAL EQUILIBRIUM OF TWO LARGE BODIES

We have seen explicitly in Section 12.1 that two small bodies which can exchange heat tend to be at the same temperature. We have also shown explicitly that the direction of flow of heat does not depend on the size of the bodies or on the actual quantity of heat involved but only on the difference in temperature. We can show explicitly that this happens for large bodies, consisting of large numbers of particles, and for any energy level system, in much the same way that we derived the Boltzmann distribution in Section 11.4 explicitly for large numbers of particles.

Suppose that we have one body A, with N_A particles, with a set of energy levels given by ϵ_{sA} with $s = 1, 2, \ldots$ and the population or number of particles in those levels given by n_{sA}. Another body B, with N_B particles, has energy levels ϵ_{tB} and populations n_{tB}. We know that the total number of complexions $\mathcal{N}_a$ of both bodies taken together is the product $\mathcal{N}_A \mathcal{N}_B$ of the number of complexions for each separately. For each body separately, we use the expression given in Section 11.4, so that

$$\mathcal{N}_a = \mathcal{N}_A \mathcal{N}_B = \frac{N_A!}{n_{1A}! \, n_{2A}! \ldots n_{sA}! \ldots} \frac{N_B!}{n_{1B}! \, n_{2B}! \ldots n_{tB}! \ldots}.$$

In evaluating this expression, we must remember that it is subject to the two restrictive conditions $\sum_s n_{sA} = N_A$ and $\sum_t n_{tB} = N_B$; since the two bodies remain distinct, they cannot exchange particles. Also the total energy U is fixed but it can be shared in any way between A and B, so that we also have the condition

$$\sum_s n_{sA}\epsilon_{sA} + \sum_t n_{tB}\epsilon_{tB} = U.$$

Proceeding in just the same way as in Section 11.4, we have

$$\alpha_A \sum_s \Delta n_{sA} = 0, \quad \alpha_B \sum_t \Delta n_{tB} = 0 \quad \text{and} \quad \beta(\sum_s \epsilon_{sA} \Delta n_{sA} + \sum_t \epsilon_{tB} \Delta n_{tB}) = 0,$$

where we now require three Lagrange undetermined multipliers, α_A, α_B, and β. As before

$$\frac{\partial(\ln \mathcal{N}_a)}{\partial n_{sA}} = -\ln n_{sA} \quad \text{and} \quad \frac{\partial(\ln \mathcal{N}_a)}{\partial n_{tB}} = -\ln n_{tB}.$$

Hence for a maximum of $\mathcal{N}_a$, we have the condition

$$\sum_s (-\ln n_{sA} + \alpha_A + \beta\epsilon_{sA})n_s A + \sum_t (-\ln n_{tB} + \alpha_B + \beta\epsilon_{tB}) \Delta n_{tB} = 0.$$

If this is to be true for all Δn_{sA} and all Δn_{tB}, we must have

$$-\ln n_{sA} + \alpha_A + \beta\epsilon_{sA} = 0, \qquad \text{for all } s$$

and

$$-\ln n_{tB} + \alpha_B + \beta\epsilon_{tB} = 0, \qquad \text{for all } t.$$

Therefore,

$$n_{sA}^* = \exp \alpha_A \exp \beta\epsilon_{sA} \quad \text{and} \quad n_{tB}^* = \exp \alpha_B \exp \beta\epsilon_{tB}.$$

The populations n_{sA}^* and n_{tB}^* and the corresponding number of complexions for this arrangement, $\mathcal{N}^*$, are so designated because they refer to the special values of n_{sA} and n_{tB} for the most probable distribution. Thus we get formulae similar to those of Section 11.4. The important point here is that we have the *same β* for both bodies A and B and this arose directly from the fact that we placed no restriction on the sharing of energy between the two bodies. This again suggests very strongly that β is closely related to the temperature, since this is the most obvious property that is the same for two bodies of arbitrary size and with arbitrary energy level systems which are in thermal contact. It can be shown that $\beta = -1/kT$, as in Section 11.4.

Strictly speaking, the two sets of energy levels in the analysis above cannot be entirely arbitrary. Incompatibility between the energy level spacing could prevent the free flow of energy between the two bodies and so additional restrictive conditions may apply. However, this situation rarely arises.

Thus we now have a physical idea of thermodynamic quantities such as temperature, internal energy, and specific heat. We even have some understanding of the second law of thermodynamics, since this is mostly about the way heat flows. We see that, in fact, the second law of thermodynamics is only statistical.

It is very probable that it will be obeyed but not absolutely certain. Thus, when we put together the two bodies with $N = 5$ and $U = \epsilon$ and 5ϵ, respectively, we found it most probable, with probability 0.25, that the energy would be shared equally. However, there is a finite probability that the heat flows the wrong way. The probability is 0.04 for *all* the heat to flow into B. Heat flow the "wrong way" is extremely unlikely for systems with large numbers of particles, so unlikely that it is never observed.

12.3 STATISTICAL ENTROPY

There is one more thermodynamic quantity which we can investigate fairly easily, namely entropy.

In thermodynamics, it is found most useful to introduce a quantity, the entropy, which is such that, when we add heat Δq reversibly at temperature T, we speak of an increase in entropy, $\Delta S = \Delta q/T$. If the temperature increases from T_1 to T_2, the increase in entropy is

$$S_2 - S_1 = \int_{T_1}^{T_2} dq/T$$

just as the energy put in is

$$q_2 - q_1 = \int_{T_1}^{T_2} dq.$$

In thermodynamics, the notion of entropy is rather mysterious but it is often vaguely suggested that S is associated with disorder or lack of knowledge of the body.

$$\text{Entropy} \leftrightarrow \begin{cases} \text{disorder} \\ \text{uncertainty} \end{cases}$$

Thus, in general, if we add heat not only does the temperature rise but the particles of which it is composed become more disordered; we are less certain where they are and how they move. In particular, we are less certain of the energy of the individual constituent particles. When the internal energy is zero (if the lowest energy level does not correspond to the zero of energy, when the total energy of the particles is as low as possible), we expect from our analyses of Chapter 11 that there is only one complexion whatever the number of particles. For $U = 0$, $\mathcal{N} = 1$ and all the particles are in the lowest level. In this situation, we are *certain* of the energy of every particle. To be explicit, consider now the five-particle system, $N = 5$ (Fig. 12.7). If we add one unit of energy ϵ, we then become less certain of the energy of each particle at any particular moment. We now only know (Fig. 11.15a for $U/\epsilon = 1$) that the probability of a particle having zero energy is $P(0) = 0.8$, which is not quite 1, that is, not quite certainty. However, the overall uncertainty is not great. The probability of a particle having an energy ϵ, $P(\epsilon)$, is only 0.2. Moreover we are *certain* that no particle has energy 2ϵ. The

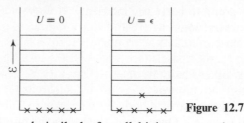

Figure 12.7

probability $P(2\epsilon)$ is zero, and similarly for all higher energy levels. Increasing the temperature further by adding energy, or heat, we get the particles spread over more and more energy levels and so we are more and more uncertain what the energy of a particular particle is likely to be. For $U = 5\epsilon$, for instance (Fig. 11.15a for $U/\epsilon = 5$), a particle is still most likely, as always, to have zero energy but there is appreciable probability of its having an energy as high as 5ϵ. We therefore need a quantity to relate to entropy S, which increases with increasing total energy U. We have such a quantity in the number of complexions, $\mathcal{N}$. For $N = 5$, $\mathcal{N}$ is given in the second row of Table 12.3. The entries for $\mathcal{N}$ and T are obtained from Chapter 11. Since the increments in energy ϵ have a large effect on the system, the *meaning* of T_{av} in Table 12.3 is not as obvious as it would be for a classical system (to which this one approximates at the higher temperatures) for which the definition $dS = dq/T$ is more appropriate. In order to calculate the thermodynamic entropy S from the formula $\Delta S = \Delta q/T$, we note that $\Delta q = \Delta U = \epsilon$ and use $T = T_{av}$ and so get the increments in S as U increases. We have taken the "averaged temperature" T_{av}, associated with two adjacent U values, to be the temperature on the curve in Fig. 11.17(b) corresponding to the mid-point between the corresponding adjacent discrete U values. This is more sensible than using the average of the two temperature values. Alternatively, we could take the average of the $1/T$ values which gives virtually the same result. In order to get S at a given temperature or value of U, we simply add up the increments as U increases, *assuming S to be zero for $U = 0$*, i.e. for $T = 0$. (Only differences in S are defined in classical thermodynamics. The assumption that $S = 0$ for $T = 0$ is not a trivial one.)

It is clear that $\mathcal{N}$ is a measure of uncertainty since, as we have already noted, the more possible complexions there are the less sure we are of what the energy

Table 12.3

U/ϵ	0		1		2		3		4		5
$\mathcal{N}$	1		5		15		35		70		126
"T"	0		0.72		1.08		1.44		1.78		2.10
"T"$_{av}$		0.55		0.92		1.26		1.60		1.94	
$\Delta S = \Delta U/T_{av}$		1.8		1.1		0.8		0.6		0.5	
$S = \sum \Delta S$	0		1.8		2.9		3.7		4.3		4.8
$\ln \mathcal{N}$	0		1.6		2.7		3.5		4.2		4.8
$S/\ln \mathcal{N}$	—		1.1		1.1		1.1		1.0		1.0

of a particle is going to be at any moment. However, it is clear from Table 12.3 that S is not proportional to $\mathcal{N}$ and that $\mathcal{N}$ increases much faster than S. A possibility is therefore that S is proportional to $\ln \mathcal{N}$, since $\ln \mathcal{N}$ increases more slowly with $\mathcal{N}$ than $\mathcal{N}$ itself (see Fig. 11.15b). So do, of course, the function $\mathcal{N}^{1/2}$ and many other functions of $\mathcal{N}$. However, it turns out that the appropriate "slowly varying" function of $\mathcal{N}$ is $\ln \mathcal{N}$. This is shown explicitly to be so for our rather special five-particle body by reference to Table 12.3. It is clear that S is proportional to $\ln \mathcal{N}$. Once again, the larger the number of particles, the more exactly this result is true. We shall not give the solution for a large number of particles here but it can be done by a method analogous to that of Section 12.3. We can also find the proportionality constant between the thermodynamic entropy S and the statistical entropy $\ln \mathcal{N}$. We have not been very careful about units in Table 12.3 and we now rectify this. "T" is in units of ϵ/k if we assume the Boltzmann relation is true. U is in units of ϵ. Therefore S is in units of $\epsilon/(\epsilon/k)$, i.e. of k. $\mathcal{N}$ is a number and $\ln \mathcal{N}$ is a number and so has no units. Hence the result for $S/\ln \mathcal{N}$, if it is a constant, as it is, is in units of k. From Table 12.3, the number of units of k in $S/\ln \mathcal{N}$ is unity, therefore

$$S = k \ln \mathcal{N}.$$

This gives the thermodynamic entropy S in terms of the statistical quantity $\mathcal{N}$. This result is really much more basic and fundamental than the Boltzmann distribution and is often used as the starting point for statistical mechanics. The other thermodynamic quantities can be deduced from S. We now see that the $\ln \mathcal{N}$ which turned up naturally in the derivation of the Boltzmann distribution (Section 11.4) and in the analysis of heat flow for large numbers of particles (Section 12.2) was, in fact, the statistical entropy and the physically interesting quantity is indeed $\ln \mathcal{N}$ rather than $\mathcal{N}$. Notice that an error in $\mathcal{N}$ causes a much smaller relative error in $\ln \mathcal{N}$ than in $\mathcal{N}$ if $\mathcal{N}$ is large. For example, if $\mathcal{N}_1 = e^{10}$ and $\mathcal{N}_2 = e^{11}$, $\mathcal{N}_2/\mathcal{N}_1 = e = 2.72$, i.e. 172% difference, but $\ln \mathcal{N}_2/\ln \mathcal{N}_1 = \frac{11}{10} = 1.1$ i.e. 10% difference. It is for this reason that it is good enough to use $\mathcal{N}_a$ (Section 12.2) instead of $\mathcal{N}$ if $\mathcal{N}$ is sufficiently large.

Our example rather overemphasizes the energy and the association of entropy with energy. This is largely because we have a system with a constant volume. It is clear that other things being equal, for example at constant temperature, an increase in volume must correspond to an increase in entropy, since we are more *uncertain* of the positions of the molecules in the larger volume (Fig. 12.8). The precise dependence of entropy on volume is given in Section 13.3.

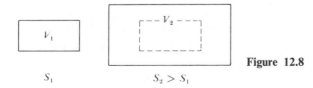

Figure 12.8

It is clear that the entropy of a body in equilibrium is a function only of the state of the body and does not depend on the way in which it reached that state. This is a somewhat subtle matter in conventional thermodynamics but in statistical mechanics it is obvious. The body in a defined state has a fixed number of complexions $\mathcal{N}$, and this number clearly does not depend on the way in which these complexions become possible. Since $S = k \ln \mathcal{N}$, the same is true of S, the thermodynamic entropy. Similarly, the difference in entropy between two states with entropies S_1 and S_2 is $S_2 - S_1$ and is independent of the way in which the body was changed from state 1 to state 2. Similar considerations apply to U and various other quantities. The situation is reminiscent of the potential energy of a conservative mechanical system. State functions like U and S are of special importance in thermodynamics. On the other hand, changes in the quantity of heat q supplied or abstracted in going from state 1 to state 2, $q_2 - q_1$, depends not only on the states 1 and 2 but on the *way* in which one went from 1 to 2. It is a quantity of a different nature, not a state function, and that is why we use the symbol q rather than Q.

Incidentally, we found it quite natural to take $S = 0$ at $T = 0$, i.e. zero entropy at the absolute zero of temperature. In thermodynamics, as we have already pointed out, only differences in entropy are defined and great difficulties arise in attempting to go to the absolute zero of temperature, $T = 0$. The difficulties are only resolved by an appeal to quantum statistical mechanics—as we have done. In quantum mechanics, an isolated body can have only distinct states. One of these states has a lower energy than all the others. At absolute zero, this state and this alone is realized, therefore $\mathcal{N} = 1$ at $T = 0$ and so if we define S by the relation $S = k \ln \mathcal{N}$, we have $S = 0$ at $T = 0$.

Since we now have a way of calculating entropy, we can test another form of the second law of thermodynamics, namely, that an isolated system left to itself will take up the state corresponding to maximal entropy.

12.4 ENTROPY INCREASES FOR APPROACH TO EQUILIBRIUM

Suppose we have two initially isolated bodies at different temperatures. If we put them in thermal contact we can easily show that the flow of heat from the hotter to the colder body results in an increase in the *thermodynamic* entropy. For the flow of a small quantity of heat Δq from the hot body A to the cold body B, we have for the increase in the thermodynamic entropy (see Fig. 12.9)

$$\Delta S = \frac{-\Delta q}{T_A} + \frac{\Delta q}{T_B} = \Delta q \left(\frac{1}{T_B} - \frac{1}{T_A} \right).$$

Since $T_A > T_B$, we have $1/T_B > 1/T_A$ and so $1/T_B - 1/T_A > 0$. Since Δq and $1/T_B - 1/T_A$ are both positive, ΔS is positive, i.e. the entropy increases. We note also that, if B is hotter than A, then Δq and $1/T_B - 1/T_A$ are *both* negative and so ΔS is again positive. The direction of flow of heat and increase in entropy are clearly related.

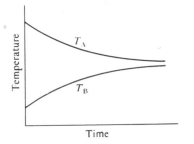

Figure 12.9

Let us see if there is a corresponding increase in *statistical* entropy when a hot and a cold body are put in thermal contact by calculating it explicitly for our small bodies. Take the case, analysed in Section 12.1, of two bodies each with $N = 5$ one of which, A, has $U = \epsilon$ (cold) and the other, B, $U = 5\epsilon$ (hot). We found in Section 12.1 that the heat flowed from the hot to the cold body and the final result was that it was most probable that the two bodies shared the energy equally when in equilibrium, that is $U_A = U_B = 3\epsilon$. We found in Section 11.2 that the body A has 5 complexions and B has 126 complexions, that is $\mathcal{N}_A = 5$ and $\mathcal{N}_B = 126$. Hence the initial entropy of A is $S_A = k \ln \mathcal{N}_A = k \ln 5$. Similarly, $S_B = k \ln \mathcal{N}_B = k \ln 126$. Therefore the total initial entropy S_i is $S_A + S_B = k \ln 5 + k \ln 126 = k \ln 630$. After the flow of energy, we have a combined body with $\mathcal{N} = 5005$ (see Table 12.1) so that the final entropy S_f is $k \ln 5005$. Therefore $S_f > S_i$, so that the entropy has increased, as expected. Even if only the most probable distribution of energy, $U_A = U_B = 3\epsilon$, was realized, we have an increase in entropy, since the number of complexions for this distribution is $\mathcal{N}_{eq} = 1225$ (see Table 12.1) which is larger than 630. For large bodies, we need in fact only calculate the number of complexions for the most probable distribution of energy, since this is overwhelmingly the most probable situation and $k \ln \mathcal{N}_{eq}$ is indistinguishable from $k \ln \mathcal{N}$.

Incidentally, we note that the entropy is an additive quantity, as assumed above, since the corresponding complexions must be multiplied. If $S_A = k \ln \mathcal{N}_A$ and $S_B = k \ln \mathcal{N}_B$, we have $S_A + S_B = k(\ln \mathcal{N}_A + \ln \mathcal{N}_B) = k \ln \mathcal{N}_A \mathcal{N}_B = k \ln \mathcal{N}_{AB} = S_{(A+B)}$. Entropy is therefore a so-called extensive property. We can speak of entropy per unit volume or per unit mass just as we do of energy per unit volume or per unit mass. The fact that on joining two bodies in the same conditions of temperature, pressure, etc., the entropies S must add, $S = S_A + S_B$, whereas the complexions multiply, $\mathcal{N} = \mathcal{N}_A \mathcal{N}_B$, means that, *if* S and $\mathcal{N}$ are related, the simplest possible relation is $S \propto \ln \mathcal{N}$.

The concept of entropy is a very powerful one in explaining a vast range of phenomena. One important common phenomenon is the degradation of mechanical energy into heat. Consider a body sliding on a rough surface where the kinetic energy of translation of the body disappears and the surface is warmed. This is clearly a case of spontaneous increase in entropy. Initially we know that all the particles in the moving body are moving in the same direction with the same velocity. There is of course in addition an uncertainty of position and velocity of the particles of both body and track since they are at a finite temperature. After the body has come to rest we are considerably less certain about all the particles involved since the amount of random or unpredictable motion has increased in the heated parts of the body and track (see Problem 12.1).

A rather different example of the power of the entropy concept is to note that the entropy is likely to increase for a change in which the number of particles increases. If we were uncertain about the position of one initial particle, we are twice as uncertain if it breaks into two particles whose positions are not known! This is of particular importance in chemical reactions. Other things being equal, reactions which increase the number of individual molecules are more likely to "go", since the equilibrium situation is that of maximal entropy* and this tends to be so when the number of particles is greatest. On the other hand, in a reaction where the number of particles of the product is smaller, for instance as in the formation of a long polymer molecule from a large number of monomer molecules, the amount of the product in equilibrium is likely to be small. The actual considerations are more complicated and are discussed in Section 13.2.

12.5 FLUCTUATIONS

When we began to deal with large numbers of particles in Chapter 10, we noted that it would be profitable to look at averaged properties of the whole system. Nevertheless, we noted also that many properties of the whole system would vary with time. We gave the example of the variation in the force F on a given area A of the wall of a container of a gas. The mean value of F/A is the pressure but F/A itself varies with time. It is clearly only useful to speak of pressure when the variations of F/A are "not too large". F/A is said to be a fluctuating quantity and it fluctuates about the mean, $P = \bar{F}/A$ (Fig. 10.1). A convenient measure of the importance of the fluctuations is the relative root mean square (r.m.s.) deviation from the mean value, $\overline{[(F - \bar{F})^2]}^{1/2}/\bar{F}$. If this is small, the fluctuations are small and the mean value $\bar{F}$ describes the situation adequately.

We have many times asserted that the most probable situation and situations similar to it are much more probable than any situation that is significantly different and that this becomes more and more marked as the number of particles increases. This is closely related to the statement that the relative fluctuations decrease with increasing numbers of particles and allows us to place such assertions on a more numerical basis. For almost all measurable properties of a thermodynamic system having a large number of particles, the property has a probability distribution which is sharply peaked about the mean value. This corresponds to a small value of the relative r.m.s. fluctuation. In practice, we want the probability of the observed quantity, say s, being in the range Δs at s, rather than the probability that some *precise* value of s is observed. The latter probability is

---

* This is for an isolated system; more usual situations are dealt with in Sections 13.2 and 13.6.

very small indeed because, for large systems, the number of possible precise values of s is extremely large. The former probability is a probability density $p(s)$ such as we had in the drum experiment (Section 10.4). The peaking in probability as systems get larger, which we have often referred to, is a peaking in probability or probability density, as we have tried to suggest, for instance, in the curve of $P(U_A)$ plotted against the observable U_A in Fig. 12.2(b). A significantly different arrangement for this example is one for which U_A differs from $\bar{U}_A$ by a measurable amount. If this minimal measurable difference is much greater than the r.m.s. fluctuation $[\overline{(U_A - \bar{U}_A)^2}]^{1/2}$, then it is certainly true that, for large systems, the most probable arrangement is overwhelmingly more likely to be observed than a physically significantly different one.

For an isolated system in thermal equilibrium, the thermodynamic entropy is constant, since $\Delta q = 0$. The statistical entropy is fixed, since $\mathcal{N}$ is fixed. There are, however, fluctuations in the system as the body goes through the $\mathcal{N}$ complexions. For large numbers of particles, a particular set of these complexions, those corresponding to the Boltzmann distribution and similar ones, are overwhelmingly more frequent than any which are significantly different and so the fluctuations are small. We have used this fact in calculating the Boltzmann distribution (Sections 11.4 and 12.2) where $\mathcal{N}^*$ was the number of complexions of the most probable distribution or arrangement. If we look at an isolated body, we are overwhelmingly likely to see it in one of the most probable complexions corresponding to $\mathcal{N}^*$. The probability of finding it in any other complexion corresponding to another arrangement is $\mathcal{N}'/\mathcal{N}$ where $\mathcal{N}'$ is the number of complexions in that arrangement. We could formally associate an entropy with $\mathcal{N}'$ through $k \ln \mathcal{N}'$ and it is in this sense that we sometimes talk loosely of the fluctuations in entropy of an isolated body. It is more appropriate to speak of temperature fluctuations but this is a rather too subtle matter to deal with here.

If we look at two bodies A and B which are in thermal contact but are isolated from their surroundings, we have seen that they tend to attain a common temperature for which the total energy is shared in a particular way. However, there is a finite probability of the energy being shared differently as we have explicitly calculated in Section 12.1 and expressed in Fig. 12.2 and 12.4. The energy of one or the other body, U_A or U_B, has a finite probability of deviating from the mean value $\bar{U}_A$ or $\bar{U}_B$. We can measure the importance of the fluctuations by actually calculating $[\overline{(U_A - \bar{U}_A)^2}]^{1/2}/\bar{U}_A$ and similarly for U_B. We shall do this for one of our bodies with a small number of particles.

Consider, as in Section 12.1, two bodies A and B where $N_A = 5$ and $N_B = 3$ and the total energy is 6ϵ. Once the bodies are in equilibrium, we know that the most probable situation is that $U_A = 4\epsilon$ and $U_B = 2\epsilon$. However, other distributions of energy are possible and have a probability P_{AB} as quoted from Section 12.1 and given in Table 12.4. The mean energy per particle of the whole body is the total energy divided by the number of particles, which is $6\epsilon/8 = 0.75\epsilon$. Hence $\bar{U}_A = 5 \times 0.75\epsilon = 3.75\epsilon$ and $\bar{U}_B = 3 \times 0.75\epsilon = 2.25\epsilon$. Note once more

Table 12.4

U_A/ϵ	P_{AB}	$(U_A - \bar{U}_A)^2/\epsilon^2$	$[(U_A - \bar{U}_A)^2/\epsilon^2] \times P_{AB}$
0	0.02	14.1	0.28
1	0.06	7.5	0.45
2	0.13	3.1	0.40
3	0.20	0.6	0.12
4	0.25	0.1	0.03
5	0.22	1.6	0.35
6	0.12	5.0	0.60
			1.93

a difference between the mean and most probable values of U_A and U_B. This arises here because we have a small number of particles and only a few energy levels involved. The same result for $\bar{U}_A$ and $\bar{U}_B$ is obtained by calculating $\sum_A U_A P_{AB}$ and $\sum_B U_B P_{AB}$. We calculate $\overline{(U_A - \bar{U}_A)^2} = \sum (U_A - \bar{U}_A)^2 P_{AB}$ and the result is shown in Table 12.4. We can show that $\overline{(U_A - \bar{U}_A)^2} = \overline{(U_B - \bar{U}_B)^2}$ (see Problem 12.5). The relative r.m.s. deviations from the mean are therefore

$$[\overline{(U_A - \bar{U}_A)^2}]^{1/2}/\bar{U}_A = 1.93^{1/2}/3.75 = 0.37$$

and

$$[\overline{(U_B - \bar{U}_B)^2}]^{1/2}/\bar{U}_B = 1.93^{1/2}/2.25 = 0.62.$$

Hence the body with the smaller number of particles, B, has larger relative r.m.s. fluctuations in its energy than the body with the larger number of particles. We can go further. It is clear that $[\overline{(U_A - \bar{U}_A)^2}]^{1/2}$ ($=1.39\epsilon$) is independent of the number of particles N_A in A, provided that the total number of particles N and the total energy U are constant. Moreover, the mean energy per particle U/N ($=0.75\epsilon$) is then also constant. Hence, for *any* particular subdivision such that the number of particles in A is N_A, we have

$$[\overline{(U_A - \bar{U}_A)^2}]^{1/2}/\bar{U}_A = 1.39\epsilon/(0.75\epsilon N_A) = 1.86/N_A.$$

This shows explicitly how, in this special case, the relative fluctuations decrease with increasing number of particles in the subsystem. This tendency is enhanced for large numbers of particles and is found also for other properties besides the energy. The smaller the fluctuations, the more precise are the results from statistical mechanics or thermodynamics which relate to average or mean properties.

PROBLEMS

12.1. A body has an amount of directed kinetic energy (K.E.) which is degraded into heat at temperature T. Show that the number of complexions of the body increases in the ratio exp (K.E./kT).

12.2. The number of particles in a colloidal suspension of given volume fluctuates with time. The number was observed at fixed intervals over a long period with the following results.

No. of particles	0	1	2	3	4	5	6	7	8
No. of times observed	15	36	24	14	8	2	1	0	0

Find the mean and the relative r.m.s. fluctuation from the mean. If the volume being observed is doubled, what change in these figures would be expected?

12.3. A galvanometer is an oscillator and therefore has a mean thermal energy kT which results in spontaneous fluctuations in the deflexion. Estimate the order of magnitude of the deflexion for a typical galvanometer.

12.4. The fluctuations discussed in Problem 12.3 are often ascribed to collisions with gas molecules. However, we still get fluctuations *in vacuo*. Why is this? (HINT: How is thermal equilibrium maintained?)

12.5. Prove the relation $\overline{(U_A - \overline{U}_A)^2} = \overline{(U_B - \overline{U}_B)^2}$ given in Section 12.5 where the total energy of the two bodies A and B is fixed.

12.6. The nuclei of some atoms have a spin one-half and in this case, in a small magnetic field, each nucleus has two possible states, spin-up and spin-down with equal probability (cf. the silver atoms of Section 6.3). If the sample contains N atoms, what is the contribution to the entropy due to the nuclear spin states?

12.7. The number of configurations $\mathcal{N}$ increases rapidly with the energy U and the number of particles N. Suppose that $\mathcal{N} \propto U^{(1/2)fN}$ where f is a constant. Show that the mean energy of a particle at temperature T is $\frac{1}{2}fkT$; f is therefore the number of degrees of freedom of each particle.

12.8. If angular momentum is quantized, it can only have the values $J\hbar$ where $J = 0, 1, 2, \ldots$, and $\hbar$ is Planck's constant divided by 2π. Show that the energy of a rotator with moment of inertia I is $J^2\hbar^2/2I$ (more precisely it is $J(J + 1)\hbar^2/2I$). However, the degeneracy of each level is $(2J + 1)$. Show that allowing for the degeneracy the number of levels per unit of energy (the density of states) is almost independent of J for large J. The level system is therefore not so different from that of a harmonic oscillator as at first appears.

12.9. In the first example given in Section 12.1, it was found that, for two bodies each with five particles and with a total energy $U = 6\epsilon$, the most probable distribution of the energy is when $U_A = U_B = 3\epsilon$. Show that, whatever the total energy, the most probable distribution is when $U_A = U_B = U/2$ if $U/2$ is even and that, if $U/2$ is odd, there are two most probable states.

12.10. Two bodies A and B have the same energy level system, $\mathcal{E} = n\epsilon$, where $n = 0, 1, 2, \ldots$, and equal numbers of particles $N_A = N_B = 5$. Show, by explicit calculation for $U = 2\epsilon$ and 4ϵ and by using the result in Section 12.1, that with increasing energy the most probable energy distribution becomes relatively more probable than the least probable distribution.

CHAPTER 13

The partition function

Not that it matters, but a great deal of the background to this
story is accurate. IAN FLEMING (*From Russia with Love*)

13.1 RELATION TO THERMODYNAMIC QUANTITIES

We now return to the Boltzmann distribution and investigate its properties
further. We have shown that the Boltzmann distribution is true for the translational motion of the molecules in a gas, for the distribution of density of a gas in a
gravitational field, for our rather special systems of small numbers of particles,
and for large numbers of particles for any set of energy levels, provided that the
most probable distribution is much more probable than any of the others. We
shall now assume that the distribution is true for all cases for a body in equilibrium
at temperature T, that is to say not only whether the energy levels are uniformly
spaced or not but whatever the type of energy concerned.

It is now of interest to show that all thermodynamic functions can be obtained
from the Boltzmann distribution. (Strictly speaking, we only need to know the
energy levels.) We have $P(\varepsilon)$ is proportional to $\exp(-\varepsilon/kT)$. Since

$$\sum_{\substack{\text{all values} \\ \text{of } \varepsilon}} P(\varepsilon) = 1, \qquad P(\varepsilon) = \exp(-\varepsilon/kT)/ \sum_{\substack{\text{all values} \\ \text{of } \varepsilon}} \exp(-\varepsilon/kT).$$

The quantity $\sum \exp(-\varepsilon/kT)$, although apparently only a normalizing factor,
turns out to be extremely important and hence has a special name, the partition
function*, and we write

$$Z = \sum \exp(-\varepsilon/kT).$$

We can write the probability of finding a particle in the level ϵ_s in the form

$$P(\epsilon_s) = [\exp(-\epsilon_s/kT)]/Z.$$

---

* Those who have already encountered partition functions and wish to pursue this matter
in more advanced applications should note that the partition function defined here is for *one*
particle in a system of almost independent particles. In that case, the partition function
Z_N for N independent particles is Z^N. More generally, if the N particles interacting in any
way have as a whole the energy levels E_r, then the partition function for the whole system is
$Z_N = \sum_r \exp(-E_r/kT)$.

If the actual number of particles in level s is n_s and the total number of particles is N, then clearly

$$P(\epsilon_s) = n_s/N,$$

so that

$$n_s = \frac{N}{Z} \exp(-\epsilon_s/kT).$$

The internal energy U is given by

$$U = \sum_s n_s \epsilon_s.$$

Substituting for n_s we get

$$U = \sum \frac{N}{Z} \epsilon_s \exp(-\epsilon_s/kT) = \frac{N}{Z} \sum_s \epsilon_s \exp(-\epsilon_s/kT).$$

Consider $\partial Z/\partial T$, which is

$$\frac{\partial}{\partial T} \sum \exp(-\epsilon_s/kT) = \sum \left(-\frac{\epsilon_s}{k}\right)\left(-\frac{1}{T^2}\right) \exp(-\epsilon_s/kT)$$

$$= \sum \left(\frac{\epsilon_s}{kT^2}\right) \exp(-\epsilon_s/kT) = \frac{1}{kT^2} \sum \epsilon_s \exp(-\epsilon_s/kT)$$

$$= \frac{1}{kT^2} \frac{ZU}{N}.$$

$$\therefore \quad U = \frac{NkT^2}{Z} \frac{\partial Z}{\partial T},$$

which may also be written $NkT^2[\partial(\ln Z)/\partial T]$. Hence we can calculate the internal energy U, which is a thermodynamic function, from Z. (Note that the mean energy per particle is U/N.)

It is now a simple matter to calculate the entropy S in terms of Z. We have, by definition, $dS = dq/T$ and also $dq + dw = dU$, but in our formulation $dw = 0$, therefore $dS = dU/T$. Integrating by parts, we get

$$S = \int \frac{dU}{T} = \left(\frac{1}{T}\right)(U) - \int U d\left(\frac{1}{T}\right) = \frac{U}{T} + \int \frac{1}{T^2} U \, dT.$$

Substituting for U in terms of Z in the second term, we get

$$S - \frac{U}{T} = \int \frac{1}{T^2}\left\{NkT^2 \frac{\partial(\ln Z)}{\partial T}\right\} dT = Nk \int \frac{\partial(\ln Z)}{\partial T} dT = Nk \ln Z,$$

or

$$S = U/T + Nk \ln Z.$$

Substituting for U again, we get

$$S = Nk \ln Z + NkT \frac{\partial}{\partial T}(\ln Z)$$

or

$$S = Nk \left[\ln Z + T \frac{\partial}{\partial T} \ln Z \right].$$

Actually, this relation is true even when dw is not zero.

We can also express the entropy in terms of the probability of finding a particle on a given level, $P(\epsilon_s)$. It is easily shown that

$$S = - Nk \sum_s P(\epsilon_s) \ln P(\epsilon_s),$$

by substituting $P(\epsilon_s) = [\exp(-\epsilon_s/kT)]/Z$ in this expression. This definition of S is therefore consistent with the relation $S - U/T = Nk \ln Z$ given above. The definition of the entropy in terms of the probabilities $P(\epsilon_s)$ is a fundamental one and is sometimes used as an alternative starting point for the statistical theory to the definition $S = k \ln \mathcal{N}$ which we have used. The two definitions are, of course, equivalent. Although we use the definition in terms of $\mathcal{N}$ rather than $P(\epsilon_s)$ in this book, it is of interest to show that they are equivalent by explicit calculation for small numbers of particles in the spirit of Chapter 11. In Section 11.2, we found for $N = 5$ and $U = 4\epsilon$ that $\mathcal{N} = 70$ and $P(0) = 0.50$, $P(\epsilon) = 0.29$, $P(2\epsilon) = 0.14$, $P(3\epsilon) = 0.06$, and $P(4\epsilon) = 0.01$. By explicit calculation we can show (see Problem 13.5) that $\ln \mathcal{N} = 4.2$ and $-N \sum_s P(\epsilon_s) \ln P(\epsilon_s) = 5.9$ so that the two definitions are already virtually equivalent even for only five particles.

An important quantity which arises in thermodynamics as a sort of potential energy is the Helmholtz free energy, F. F is a thermodynamic state function (see Section 12.3, p. 202). It is defined as

$$F \equiv U - TS.$$

We have shown above that $S - U/T = Nk \ln Z$ or $U - TS = -NkT \ln Z$, so that

$$F = -NkT \ln Z.$$

This is a very important result not only because F is an important quantity itself (it is discussed in Section 13.2) but because all other thermodynamic quantities can be conveniently derived from F. For example, we have for the entropy and pressure

$$S = -\left(\frac{\partial F}{\partial T} \right)_V \quad \text{and} \quad P = -\left(\frac{\partial F}{\partial V} \right)_T,$$

where, of course, the subscript emphasizes that that quantity must be regarded as a constant in the differentiation.

The important result, $F = -NkT \ln Z$, can also be obtained directly from the distribution of the particles, as used in the derivation of the Boltzmann distribution for large numbers of particles. We found in Section 11.4 that, for the most probable arrangement, the number of complexions $\mathcal{N}^*$ is given by

$$\mathcal{N}^* = N!/n_1! n_2! \ldots n_s! \ldots, \quad \text{with} \quad n_s/N = [\exp(-\epsilon_s/kT)]/Z.$$

Using Stirling's theorem in the first relation, we easily show that

$$\ln \mathcal{N}^* \approx N \ln N - \sum_s n_s \ln n_s.$$

Using the second relation, we see that $n_s \ln n_s = n_s \ln N/Z - n_s \epsilon_s/kT$ so that $\sum_s n_s \ln n_s = N \ln N/Z - U/kT$, since $\sum n_s = N$ and $\sum n_s \epsilon_s = U$.

$$\therefore \quad \ln \mathcal{N}^* \approx N \ln N - N \ln N/Z + U/kT = N \ln Z + U/kT.$$

But for N large, $\ln \mathcal{N}^* \to \ln \mathcal{N} = S/k$,

$$\therefore \quad S/k = N \ln Z + U/kT,$$

$$\therefore \quad F = -NkT \ln Z.$$

13.2 FREE ENERGY

We know that, in a simple mechanical system, the tendency is for it to get into a situation in which the energy is a minimum—if it can do so. The question of entropy does not arise, since the system usually has only one configuration. There is no uncertainty or ignorance about the state of the system; in other words, $\mathcal{N} = 1$ and $S = 0$. For a many-particle system, the problem is more complicated. It also will tend to get into its lowest energy state—if it can—that is U will get as small as possible. But in addition, the entropy will try to get as large as possible, as we have seen. Thus we have two factors to consider in deciding whether a system will change from one situation to another: U wants to decrease and S wants to increase, the two generally opposing each other. For instance, for any of our sets of particles on energy levels, a decrease in U means moving particles to lower levels but then we find that $\mathcal{N}$ is smaller and so therefore is S. Thus a decrease in U will imply a decrease in S and vice versa. It is clear that some quantity that will express *both* tendencies ought to be very useful. Such a quantity is the free energy F which we have already introduced, $F = U - TS$. F has the property that it decreases with decrease in U and with increase in S. We must put the factor T in to keep the dimensions right! Hence F should be a suitable measure of spontaneous changes and a way of deciding which of several alternatives will be the equilibrium state. Notice that for an isolated system U must be constant and so the sole criterion of equilibrium is maximal entropy. However, we have now opened the possibility of exchange of energy with the surroundings. Now the criterion of maximal entropy is clearly inadequate because this just increases with the energy and we must therefore consider the probability of the body acquiring a certain energy. We therefore need a more elaborate criterion for equilibrium. Since U tends to decrease and S to increase in an approach to equilibrium, we expect F to be a minimum in equilibrium. In the equilibrium state, F is a minimum for small changes in the parameters of the system in much the same way that we have that the potential energy is a minimum for mechanical equilibrium. If there are two possible situations for given fixed parameters then the one taken up is the one with the lower *free* energy. Thus, for example, we can

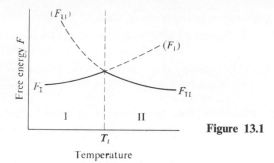

Figure 13.1

explain a change of phase, say, as a function of temperature as occurring when the two free energy curves cross over. For the situation shown in Fig. 13.1, phase I is adopted below the crossover temperature and phase II above. It is clearly a subtle matter to calculate precisely at what temperature a phase change occurs, since to determine F both U and S have to be evaluated. Let us compare a substance as a solid and as a liquid at the same temperature, the melting temperature. It is clear that, in the liquid, U is larger, since the molecules are not always as near the minimum of interaction energy and they also have greater kinetic energy. However S is also larger in the liquid because the position and velocity of any particular molecule is less certain. It is not obvious therefore whether F is larger or smaller in the liquid or the solid. (Actually, for the more familiar phase changes, there is also a change in volume and then a different free energy from F must be used; in fact, we must use the Gibbs free energy as described below.)

Free-energy considerations often provide a helpful qualitative indication of what will happen. As an example, consider what happens as we raise the temperature of a perfect crystal from the absolute zero. At the absolute zero, the crystal must be in its lowest energy state; the atoms are all arranged perfectly on the lattice and are not moving—apart from the zero-point motion, a complication which need not detain us here. It is usually said that the atoms of the crystal vibrate more vigorously as the temperature increases. This is true and so U increases because of the energy of vibration and S increases because the positions and velocities of the atoms are not as well known as they were when the atoms were fixed at the lattice points. However, a more interesting thing than just atomic vibrations can happen. Suppose an atom jumps right out of its proper position in the lattice into an interstitial position. This requires a considerable amount of energy but there is certainly a finite probability, given by the Boltzmann formula, of this happening at a temperature above absolute zero. However, in this process the entropy also increases, since the atom in question may be *any* one of the atoms in the crystal and so we are now considerably less certain where an atom is. It is clearly possible for F to be lower for an imperfect crystal than for a perfect one at a finite temperature and a calculation of U and S for a given T shows that $U - TS$ is indeed smaller if some of the atoms are in interstitial positions than if they are all vibrating about their lattice sites. There is a minimum of F for a certain density of defects at a given temperature and so there is no such thing in nature as a perfect crystal at a finite temperature.

In a more precise sense, a crystal at a finite temperature is also imperfect because its atoms are vibrating as a result of the thermal energy. Connected with this increase in vibrational energy with increasing temperature, there is an increase in entropy because we are not so sure where the atoms are as we were at the lower temperature. We again, therefore, have an increase in energy associated with an increase in entropy and we have to calculate a free energy and minimize it to decide what actually happens as the temperature increases. What happens, of course, is that the crystal expands. Considerations of this sort lead to a more satisfactory many-body treatment of the thermal expansion of crystals than the essentially two-body treatment given in Section 4.2.

The practical situation which we usually have to deal with is somewhat more complicated. In order to deal with a variety of problems, several different free energies are needed. The free energy F is appropriate to changes at constant volume and temperature. We notice that our analysis, which was an essentially constant volume one, rather naturally produced the function F. It often happens that we study changes at constant pressure (atmospheric usually!) and temperature. Then the Gibbs free energy, $G \equiv U - TS + PV$, is more useful. This is true particularly of chemical changes. For changes at constant pressure, the quantity $U + PV$ plays the same role as U for changes at constant volume. $U + PV$ is called the enthalpy H, and we can write $G = H - TS$ which shows the relation of G to $F \equiv U - TS$. For changes at constant pressure, H tends to get smaller and S tends to get larger. For equilibrium, G is a minimum. An important quantity is the rate of change of G (or F) as the number of particles is varied, $\partial G/\partial N$. This is called the chemical potential. It is a measure of the tendency for change to occur, particularly where the change results in a different total number of particles.

13.3 THE CLASSICAL CASE AS A LIMIT

In many cases, the energy levels are sufficiently close together that we can proceed somewhat differently. The sum in the partition function

$$Z = \sum_{s=1}^{\infty} \exp\left(-\epsilon_s/kT\right),$$

can sometimes be replaced to a good approximation by an integral. Z is the sum of all the vertical lines in Fig. 13.2(a). Suppose the energy depends on some coordinate q. Then we can plot the terms of the partition function, which are now $\exp\left(-\epsilon(q)/kT\right)$ against q instead of against ϵ_s. In Fig. 13.2(b), we assume that q is positive and that $\epsilon(q)$ increases steadily with q. Neither of these conditions may necessarily be realized but the conclusions are not affected. Z is the sum of the vertical lines of Fig. 13.2(b) just as it was of Fig. 13.2(a); we have just changed the position of the lines on the axis of abscissae. If the lines are close together, the

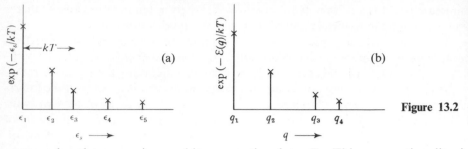

Figure 13.2

area under the curve is roughly proportional to Z. This proportionality is clearly more exact the smaller the spacing between the lines as compared with kT; in other words, we require $\epsilon_{r+1} - \epsilon_r \ll kT$. We therefore have

$$Z = C \int_{-\infty}^{\infty} \exp\left(-\mathcal{E}(q)/kT\right) dq,$$

where C is a constant which can be found if we know the actual energy as a function of q, $\mathcal{E}(q)$. More generally, the energy may depend on several coordinates q_1, $q_2, \ldots$ If the energy is an additive function of the q values, i.e. if $\mathcal{E}(q_1, q_2, \ldots) = \mathcal{E}_1(q_1) + \mathcal{E}_2(q_2) + \cdots$, the partition function Z factorizes. For example, for two coordinates only, q_1 and q_2,

$$Z_{q_1, q_2} \equiv \sum_{q_1, q_2} \exp\left[-\mathcal{E}(q_1, q_2)/kT\right] = \sum_{q_1, q_2} \exp\left[-\mathcal{E}_1(q_1)/kT\right] \exp\left[-\mathcal{E}_2(q_2)/kT\right]$$

$$= \{\sum_{q_1} \exp\left[-\mathcal{E}_1(q_1)/kT\right]\}\{\sum_{q_2} \exp\left[-\mathcal{E}_2(q_2)/kT\right]\} = Z_{q_1} Z_{q_2}.$$

The corresponding result in the classical case is

$$Z \equiv C \int_{q_1=-\infty}^{\infty} \int_{q_2=-\infty}^{\infty} \exp\left[-\mathcal{E}(q_1, q_2)/kT\right] dq_1 \, dq_2$$

$$= C \left\{ \int_{q_1=-\infty}^{\infty} \exp\left[-\mathcal{E}_1(q_1)/kT\right] dq_1 \right\} \left\{ \int_{q_2=-\infty}^{\infty} \exp\left[-\mathcal{E}_2(q_2)/kT\right] \right\}.$$

This result can be readily generalized to any number of coordinates. Consider, for example, a perfect monatomic gas where we have

$$q_1 = v_x, q_2 = v_y, q_3 = v_z$$

and

$$\mathcal{E}(v_x, v_y, v_z) = \tfrac{1}{2}m(v_x^2 + v_y^2 + v_z^2).$$

$$\therefore \quad Z = C \int_{v_x=-\infty}^{\infty} \int_{v_y=-\infty}^{\infty} \int_{v_z=-\infty}^{\infty} \exp\left[-\tfrac{1}{2}m(v_x^2 + v_y^2 + v_z^2)/kT\right] dv_x \, dv_y \, dv_z$$

$$= C \left\{ \int_{-\infty}^{\infty} \exp\left(-\frac{m}{2kT} v_x^2\right) dv_x \right\} \left\{ \int_{-\infty}^{\infty} \exp\left(-\frac{m}{2kT} v_y^2\right) dv_y \right\}$$

$$\times \left\{ \int_{-\infty}^{\infty} \exp\left(-\frac{m}{2kT} v_z^2\right) dv_z \right\}.$$

Put $(m/2kT)v_x^2 = u^2$ so that $dv_x = (2kT/m)^{1/2}\,du$; hence

$$\int_{-\infty}^{\infty} \exp\left(-\frac{m}{2kT}v_x^2\right) dv_x = \int_{-\infty}^{\infty} \exp\left(-u^2\right) \left(\frac{2kT}{m}\right)^{1/2} du = \left(\frac{2kT}{m}\right)^{1/2} \pi^{1/2}$$

$$= \left(\frac{2\pi kT}{m}\right)^{1/2}.$$

Similarly for v_y and v_z. Hence we have

$$Z = C\left(\frac{2\pi kT}{m}\right)^{3/2}$$

for the partition function of a perfect monatomic gas.

This is a very important formula in all considerations of gases, and particularly for chemical reactions in gases. However, we must take care to find the value of C before we use the expression too widely and this is done below. We can see immediately, nevertheless, that this expression for Z already embodies some well-known properties of the perfect gas.

We can, for instance, calculate the internal energy U of a perfect gas from the formula $U = NkT^2\, \partial(\ln Z)/\partial T$ which was obtained in Section 13.3. From the fact that $Z = C(2\pi kT/m)^{3/2}$, we obtain

$$\ln Z = \tfrac{3}{2}\ln T + \text{terms independent of } T,$$

since, as is shown below, C does not involve the temperature. Consequently,

$$\frac{\partial}{\partial T}\ln Z = \frac{3}{2}\frac{1}{T}.$$

$$\therefore \quad U = NkT^2\left(\frac{3}{2}\frac{1}{T}\right) = \tfrac{3}{2}NkT = N(\tfrac{3}{2}kT),$$

which is the value found in Section 10.4. Note that the value of C is not required to get U for a perfect gas. We shall see that this is so because the internal energy of a perfect gas is independent of its volume.

The precise determination of C is too difficult to go into here. However, for a perfect gas we can see that it must involve the volume. Firstly we note that in calculating Z we have only used the coordinates v_x, v_y, and v_z. However, to get a full account of the state of the atoms, we need to specify for each one not only its momentum $p_x = mv_x$, etc., but also its position x, y, and z. It would be reasonable therefore to expect that we would improve our knowledge of Z by allowing also for the coordinates x, y, and z. Since $\varepsilon(x)$, etc., are just constants, as discussed in Section 10.5, this simply amounts to multiplying Z by the additional integral $\iiint dx\,dy\,dz$. The limits of x, y, and z are defined by the vessel containing the gas and so $\iiint dx\,dy\,dz = V$ where V is the volume of the gas. Hence the classical expression for Z becomes $Z = C'V(2\pi kT/m)^{3/2}$ where C' is a new constant not involving V.

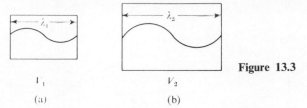

Figure 13.3

λ_1

V_1

λ_2

V_2

(a)   (b)

Secondly, for the general case, in which we must consider energy levels, we observe that if the volume increases then the quantum-mechanical wavelengths involved will also increase. The wave functions have to spread out as the volume increases as shown by comparing Figs. 13.3(a) and (b). From the de Broglie relation (Section 8.5), $p = h/\lambda$, an increase in λ means a decrease in the momentum p and therefore a decrease in the energy $p^2/2m$. Hence the energy levels will be closer together in the larger volume. Note that the smooth curves in Figs. 13.4(a) and (b) are the same exponential $\exp(-\epsilon_s/kT)$ which does not depend on V. In Fig. 13.4, (b) is for a larger volume than (a). Since the partition function $Z \equiv \exp(-\epsilon_s/kT)$ is the sum of the ordinates, clearly Z increases with volume. We can therefore guess that, in the expression $Z = C(2\pi kT/m)^{3/2}$, $C = C'V^l$ where $l > 0$, i.e. we suspect that

$$Z = C'V^l(2\pi kT/m)^{3/2}$$

for a perfect gas. We now calculate the free energy from Z using the relation given in Section 13.1.

$$F = -NkT \ln Z = -NkT[\ln C' + l \ln V + \tfrac{3}{2}\ln(2\pi kT/m)].$$

We obtain the pressure from the free energy using the relation given in Section 13.1.

$$P = -\left(\frac{\partial F}{\partial V}\right)_T = NkTl \frac{\partial}{\partial V} \ln V = l(NkT/V).$$

This may be written $PV = lNkT$. But for a perfect gas, we know that $PV = NkT$. Therefore $l = 1$ and so

$$Z = C'V(2\pi kT/m)^{3/2}$$

for a perfect gas, as we found by another method above.

If the actual energy levels for the translational motion of the atoms in a box are evaluated by quantum mechanics, it is found that $C' = (m/h)^3$, so that finally

$$Z = V(2\pi mkT/h^2)^{3/2},$$

for a perfect gas. This is the formula as it is usually employed. The relation has a much wider validity than for the case of a perfect gas. It is one factor of the complete partition function for any gas and indeed for most liquids and solids. This is because the effect on Z of every independent contribution to the energy can be calculated separately as we have already seen ($Z_{q_1,q_2} = Z_{q_1}Z_{q_2}$). In consideration of gases or liquids, the translational energy term $\tfrac{1}{2}mv^2$ is always present. Hence Z

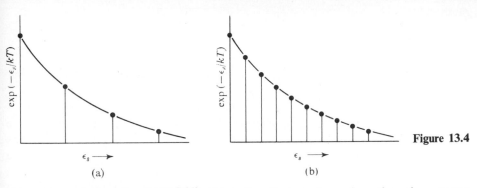

Figure 13.4

(a)   (b)

always has a factor $(2\pi mkT/h^2)^{3/2}$. The other factors depend on the other energy terms, for example internal vibrations, electronic excitation, interaction forces between the molecules, etc.

We can use the formula $S = Nk[\ln Z + T(\partial/\partial T)(\ln Z)]$ to obtain the explicit dependence of entropy on volume for a perfect gas. Substituting $Z = V(2\pi mkT/h^2)^{3/2}$ in the expression just given, we find $S = Nk \ln V +$ terms independent of V. Hence S increases with V as we conjectured in Section 12.3.

We can confirm that *any* squared term in the energy leads to a mean energy per particle of $\frac{1}{2}kT$. Let $\varepsilon(q) = cq^2$, then

$$Z_q \propto \int_0^\infty \exp\left[-cq^2/kT\right]\,dq = \left(\frac{\pi kT}{c}\right)^{1/2}$$

and so

$$U_q = NkT^2 \frac{\partial}{\partial T}(\ln Z_q) = NkT^2 \frac{\partial}{\partial T}(\tfrac{1}{2}\ln T) = \tfrac{1}{2}NkT.$$

Thus $U_q/N = \frac{1}{2}kT$. The mean energy per particle associated with the coordinate q which gives rise to an energy cq^2 in a body in equilibrium at temperature T is $\frac{1}{2}kT$. This is equipartition of energy once more and is the result which we found using the Boltzmann distribution in Section 11.4. As in the earlier derivation, the present result is only true for high enough temperatures, namely temperatures which are high enough that we may replace the sum for Z by an integral.

13.4 VOLUME CHANGES AND EXTERNAL WORK

It has really become rather embarrassing that we have not accounted for "work done" in our calculations and we have had to assert from time to time that a result is true in spite of our gross assumption that d$w = 0$. We can see from Section 13.3 how at least the effects of volume change can be introduced into our model—it changes the energy levels. We can therefore study the effect of adding both heat and work to our particles by allowing the levels to move appropriately. In general, the internal energy is $U = \sum_s \epsilon_s n_s^*$. If both the ϵ_s and the n_s^* can change as a result of adding heat Δq and doing work Δw, we have, since $\Delta q + \Delta w = \Delta U$,

$$\Delta q + \Delta w = \Delta \left(\sum_s \epsilon_s n_s^* \right), \quad \text{which equals} \quad \sum \epsilon_s \, \Delta n_s^* + \sum n_s^* \, \Delta \epsilon_s.$$

Clearly, the first term on the right-hand side is Δq and so the second term must be Δw, that is

$$\Delta w = \sum n_s^* \, \Delta \epsilon_s.$$

If we allow external work only through volume change, the most familiar case, we expect $\Delta w \approx - P \, \Delta V$, or $P \approx -\Delta w/\Delta V$. Hence

$$P \approx - \frac{1}{\Delta V} \left(\sum n_s^* \, \Delta \epsilon_s \right) = -\sum n_s^* (\Delta \epsilon_s/\Delta V).$$

In the limit of infinitesimal volume change we have $P = -\sum n_s^*(\partial \epsilon_s/\partial V)$. Using the Boltzmann distribution values for n_s^* given in Section 11.4, we have

$$P = -\sum \frac{N}{Z} \exp\left(-\epsilon_s/kT\right) \frac{\partial \epsilon_s}{\partial V} = NkT \sum \frac{1}{Z} \frac{\partial}{\partial V} \exp\left(-\epsilon_s/kT\right)$$

$$= - \frac{\partial}{\partial V} \left(-NkT \ln \sum \exp\left[-\epsilon_s/kT\right]\right) = - \frac{\partial}{\partial V} \left(-NkT \ln Z\right).$$

But the expression in the brackets is just the free energy F so that we have shown that $P = -(\partial F/\partial V)_T$. This is a correct result which was quoted in Section 13.1 and so confirms our analysis of the effect of changes of volume. Note the important explicit requirement here that T be regarded as fixed in the differentiation.

It is clear that external work can be incorporated into the statistical picture and a clear understanding of the significance of the first law of thermodynamics, $\Delta q + \Delta w = \Delta U$, can be obtained.

13.5 DISTINGUISHABILITY

Actually, we have to be rather more careful in applying our results to gases, since we have assumed we have distinguishable particles. This is only correct for molecules or atoms or fundamental particles or any other particles if we know where they are. This is true for atoms in a solid but not in a gas. Actually, in a solid the sites, not the particles, are distinguishable. If indistinguishable particles change sites, no physical change has occurred. More precisely, identical particles are distinguishable if their wave functions do not overlap. In a gas, there is really no way of knowing which molecule or atom is which, unless we change it physically, i.e. measurably, in some way. This question arises acutely in collisions if we cannot follow in detail the actual collision process. Suppose two particles A and B collide. How are we to distinguish the two different collisions of Figs. 13.5(a) and (b) for identical particles if we are unable to follow the trajectories of the particles inside the "boxes"? This problem is clearly most acute in non-classical situations.

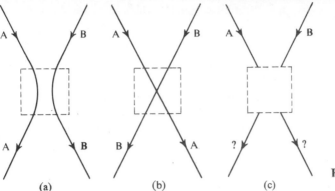

Figure 13.5

(a)   (b)   (c)

Because of the Heisenberg uncertainty of position (Section 4.5) we are not able to say exactly where the particles are and so we are always uncertain to some extent which is which. On the other hand, if we know rather precisely where the particles are ($\Delta x \to 0$), we know their velocities rather imperfectly ($\Delta p \geq \hbar/\Lambda x$) and so we cannot describe their trajectories at all well and they soon get mixed up. The number of complexions is therefore less than if the particles were distinguishable. In the collision of the two identical particles, the collision is completely described by the one diagram (c) of Fig. 13.5, not two. If the particles are distinguishable, we must have the two diagrams (a) and (b) of Fig. 13.5. This is because we could do an experiment for instance which would distinguish whether the particle which is going off to the lower right is A or B by measuring the property or properties on which we base the assertion that A and B are distinguishable, its mass for instance. Returning to our familiar energy diagrams as in Fig. 13.6, the two complexions (a) and (b) are not now distinguishable and so count as one complexion (c), not two. Hence the number of complexions $\mathcal{N}$ is smaller and so therefore is the entropy S for indistinguishable particles as compared with the same set of distinguishable ones.

Since we can no longer identify the particles, it seems reasonable to expect $\mathcal{N}$ to be smaller by the factor $N!$, since this is the number of different ways we could label N particles. This is true to a sufficiently good approximation for large N and when the temperature is high enough. A more precise treatment of the statistics of indistinguishable particles is given in Section 14.1. S is therefore smaller for indistinguishable particles by the amount $k \ln N!$ which by Stirling's theorem is $k(N \ln N - N)$ or $Nk \ln N$, for large N. Hence the formula $S_s = U/T + Nk \ln Z$ appropriate to a solid is replaced for a gas by $S_g = U/T + Nk \ln Z - Nk \ln N$ or

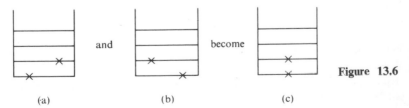

and   become

Figure 13.6

(a)   (b)   (c)

$S_g = U/T + Nk \ln Z/N$. Consequently, the expression for the free energy must also be modified to $F_g \equiv U - TS_g = -NkT \ln Z/N$. Z is still defined as $\sum_s \exp(-\epsilon_s/kT)$ which involves only the energy levels and not the particles, except in so far as these determine the levels, and so does not depend on whether the particles are distinguishable or not.* It should be noted that sometimes the correction is made to the definition of the partition function; $Z/N!$ is used instead of Z as defined above. It would seem more fundamental to modify the entropy, since this is directly related to the number of distinguishable configurations. The matter is more logical if we deal with the general case of many interacting particles but the reader should look elsewhere for this (e.g. Further Reading, No. 14).

13.6 EQUILIBRIUM CONSTANTS AND REACTION RATES

Now consider a reaction in which one species is converted into another, say $A \rightleftharpoons B$. Suppose we have an isolated container with a total of N particles inside, so that

$$N = N_A + N_B.$$

But what are N_A and N_B, i.e. what are the equilibrium concentrations? What also is the value of the equilibrium constant, which is defined as $K \equiv N_B/N_A = (N_B/N)/(N_A/N) = [B]/[A]$ where [A] and [B] are the concentrations of A and B, respectively? If we know the energy levels of the constituents A and B, we can calculate the corresponding partition functions Z_A and Z_B at a temperature T. If the substances A and B are gases, they occupy the same volume independently, so that

$$S_A = U_A/T + N_A k \ln Z_A/N_A \quad \text{and} \quad S_B = U_B/T + N_B k \ln Z_B/N_B.$$

Hence the total entropy S_{AB} is

$$S_{AB} = S_A + S_B = (U_A + U_B)/T + k(N_A \ln Z_A/N_A + N_B \ln Z_B/N_B).$$

But the total number of particles N is constant for this reaction. If an A changes into a B, N_A falls by 1 and N_B increases by 1, that is $-\Delta N_A = +\Delta N_B$ (as can be seen by differentiating the equations $N = N_A + N_B$, that is $0 = \Delta N_A + \Delta N_B$). Similarly, the total internal energy is constant; thus $U_A + U_B = U_{AB} = $ constant so that $\Delta(U_A + U_B) = 0$. Therefore,

$$\Delta S_{AB} = 0 + k(\Delta N_A \ln Z_A/N_A + \Delta N_B \ln Z_B/N_B)$$

$$+ N_A\left(-\frac{1}{N_A}\Delta N_A\right) + N_B\left(-\frac{1}{N_B}\Delta N_B\right)$$

$$= k\,\Delta N_A(\ln Z_A/N_A - \ln Z_B/N_B),$$

where we have used the fact that $\Delta N_B = -\Delta N_A$.

---

* Indistinguishability may lead to restrictions on occupation of the levels however (Section 14.2).

For equilibrium S_{AB} must be a maximum with respect to progress of the reaction in either direction, hence ΔS_{AB} is zero for small changes of N_A. This is the same condition as for a minimum of the free energy F in this case, since U is fixed. ΔS_{AB} is zero if $(\ln Z_A/N_A - \ln Z_B/N_B) = 0$, i.e. if $K \equiv N_B/N_A = Z_B/Z_A$. We see therefore that the equilibrium constant can be expressed in terms of the partition functions. This is a rather remarkable result, since in order to calculate the partition functions we only need to know the energy levels (the temperature being an independent variable).

This result can be generalized. For example, if the reaction is $AB \rightleftharpoons A + B$, then $K \equiv N_A N_B/N_{AB} \propto Z_A Z_B/Z_{AB}$. For $A_2 \rightleftharpoons 2A$, $K \equiv N_A^2/N_{A_2} \propto Z_A^2/Z_{A_2}$ and so on. We note that, since K only depends on the partition functions, it is independent of the concentrations at constant temperature. Hence, for instance, in the reaction $AB \rightleftharpoons A + B$, $K = [A][B]/[AB]$ is constant and is a property of the *reaction* and does not depend on the amounts of the constituents. Thus, if we try to increase the amount of A, $[A]$ increases. Therefore, $[B]$ must decrease and $[AB]$ must increase in order to keep K constant. In other words, the reaction is "driven" to the left by excess of A (or, in fact, of B). This is physically understandable, since increasing the number of particles A increases the probability of an A meeting a B and forming an AB. It is clear that the rate of reaction to the left k_1 is proportional to $[A][B]$ and the rate to the right k_{-1} is proportional to $[AB]$. At equilibrium $k_{-1} = k_1$ and hence $[A][B]/[AB]$ is a constant. This is an example of the law of mass action. It is, however, quite a subtle matter to actually calculate this constant— we have found it to be given simply by the appropriate ratio of the partition functions. In using the statistical method, we have to be a little more careful for the reactions such as $AB \rightleftharpoons A + B$ because the total number of particles is not constant, that is $(N_{AB} + N_A + N_B)$ is not constant. In fact, we have $(2N_{AB} + N_A + N_B) = $ constant and in addition $\Delta N_A = \Delta N_B$ (see Problem 13.1). This is a common situation. It would also arise, for instance, in considering the equilibrium of radiation with matter where the number of atoms is constant but the number of photons is not.

Consider the reaction $AB \rightleftharpoons A + B$ for which the equilibrium constant is $e^{-1}Z_A Z_B/Z_{AB}$ (see Problem 13.1). Let us be more specific and suppose that the mechanism of the reaction is that A and B in coming together have to surmount an energy barrier ΔE and that the final energy of AB is Q lower than that of A and B separately (Fig. 13.7). Let the zero of energy be that of $A + B$. The partition function Z_{AB} must be referred to the same zero of energy, not to an energy Q lower. Hence we get $Z_{AB} = Z'_{AB} \exp(Q/kT)$, since every term in Z_{AB} has the factor $\exp(Q/kT)$ and Z'_{AB} now contains only internal coordinates of the product molecule AB. Hence the equilibrium constant $e^{-1}Z_A Z_B/Z_{AB}$ is proportional to $\exp(-Q/kT)$.

The same result can be obtained from the Boltzmann distribution law. The probability of $A + B$ forming AB is proportional to the quantities n_A and n_B of A and B present and also to the probability of $A + B$ acquiring an energy greater than ΔE, i.e. to $n_A n_B \exp(-\Delta E/kT)$ (see Problem 11.11). Similarly, the probability

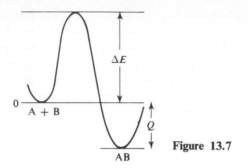

Figure 13.7

of AB breaking up into A + B is proportional to $n_{AB} \exp\left[-(\Delta E + Q)/kT\right]$. At equilibrium, the two rates are equal and so

$$n_A n_B \exp\left(-\Delta E/kT\right) \propto n_{AB} \exp\left[-(\Delta E + Q)/kT\right],$$

or

$$\frac{n_A n_B}{n_{AB}} \propto \exp\left(-Q/kT\right),$$

as above. Note that ΔE does not affect the *equilibrium* concentrations. It does, however, determine the *rate* of attainment of equilibrium, since the probability of the reaction going either way depends among other things on $\exp\left(-\Delta E/kT\right)$. Strictly speaking, the reaction must involve at least a third body C, so that momentum and energy can be conserved during the reaction. This affects the rates either way which are now proportional to

$$n_A n_B n_C \exp\left(-\Delta E/kT\right) \quad \text{and} \quad n_{AB} n_C \exp\left[-(\Delta E + Q)/kT\right],$$

respectively. But the third body does not affect the equilibrium, since in equilibrium we still get $n_A n_B/n_{AB} \propto \exp\left(-Q/kT\right)$, the n_C cancelling out. A similar argument holds for the partition function expression for K since, with the third body present,

$$K = e^{-1} Z_A Z_B Z_C/(Z_{AB} Z_C) = e^{-1} Z_A Z_B/Z_{AB},$$

which is the same result as before.

For the rate of reaction between atoms or molecules in a gas, we need the number of collisions of the molecules in the gas. If the collision cross-section (Section 7.1) is $\mathscr{A}$, the mean velocity (Section 10.4) is $(8kT/\pi m)^{1/2}$ and if there are n_A molecules of A per cm³, the number of collisions per molecule of B per second is $\sqrt{2}\mathscr{A}(8kT/\pi m)^{1/2} n_A$ where the factor $\sqrt{2}$ allows approximately for the fact that the molecules of both A and B are moving. For example, in a typical gas at n.t.p., there are about 10^{10} collisions per molecule per second (see Problem 13.10). The total number of collisions of A and B molecules per sec per cm³ is

$$\sqrt{2}\mathscr{A}(8kT/\pi m)^{1/2} n_A n_B.$$

We have already discussed the additional factor $\exp\left(-\Delta E/kT\right)$, which also determines the rate of the reaction but even so not all these collisions lead to a reaction and so reaction rates are expected to be slower than given by this formula for the number of collisions.

Formulae for equilibrium constants in terms of partition functions are extremely useful in many branches of physics and chemistry, since the partition function can be calculated from the energy levels, that is from the physical properties of the atoms, molecules, electrons, nuclei, or whatever the systems happen to be. The relation is often used in reverse. We measure the equilibrium constant K as a function of temperature say, and try to deduce from it the physical properties of the particles involved.

13.7 EXCITED PARTICLES

An important special case of a reaction is $A \rightleftharpoons A^*$ where A^* is an "excited" form of A in equilibrium with A. For example, we may have a partially ionized gas or plasma, which is say emitting light, or a molecule which has been twisted or excited into vibration. Then the energy levels of A^* are the same as those of A except that the energy of A^* relative to A is, say, ΔE higher (Fig. 13.8). The relative concentrations are given by the general formula

$$K = \frac{[A^*]}{[A]} = \frac{N_{A^*}}{N_A} = \frac{Z_{A^*}}{Z_A}.$$

But the Z terms must refer to a common zero of energy. Therefore

$$Z_{A^*} = \sum_s \exp\left(-\epsilon_s^*/kT\right) = \sum_s \exp\left(-\Delta E + \epsilon_s\right)/kT$$

$$= \exp\left(-\Delta E/kT\right) \sum_s \exp\left(-\epsilon_s/kT\right) = Z_A \exp\left(-\Delta E/kT\right).$$

Therefore the equilibrium constant, which is Z_{A^*}/Z_A, is $\exp\left(-\Delta E/kT\right)$.

The relative population of excited systems varies as the Boltzmann factor. This is obviously true if $\Delta E = 0$, since then A and A^* are indistinguishable and $N_A = N_{A^*}$, that is $K = 1$.

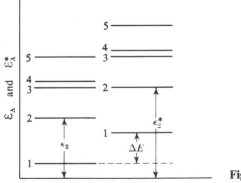

Figure 13.8

13.8 FURTHER DEVELOPMENTS

We have actually been mostly concerned with what is technically called the micro-canonical ensemble. The field of application of statistical mechanics can be widened by relaxing our restrictions for both mathematical and physical reasons. It is desirable for instance to relax the restrictive condition that the energy $\sum n_s \epsilon_s$ is held constant. Thus, instead of considering an isolated body, we might consider one in thermal contact with another at fixed temperature T. This is then called a canonical ensemble. We may even relax the restriction on the number of particles $\sum n_s$ by letting our body exchange particles with other identical ones. This is then called the grand canonical ensemble. This is found to be helpful in dealing with such apparently different topics as radiation and chemical reactions.

There is a sense in which all physically observable effects are "many-body" problems, since we must have a macroscopic effect to make an observation and so what we have been doing is more fundamental than would appear at first sight.

PROBLEMS

13.1. Show that the equilibrium constant $(N_A N_B / N_{AB})$ for the reaction $AB \rightleftharpoons A + B$ is given by $e^{-1} Z_A Z_B / Z_{AB}$.

13.2. The energy levels of a harmonic oscillator are given by $\epsilon_n = (n + \frac{1}{2})hv$ where $n = 0, 1,$ 2, ... and v is the classical oscillator frequency. Show that the partition function $Z = \sum_n \exp(-\epsilon_n/kT)$ is given by $\exp(-\frac{1}{2}hv/kT)(1 - \exp[-hv/kT])^{-1}$. Find an expression for the mean energy of N identical oscillators at temperature T using the formula $U = NkT^2(\partial/\partial T)(\ln Z)$. (These results are very important, since harmonic oscillators arise frequently, e.g. they apply to things as diverse as molecules and black-body radiation.)

Show that U rises with temperature from $\frac{1}{2}Nhv$ to RT and that it is changing most significantly when $hv \approx kT$. Give a simple explanation of the extreme values of U.

For molecules, v is of order 10^{14} Hz. Show that internal vibrations are not excited to an appreciable extent at room temperature and so do not contribute much to the specific heat.

13.3. Show that $dF = -P\,dV - S\,dT$ and $dG = V\,dP - S\,dT$ and hence that, for changes at constant volume and temperature, F is constant but that, for changes at constant pressure and temperature, G is constant.

13.4. Show that $P = -(\partial F/\partial V)_T$.

13.5. In showing that $\ln \mathcal{N}$ and $-N \sum_s P(\epsilon_s) \ln P(\epsilon_s)$ are equivalent in Section 13.1 for $N = 5$, we might have been worried perhaps that for $s \geq 5$, $P(\epsilon_s) = 0$. Show that this causes no difficulty because $-x \ln x \to 0$ as $x \to 0$.

13.6. Show that, if the ground state energy is zero and Z is the partition function, then $1/Z$ is the number fraction of particles in the ground state.

13.7. Show that, if the ground state energy is zero, then as $T \to 0$, $Z \to 1$ and that, for $T > 0$, $Z > 1$.

13.8. Show that, in general, the closer the energy levels the larger is Z for a given temperature. If we know the energy levels for translation, rotation, and vibration of molecules we shall then expect that $Z_{trans} \gg Z_{rot} > Z_{vib}$.

13.9. Show that Z is approximately equal to the number of energy levels in the energy range zero to kT.

13.10. Use the formula given in Section 13.6 to show that the number of collisions per second per molecule for a gas at n.t.p. is about 10^{10}.

CHAPTER 14

Non-classical distributions

The old shop fell to pieces with the shock.   W. HEATH ROBINSON

14.1 BOSE–EINSTEIN STATISTICS

The Boltzmann distribution is the "classical" one. In deriving it, we assumed we could distinguish one particle from another. However, in many cases, the particles are not distinguishable as, for example, in a gas and we have already discussed some modifications to the statistics of many particle systems in Section 13.5. The treatment there, however, was somewhat superficial, since it was still based on the Boltzmann distribution and we should really enquire whether the Boltzmann distribution itself is still the same if the particles are indistinguishable. On the other hand, if the particles are "localized" as for the atoms in a crystal, they are distinguishable because we know where they are. However, in a crystal, the particles are subject to considerable forces to keep them in place and so are not by any means independent particles. There are clearly many subtleties in the analysis of many particle systems which we shall not be able to explore fully here.

We now look more closely at what changes have to be made in the case of indistinguishable particles. We shall do this again for small numbers of particles and hope that it will be possible to extrapolate to a large number of particles and so gain a physical feeling for the behaviour of macroscopic systems. We shall find that certain important modifications to the results obtained in Chapters 10 to 13 are necessary. On the other hand, we shall be able to show that there is a wide range of important and commonly occurring circumstances when the indistinguishability of the particles makes very little difference to observable results or at least the simple theories we have developed can be adequately patched up as was done in Section 13.5. If the particles are indistinguishable, we have to use Bose–Einstein or Fermi–Dirac statistics, rather than Boltzmann or classical statistics. We now discuss Bose–Einstein statistics; Fermi–Dirac statistics are discussed in Section 14.2. It should be noted here that not all indistinguishable particles obey Bose–Einstein statistics (see Section 14.2).

Consider once more the energy distribution diagram for five particles with uniformly spaced energy levels and with five units of energy, $N = 5$ and $U = 5\epsilon$.

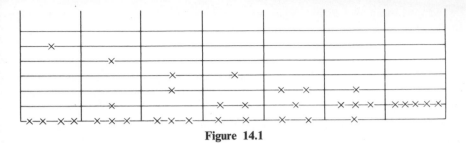

Figure 14.1

The diagram in Fig. 14.1 is similar to Fig. 11.19. If the particles were distinguishable, the arrangements shown, going from left to right, would occur 5, 20, 20, 30, 30, 20, and once, respectively. Since the particles are indistinguishable, each arrangement must now count as only *one* complexion, not $N!/n_1! n_2! \ldots n_s! \ldots$. We calculate the probability of finding a particle in a given energy level, as before, and we find $P(0) = 0.43$, $P(\epsilon) = 0.34$, $P(2\epsilon) = 0.11$, $P(3\epsilon) = 0.06$, $P(4\epsilon) = 0.03$, and $P(5\epsilon) = 0.03$. This may be compared with the result for distinguishable particles given in Section 11.2. The curve of $P(\varepsilon)$ versus ε for indistinguishable particles is compared with that for distinguishable particles in Fig. 14.2. The new Bose–Einstein distribution is not very different from the Boltzmann distribution with the same temperature which we found for distinguishable particles! The points for the Bose–Einstein distribution are more scattered because the number of complexions involved is smaller than for the Boltzmann distribution so we are less likely to get a smooth curve for $P(\varepsilon)$. The number of complexions for Bose–Einstein statistics is very much lower than for Boltzmann statistics. In this example, $\mathcal{N}$ is 7 instead of 126. $\mathcal{N}$ for Bose–Einstein statistics is, of course, just the number of *arrangements* for the classical case rather than the number of *complexions*. Hence, although the distribution is not much affected, the entropy ($k \ln \mathcal{N}$) is much lower. When we were discussing distinguishability in Section 13.5, we suggested that $\mathcal{N}$ should

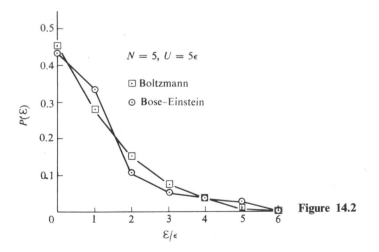

Figure 14.2

be reduced by the factor $N!$ to account for the indistinguishability of the particles. In this particular example where $N = 5$, we have $N! = 5! = 120$. The actual reduction for our system which contains only five particles is by the factor $126/7 = 18$. This, however, is again a trend which is justified as we go to larger and larger numbers of particles (Problem 14.5) and in any case this correction is only expected to be a rather approximate one unless we are in the high temperature situation (see below).

To be precise, the indistinguishability *does* affect the distribution function, which turns out to be

$$P(\varepsilon) \propto 1/\{\exp\left[-\alpha(T) + \varepsilon/kT\right] - 1\}.$$

In most situations encountered, $[\varepsilon/kT - \alpha(T)] \gg 1$ and then

$$P(\varepsilon) \propto 1/\exp\left[-\alpha(T) + \varepsilon/kT\right] = \exp\left[\alpha(T)\right]\exp\left[-\varepsilon/kT\right],$$

which is a Boltzmann distribution. Actually, this happens at "high" temperatures, although this is not obvious from the formula because of the complex dependence of $\alpha(T)$ on T. Our $N = 5$, $U = 5\epsilon$ example above must therefore be a "high temperature" case.

Bose–Einstein statistics are particularly important for dealing with photons, phonons, and superfluid helium. Strictly speaking, they should be used for gases but it turns out that actual gases are such that the Boltzmann approximation is entirely adequate. However, as we have already seen, we have to be careful about thermodynamic quantities such as the entropy. We have already noted the importance of indistinguishability in the special case of gas reactions in Section 13.6. The entropy function for distinguishable particles contains $\ln Z$ and for indistinguishable particles $\ln Z/N$. The $\ln Z$ form may give completely incorrect results. It does not lead for instance to the law of mass action (Section 13.6), which is very well supported by experiment. The laws of chemical reactions are therefore evidence that the particles taking part in the reactions are indistinguishable.

14.2 FERMI–DIRAC STATISTICS

An additional important restriction which may arise for quantum-mechanical reasons is the requirement that "there must be only one particle on each energy level". Alternatively, this is sometimes stated as the Pauli exclusion principle which forbids that any two particles may have the same set of quantum numbers— the two statements are equivalent.† The first and most obvious effect of this new restriction is that there is a lower limit to the energy that the particles may possess. There is a limit to the energy which can be extracted from the system of particles, since we cannot lower the energy of a particle if this requires it to be put on the same energy level as another particle. In particular, we cannot put all the particles on

----

† The possibility of degenerate energy levels is ignored here.

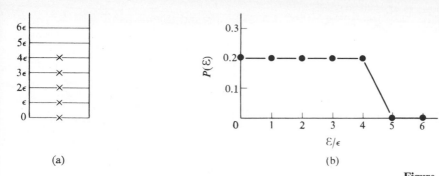

(a)   (b)

Figure 14.3

the lowest energy level. We again investigate the effect of this new restriction for
a system with a small number of particles. For $N = 5$, the lowest energy state
is as shown in Fig. 14.3(a). The energy of this arrangement is $U_0 = 10\epsilon$. This
lowest possible energy state must correspond to $T = 0$ but it has the $P(\varepsilon)$ curve
shown in Fig. 14.3(b). This is very different indeed from the Boltzmann distribution
for $T = 0$ (Fig. 11.7) which has $P(0) = 1$ and $P(n\epsilon) = 0$ for $n \geq 1$. The Bose–
Einstein distribution is also very different from the Boltzmann distribution as
$T \to 0$ but the difference is more subtle and cannot be investigated here. In all
cases where this new restriction on the population of the levels is applicable, the
particles are also indistinguishable so we have *both* differences from the Boltzmann
distribution. Particles with such restrictions are said to obey Fermi–Dirac
statistics.

Since the particles are indistinguishable, the number of complexions is again
the number of arrangements and so the diagram of Fig. 14.3(a) corresponds to
one complexion, $\mathcal{N} = 1$. Hence we again have for the entropy $S = k \ln \mathcal{N} = 0$
for $T = 0$. The statistical entropy is zero at the absolute zero of temperature for
Fermi–Dirac statistics.

If we add energy, the distribution changes and we investigate this for our
five-particle body. Take $N = 5$ and $U = 12\epsilon = U_0 + 2\epsilon$ and we get the results
shown in Fig. 14.4.

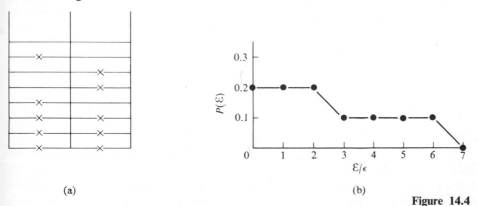

(a)   (b)

Figure 14.4

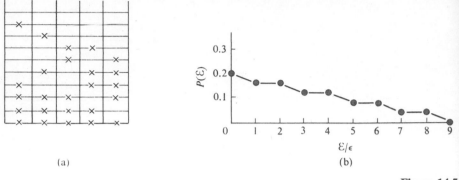

(a)

(b)

Figure 14.5

Again, for $N = 5$ and $U = 14\epsilon = U_0 + 4\epsilon$, we get the results shown in Fig. 14.5.

The number of complexions $\mathcal{N}$ is very much lower than for the Boltzmann distribution. But the most striking effects are the high minimal energy that the particles must possess and the distribution which is very different from the Boltzmann distribution of particles on the levels when the total energy U is not much greater than the minimum U_0. Nevertheless, as the energy, and therefore the temperature, increases, the distribution becomes more and more like a Boltzmann distribution for the same N and U. Even for $N = 5$ and $U = 14\epsilon = U_0 + 4\epsilon$, we have a fair approximation to a Boltzmann distribution with the temperature corresponding to the classical case with $U = 14\epsilon$.

If we solve the problem analytically for a large number of particles, we find

$$P(\varepsilon) \propto 1/\{\exp\left[-\alpha(T) + \varepsilon/kT\right] + 1\}.$$

If $\left[\varepsilon/kT - \alpha(T)\right] \gg 1$, this becomes

$$P(\varepsilon) \propto \exp\left[\alpha(T)\right] \exp\left[-\varepsilon/kT\right],$$

which is again a Boltzmann distribution. This is what we have found explicitly for $N = 5$. We again, therefore, get the "classical" result and the condition is once more that the temperature is high enough.

Since $\mathcal{N}$ is much lower, the entropy and other thermodynamic functions have again to be reconsidered, even for high temperatures. Fermi–Dirac statistics are not uncommon. The most important case is for electrons in a metal. Actually, we can have either one or two electrons in each level, since the electrons are distinguishable by their spin or magnetic moment which may be "up or down", two possibilities (see Section 6.3 and Problem 12.6). But this makes no essential difference to the analysis given here. For the electrons in a metal at room temperature, the distribution is very far from a Boltzmann distribution. In fact, the distribution is something like that in Fig. 14.6. As far as the electrons in a metal are concerned, room temperature is a low temperature and the quantum restrictions

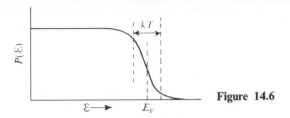

Figure 14.6

on the occupation of energy levels are of major importance. The same is true for the electrons in atoms in a body at a temperature T but this involves a complex set of energy levels and so we do not go into the question here.

14.3 PARTICLES AND ANTIPARTICLES

Since in many cases the deviation from the Fermi–Dirac zero-point distribution is not large, it is often convenient to consider the change relative to that situation rather than the actual situation. We can break down the actual distribution into the sum of the zero-point distribution together with a distribution corresponding to the difference of the actual distribution from the zero-point one. Figure 14.7 illustrates this for $N = 5$ and $U = 11\epsilon = U_0 + \epsilon$. The $-\bigcirc-$ in the third energy distribution diagram in Fig. 14.7 indicates that a particle has been removed. It is a sort of negative particle or a "hole". This is perhaps more striking for the probability distribution curves which are also shown in Fig. 14.7. The best known example of this effect is for the electrons in a metal. The excited particles are the electrons with energy greater than E_F (see Fig. 14.7) and the holes are the gaps

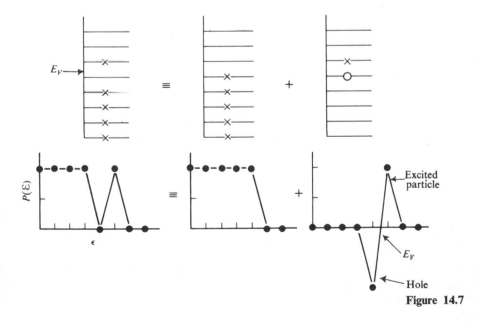

Figure 14.7

where electrons ought to be. This concept is particularly useful in semiconductors (n type and p type) and arises in much the same way. If an atom of the metal is replaced by an atom with an additional mobile electron, that electron must go into an energy level above the original Fermi level and so is an excited particle in the sense above. This is essentially the way in which an n type (n for *n*egative) semiconductor can be produced. On the other hand, if one of the original atoms is replaced by one which tends to acquire an electron, then it will take an electron out of the effectively zero-point distribution and leave a hole. Since the hole behaves like a positively charged particle, this leads essentially to a p type (p for *p*ositive) semiconductor.

For a Fermi–Dirac system at a finite temperature, the energy can be removed or emitted by allowing an electron to fall into a hole and both are thereby annihilated.

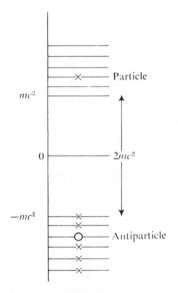

Figure 14.8

Another example of a hole is an atom with an almost complete shell of electrons. Chlorine has the electronic configuration $(Ne)(3s)^2(3p)^5$. (Ne) represents the set of inner electronic orbitals as for neon and is not of course a neon atom. The chlorine atom may be regarded as being the sum of a particle having an electronic structure which we write as $(Ne)(3s)^2(3p)^6$ (which is like argon) together with a "hole" in the $3p$ shell. Similarly, sodium has the electronic configuration $(Ne)3s$ and may be regarded as (Ne) together with a $3s$ electron. When a sodium atom and a chlorine atom come together to form a sodium chloride molecule (which can exist in a molecular beam), the process may be regarded as one in which the excited electron of the sodium atom annihilates the hole in the chlorine atom and the energy released is the energy of chemical combination. This is a physicist's way of doing chemistry!

This recombination process is reminiscent of the mutual annihilation of a particle and its antiparticle which usually produces electromagnetic radiation (Fig. 14.8). This picture is indeed a reasonable one for the electron and its anti-particle, the positive electron or positron. We must, however, put an energy gap (of $2m_ec^2$, see Section 8.3) between the top of the Fermi sea of electrons and the first available excited level, since at least this amount of energy must be produced if the two particles annihilate each other or alternatively must be provided before the two particles can materialize. In this sense, particle and antiparticle pairs are not produced from "nowhere" by energy. They come from the unobserved reservoir in free space. We suspect from this that free space, in which our particles move, is really quite complicated. The dynamics of particles will involve the so-called "vacuum states", which are the filled states in the lower part of the diagram in Fig. 14.8, if we are considering processes in which the energy available is $2m_ec^2$ or greater. For a particle of greater mass, a correspondingly greater amount of energy must be available (Problem 14.4). Since, in this sense, the vacuum contains particles of all types, free space is certainly as complicated as the ether which we discussed briefly in Chapter 9.

14.4 THE THREE STATISTICS

The situation may be summarized as in the following table. Under suitable conditions (see Section 14.1), both the Bose–Einstein and the Fermi–Dirac

Boltzmann	Bose–Einstein	Fermi–Dirac
Distinguishable or localized particles. (Classical case, no wave functions)	Indistinguishable particles. (Symmetric wave functions)	Indistinguishable particles and the number of particles on any given level restricted to a small integral number. (Antisymmetric wave functions)

distributions are effectively indistinguishable from the Boltzmann distribution. In other words, in many circumstances the fact that particles may be indistinguish-able and that there are severe restrictions on the occupation of energy levels makes little difference to the observable results. This is one reason why "classical" physics works so well. Classical physics, as we have seen many times by now, tends to be a correct description of nature for high enough temperatures. It so happened that the temperatures at which the first physical experiments were done (mostly room temperature!) were high temperatures in this sense. Otherwise science might have developed in a very different way and the history of science might have started with quantum mechanics and Fermi–Dirac and Bose–Einstein statistics and proceeded to have had great difficulty in explaining classical mechanics and Boltzmann statistics.

Particles which obey Bose–Einstein statistics are called bosons; they are particles with integral spin, including zero, such as photons, π mesons, ^{4}He atoms, deuterons, most molecules, etc.

Particles which obey Fermi–Dirac statistics are called fermions; they are particles with half-integral spin such as protons, electrons, μ mesons, etc.

The question of the indistinguishability of particles provides a suitable definition of a "particle" for this book. If particles are indistinguishable, they are identical and so we are led to consider electrons, protons, and, with certain reservations, atoms, molecules, and so on. On the other hand, two dust particles and similar objects are never identical; so we prefer to call them bodies and have to deal with them in a different way. Nevertheless, in some circumstances, we can treat bodies as particles as a matter of convenience. Thus in astronomy it may even be convenient to consider a galaxy as a particle.

Table 14.1

Classical or Boltzmann	Bose–Einstein	Fermi–Dirac
$\alpha(1)\alpha(2)$ $\alpha(1)\beta(2)$ $\alpha(2)\beta(1)$ $\beta(1)\beta(2)$	$\alpha(1)\alpha(2)$ $(1/\sqrt{2})[\alpha(1)\beta(2) + \alpha(2)\beta(1)]$ $\beta(1)\beta(2)$	$(1/\sqrt{2})[\alpha(1)\beta(2) - \alpha(2)\beta(1)]$
$\mathcal{N}_{\mathrm{B}} = 4$	$\mathcal{N}_{\mathrm{B-E}} = 3$	$\mathcal{N}_{\mathrm{F-D}} = 1$

The difference between the three types of statistics is made clear in quantum mechanics. Suppose we have two particles 1 and 2 which may exist in two different states α and β. We use the notation $\alpha(1)$ to mean that particle 1 is in state α and so on. If the particles are distinguishable, we have the four possibilities marked classical in Table 14.1 and these are distinct states so that $\mathcal{N} = 4$. However, if the particles are not distinguishable we can no longer distinguish the state $\alpha(1)\beta(2)$ from the state $\alpha(2)\beta(1)$. However, a combination which does not distinguish between particles 1 and 2 is $(1/\sqrt{2})[\alpha(1)\beta(2) + \alpha(2)\beta(1)]$ and so it is also a possible state. Notice that the states $\alpha(1)\alpha(2)$ and $\beta(1)\beta(2)$ are still admissible because they do not distinguish one particle from the other. Moreover, we can have more than one particle in one state (energy level), e.g. both particles in α or both in β. For all the three states for Bose–Einstein statistics in Table 14.1, we can exchange the labels on the particles without affecting the state. Since all observable quantities depend on the states, this means that we cannot observe the labels and so the particles are indistinguishable. This may be contrasted with, say, the state $\alpha(1)\beta(2)$ of the Boltzmann distribution which if we change the labels becomes $\alpha(2)\beta(1)$ which is not the same state. Using these wave functions then, we can in principle observe effects which result from the distinguishability of the particles. These considerations reduce the number of complexions to $\mathcal{N} = 3$ for Bose–Einstein statistics, for $N = 2$.

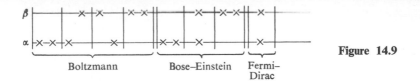

Figure 14.9

Boltzmann   Bose–Einstein   Fermi–
                                  Dirac

For Fermi–Dirac statistics, we can only have one particle in each level and so $\alpha(1)\alpha(2)$ and $\beta(1)\beta(2)$ are not allowed. The only possibility, in this case, is

$$(1/\sqrt{2})[\alpha(1)\beta(2) - \alpha(2)\beta(1)].$$

Exchanging the labels on the particles turns this state into the negative of itself so that it may appear that the particles are not indistinguishable. It turns out, however, that the mere change of sign just mentioned does not in fact imply distinguishability; it is the signal which tells us we are dealing with fermions rather than bosons. The number of complexions is reduced even further for Fermi–Dirac statistics by the increased restrictions and $\mathcal{N} = 1$ for Fermi–Dirac statistics, for $N = 2$. These results are consistent with what we found in Sections 14.1 and 14.2 and we can use the same sort of diagram to represent the possible complexions. For $N = 2$ and only *two* energy levels *all* the possible states are shown diagrammatically in Fig. 14.9 and there is a one-to-one correspondence with Table 14.1.

PROBLEMS

14.1. Show that the condition that the Bose–Einstein and Fermi–Dirac distributions $\{\exp[-\alpha(T) + \varepsilon/kT] \pm 1\}^{-1}$ go over to the Boltzmann distribution is that the temperature is high enough.

14.2. In the Fermi–Dirac distribution for "low" temperatures (Figs. 14.3, 14.6, and 14.7), there is a rather sharp value separating the filled from the empty levels which is called the Fermi energy E_F. The exact distribution is $\{\exp[-\alpha(T) + \varepsilon/kT] + 1\}^{-1}$. Show that $E_F \approx \alpha kT$.

14.3. Show qualitatively that the specific heat of a system of particles obeying Fermi–Dirac statistics and at low temperatures is proportional to the absolute temperature. (HINT: Use Fig. 14.6.) This is true for the electronic contribution to the specific heat of a metal.

14.4. Show that the minimal energy required for the production of an electron–positron pair by a γ ray is about 1 Mev. To what wavelength of the electromagnetic radiation of the γ ray does this correspond? What would be the minimal energy for production of a proton–antiproton pair?

14.5. It has been suggested that, for high enough temperatures, the Bose–Einstein statistics go over to the Boltzmann statistics except that the number of complexions is smaller by the factor $N!$ where N is the number of particles. Make explicit calculations of $(\mathcal{N}_B/\mathcal{N}_{B-E})/N!$ for $N = 5$ and $U = \epsilon, 3\epsilon, 5\epsilon, 7\epsilon,$ and 9ϵ. Hence or otherwise show that the correct result is unlikely to be attained until U is greater than about 30ϵ.

CHAPTER 15

Strongly interacting particles

Mystics always hope that science will one day
overtake them.   B. TARKINGTON

If particles interact strongly, the formalism we have used for dealing with many particles is not applicable.   The molecules in a gas may interact strongly during collisions but "most of the time" they are virtually free; consequently the treatment of gases is relatively simple.   Actually, the Boltzmann distribution in a wider sense still applies to systems of strongly interacting particles but leads less readily to actual results.   The modern tendency, however, in dealing with a system of strongly interacting particles is to "transform" the situation so that it looks like a set of weakly interacting entities which are different but behave in many ways like particles.   This is particularly fruitful in quantum-mechanical calculations.   We have, in fact, dealt with such "quasi-particles" or "collective excitations" right from the beginning.   Indeed, we are probably *always* doing so, since who can say that a fundamental particle like an electron is not composed of a set of strongly interacting particles behaving like a quasi-particle? The conclusion would be particularly difficult to avoid, for instance, if the μ meson turns out to be merely an excited electron.

A hydrogen atom is a quasi-particle.   We have two particles, the proton and the electron, in strong interaction.   The combination can be regarded as a particle provided the interactions with it are not so strong as to involve changes in its internal structure.   Similar considerations apply to a molecule.   The hydrogen molecule, for instance, can move as a whole as a particle of mass $2m_H$.   In addition, it can reorientate and we have dealt with this sort of thing in connexion with angular momentum.   Finally, we have the possibility of an internal vibration.   This latter is a motion which involves *both* atoms and is an internal property of the molecular particle; it is a motion of strongly interacting particles.   The two strongly interacting massive particles of the hydrogen molecule can be regarded in a sense as two weakly interacting quasi-particles, one of mass $2m_H$ undergoing translational motion and one of (reduced) mass $m_H/2$ undergoing vibrational motion.

In a crystal, all the atoms or molecules are relatively tightly coupled and, as for the hydrogen molecule, there are corresponding internal vibrations which are naturally more complex but the simplest of them are the sound waves.   When a sound wave passes through a crystal, there is a simple relation between the motions of the atoms over and above their thermal motion. In talking of a sound wave, we no longer need to state the motions of every individual atom so that in this sense the motion of a large number of particles is readily described. The particulate nature of the medium supporting the sound wave can be ignored in good approximation, provided the wavelength of the sound wave is much longer than the distance between the atoms. The exact analysis of the motion of large numbers of atoms in an array as in a crystal does result in the prediction of some modes of motion which correspond to sound waves with long wavelength. The actual particle properties are then only required to obtain the elastic modulus and the density of the sample which in turn determine the properties of the sound wave.

Just as the quantization of the electromagnetic field led to photons, the quantization of sound waves leads to the idea of phonons which are quasi-particles having energy and momentum and so having many of the properties of "real" particles. They can be scattered, for instance, and they can be annihilated.

A crystal at a finite temperature may be regarded as a perfect crystal in which the atoms are fixed on the lattice sites (we ignore the complication of the zero-point energy) together with certain excitations which are the thermal counterpart of the sound waves referred to above and may be called thermal phonons. We have again a case of looking at the deviation from some standard situation rather than the total situation which is similar to the analysis in terms of particles and holes of Section 14.3. This proves to be a very profitable way of proceeding in a great variety of problems.

It is clear that photons are just as much quasi-particles as phonons. It is noticeable that, the better we get to understand a quasi-particle, the more likely we are to forget the "quasi" and to speak simply of a particle.

It is probably true to say, particularly as a result of quantum mechanics and especially of second quantization, that physics is currently describable most conveniently in terms of particles. The fact that wave phenomena have been almost ignored in this book is therefore not a very serious omission!

Laboratory experiments

The following experiments are particularly recommended to be carried out in conjunction with this book. One object of the laboratory course is to have the students measure for themselves, as far as possible, all the quantities which are used in the book. This is considered to be particularly important for the fundamental constants.

(1) Electronic charge. Millikan's oil drop experiment,

$$e = 4.8^* \times 10^{-10} \text{ e.s.u.}$$

(2) e/m for the electron. Magnetron experiment. $e/m_e = 5.3 \times 10^{17}$ e.s.u. g^{-1}. Hence with the value of e above,

$$m_e = 9.1 \times 10^{-28} \text{ g.}$$

(3) Velocity of light. By rotating mirror and fringe shift.

$$c = 3.0 \times 10^{10} \text{ cm s}^{-1}.$$

(4) Universal gravitational constant. By torsion balance.

$$G = 6.7 \times 10^{-8} \text{ dyn cm}^2 \text{ g}^{-2}.$$

(5) Planck's constant. By photoelectric emission as a function of wavelength (see Section 8.4). h/e with e from Experiment 1 gives

$$h = 6.6 \times 10^{-27} \text{ erg s.}$$

(6) Boltzmann constant. By Brownian motion of small spherical particles in solution (see Section 2.3).

$$k = 1.4 \times 10^{-16} \text{ erg deg}^{-1}.$$

(7) Gas constant. By weighing a gas.

$$R = 8.3 \times 10^7 \text{ erg mol}^{-1} \text{ deg}^{-1}.$$

---

* The constants are given to two significant figures only, since this is sufficient for the calculations in the text and in the problems.

Since Avogadro's number $N_0 = R/k$, with k from Experiment 6 gives

$$N_0 = 6.0 \times 10^{23} \text{ mol}^{-1}.$$

(Proton mass $m_p \approx 1/N_0 = 1.7 \times 10^{-24}$ g.)

(8) **Faraday constant.** By electrical deposition of copper.

$$F = 96,500 \text{ coulombs.}$$

Since $F = N_0 e$, with e from Experiment 1 gives N_0 again.

(9) **Bohr magneton.** By electron spin resonance.

$$\mu_B = 9.3 \times 10^{-21} \text{ erg gauss}^{-1}.$$

This is consistent with Experiments 1, 2, 3, and 5, since $\mu_B = eh/4\pi m_e c$.

(10) **The Rydberg constant, R_∞.** Measure the wavelength of three Balmer lines of hydrogen in the visible region and use the relation $R_H(2^{-2} - n^{-2}) = \lambda^{-1}$. Correct to infinite nuclear mass to get $R_\infty = 1.1 \times 10^5$ cm^{-1}. This can be checked with the fundamental constants already measured because

$$R_\infty = 2\pi^2 m_e e^4 / h^3 c.$$

(11) **The proton magnetic moment.** By nuclear magnetic resonance.

$$\mu_p = 1.4 \times 10^{-23} \text{ erg gauss}^{-1}.$$

Since $\mu_B/\mu_p \approx m_p/m_e$, this gives a rough estimate of the proton mass without reference to atomic weights or chemical reactions.

(12) **Mass of proton.** From measurement of the isotope shift in the Balmer spectrum of hydrogen with respect to deuterium, we can obtain the ratio m_e/m_p. Hence with m_e from Experiment 2, we get m_p.

(13) **Molecular size.** Spreading experiment of fatty acid on water to give a monomolecular layer (see Section 3.2). This gives an estimate of the length of the molecule.

(14) **Model scattering experiment.** Steel balls are projected at a perspex cylinder for various impact parameters and the scattering pattern measured from the point of impact of the balls on an enclosing cylinder. The target diameter can be determined from the scattering pattern (see Section 7.2, but note that there is a considerable difference in detail between the scattering in a plane of this experiment and the scattering in space of Section 7.2).

(15) **Probability distributions.** Experimental determination of probability distributions by rolling steel balls through a pin table (Section 10.3).

(16) **Young's modulus E and Poisson's ratio σ.** Measured by longitudinal and transverse strain gauges on a bent beam. Gives the axial modulus of elasticity (Section 4.2) via $M = E(1 - \sigma)/(1 + \sigma)(1 - 2\sigma)$.

(17) Viscosity of gases. By comparing the viscosities of gases, measured by flow through a capillary tube, the molecular diameters can be compared since $d_m \propto \eta^{-1/2}$ (Section 7.1).

(18) Magnetic susceptibility. Gouy's method for copper sulphate gives a value for the Bohr magneton by weighing.

USEFUL QUANTITIES

The fundamental constants are given in the experiments described above. The following additional constants will be useful in connexion with the problems. All constants are given to two significant figures only. This is almost always sufficient for rough calculations which illustrate physical principles.

Radius of the Earth	6.4×10^8 cm
Mass of the Earth	6.0×10^{27} g
Radius of the Sun	6.9×10^{10} cm
Mass of the Sun	2.0×10^{33} g
Mass of the Moon	7.3×10^{25} g
Radius of the Moon	1.7×10^8 cm
Distance from Earth to the Sun	1.5×10^{13} cm
Distance from Earth to the Moon	3.8×10^{10} cm
Wavelength of visible light	5000 Å approx.

CONVERSION FACTORS

1 calorie $\equiv$ 4.2 joule $\equiv$ 4.2×10^7 erg

1 coulomb $\equiv$ 3×10^9 e.s.u. of charge

1 volt $\equiv$ 1/300 e.s.u. of potential difference

1 wb m^{-2} $\equiv$ 10^4 gauss

1 newton $\equiv$ 10^5 dyn

1 ev $\equiv$ 1.6×10^{-19} joule $\equiv$ 1.6×10^{-12} erg $\equiv$ 23 kcal mol^{-1}

1 a.m.u. $\equiv$ 931 Mev

1 debye unit $\equiv$ 10^{-18} e.s.u. of charge cm.

Further reading

1. G. HOLTON and D. H. D. ROLLER, *Foundations of Modern Physical Science*, Addison-Wesley, Reading, Mass. (1958).

2. R. P. FEYNMAN, R. B. LEIGHTON, and M. SANDS, *The Feynman Lectures on Physics*, Vol. 1, Addison-Wesley, Reading, Mass. (1963).

3. R. W. CHRISTY and A. PYTTE, *The Structure of Matter*, Benjamin, New York (1965).

4. N. FEATHER, *Mass, Length and Time*, Penguin, London (1963).

5. C. KITTEL, *Berkeley Physics Course*, Vol. 1, "Mechanics", McGraw-Hill, New York (1965).

6. J. H. SANDERS, *The Fundamental Atomic Constants*, Oxford University Press, London (1961).

7. D. L. ANDERSON, *The Discovery of the Electron*, Van Nostrand, New York (1964).

8. A. H. COTTRELL, *The Mechanical Properties of Matter*, Wiley, New York (1964).

9. C. V. DURELL, *Readable Relativity*, Bell, London (1938).

10. T. M. HELLIWELL, *Introduction to Special Relativity*, Allyn and Bacon, Boston (1966).

11. W. FELLER, *An Introduction to Probability Theory and its Applications*, Wiley, New York (1950).

12. E. A. GUGGENHEIM, *The Boltzmann's Distribution Law*, North Holland, Amsterdam (1959).

13. J. WILKS, *The Third Law of Thermodynamics*, Oxford University Press, London (1961).

14. F. REIF, *Berkeley Physics Course*, Vol. 5, "Statistical Physics", McGraw-Hill, New York (1967).

15. R. W. GURNEY, *Introduction to Statistical Mechanics*, McGraw-Hill, New York (1949).

16. C. E. SWARTZ, *The Fundamental Particles*, Addison-Wesley, Reading, Mass. (1965).

17. G. STEPHENSON, *Mathematical Methods for Science Students*, Longmans Green, London (1961). (This book gives a suitable mathematical background.)

Solutions to problems

CHAPTER 2

2.1. Footnote to Table 1.1.

2.2. $F = N_0 e$.

2.6. As for CO and CO_2 discussed in the text. If $N_n O_m$, ratios given are $16m/14n$, that is $\frac{1}{2}(1:2:3:4:5)$. The gases are nitrous oxide, nitric oxide, nitrous anhydride, nitrogen dioxide, and nitric anhydride (i.e. N_2O, NO, N_2O_3, NO_2, and N_2O_5).

2.7. No.

2.8. $(800)^{1/3} \approx 9$.

2.9. $\overline{r^2} = (6kT/6\pi\eta a)t \sim 10^{-12} t/a$ for water, $\sqrt{\overline{r^2}} \sim 10^{-5} a^{-1/2}$. (a) 10^{-7} (b) 5×10^{-6} (c) 10^{-4} (d) 5×10^{-2} cm approx.

2.10. $\frac{1}{2}m\overline{v^2} = \frac{3}{2}kT$, $m \sim 10^{-12}$ g. $\therefore (\overline{v^2})^{1/2} \sim 0.3$ cm s^{-1}.

2.11. $\overline{t \cos \omega t}/\bar{t} = (2/\omega T)[\sin \omega T + (1/\omega T)(\cos \omega T - 1)] \to 0$ as $\omega T \to \infty$.

CHAPTER 3

3.1. Volume per atom is $d_0^3/\sqrt{2}$ if d_0 is the nearest neighbour distance $\therefore$ $d_{0,\text{fcc}} = 2^{1/6} d_{0,\text{sc}}$.

? Volume occupied by one mole $= (1/1.14) \times 32 = 28$ cm^3. If simple cubic packing, this is $d_0^3 N_0$.
Volume of one mole of spherical molecules is $\frac{4}{3}\pi(d_0/2)^3 N_0 = (\pi/6)d_0^3 N_0$ and this is $b/4$.
$\therefore$ volume occupied by one mole is $(3/2\pi)b = 15$ cm^3. Or compare two estimates of d_0.

3.4. $R \approx r_0 A^{1/3}$ where $r_0 = 1.3 \times 10^{-13}$ cm. For simple cubic packing, volume per nucleus of atomic number A (i.e. of mass Am_p) is R^3 $\therefore$ $\rho \approx Am_p/R^3 = m_p/r_0^3 = 1.67 \times 10^{-24}/1.3^3 \times 10^{-39} \approx 10^{15}$ g cm^{-3}.

3.5. Electrostatic repulsion.

3.6. (a) $r > a, E = \dfrac{e}{r^2}$; $r < a, E = e\dfrac{r}{a^3}$. $\mathcal{E}_{r>a} = \displaystyle\int_a^\infty \left(\dfrac{e}{r^2}\right)^2 \times \dfrac{1}{8\pi} \times 4\pi r^2\, dr = \dfrac{e^2}{2a}$,

$$\mathcal{E}_{r<a} = \int_0^a \left(\dfrac{er}{a^3}\right)^2 \times \dfrac{1}{8\pi} \times 4\pi r^2\, dr = \dfrac{e^2}{10a}.$$

$$\therefore\ \mathcal{E} = \tfrac{3}{5}(e^2/a) = m_e c^2, \quad \therefore\ a = \tfrac{3}{5}(e^2/m_e c^2).$$

(b) When sphere is of radius r, $q = (r^3/a^3)e$. Energy to bring up Δq is

$$\dfrac{q\,\Delta q}{r} = \left(e\dfrac{r^3}{a^3}\right)\left(e\dfrac{3r\,\Delta r}{a^3}\right)\dfrac{1}{r} = \dfrac{3e^2}{a^6} r^4\,\Delta r.$$

$$\therefore\ \mathcal{E} = \int_0^a \dfrac{3e^2}{a^6} r^4\, dr = \dfrac{3}{5}\dfrac{e^2}{a}, \text{ as before.}$$

3.9. $d_0 = 3.4$ Å.

CHAPTER 4

4.1. Before removal, the atom is being compressed but the ion is under tension.

4.2. The work done to bring a molecule to the surface from the body of the liquid decreases as the density of the liquid ρ_1 decreases, since the molecules are farther apart. On the other hand, the surface molecules may come from the vapour where they are already free of bonding to other molecules so the surface tension should fall with increasing ρ_v. Hence possibly surface tension $\propto f(\rho_1 - \rho_v)$. Actually, it depends roughly on $(\rho_1 - \rho_v)^4$ near the critical temperature.

4.3. $\kappa = (d^2E/dx^2)_{d_0} = 2\,\Delta E/a^2$; $\nu_{\text{vib}} = (1/2\pi)[\kappa/(m/2)]^{1/2} = (\pi a)^{-1}(\Delta E/m)^{1/2}$; 1.4×10^{14} Hz.

4.4. Thermal expansion.

4.5. Hydrogen bonding.

4.6. $x = a_0 \cos \omega t$, $\therefore\ \Delta x = -a_0\omega \sin (\omega t)\,\Delta t$. $p(x)\,\Delta x \propto \Delta t$, that is $p(x) = c(dt/dx) = c(a_0\omega \sin \omega t)^{-1} - c(a_0\omega)^{-1}[1 - (x/a_0)^2]^{-1/2}$. c from $\int p(x)\,dx = 1$. S.H.M. is projection of circular motion, $\therefore\ t_1/t_2 = \theta_1/\theta_2 = \cos^{-1}\tfrac{1}{2}/\sin^{-1}\tfrac{1}{2} = 60°/30° = 2$.

4.7. $mv^2/r = e^2/r^2$ and $mvr = n\hbar$, $\therefore\ r = n^2\hbar^2/me^2$, $\therefore\ \mu \equiv er = n^2\hbar^2/me = 2.5n^2$ debye units.

4.8. Need $dF/dx = 0$, that is $d^2E/dx^2 = 0$ and this occurs for $(x - d_0) = a \ln 2$ and then $E = -\tfrac{3}{4}\Delta E$, i.e. thermal energy must be $\tfrac{1}{4}\Delta E$ $\therefore\ T_m = \tfrac{1}{4}\Delta E/k$.

4.9. For salt, Na^+ and Cl^- are at 2.81 Å and $e^2/d = 5.1$ ev per pair. Linear array energy $= (e^2/d)[-\tfrac{2}{1} + \tfrac{2}{2} - \tfrac{2}{3} + \cdots] = -2(e^2/d) \ln 2 = -1.39(e^2/d)$. (For the actual crystal, energy per ion pair is $-1.75(e^2/d)$.)

4.10. $(e^2/d)[-6 + 12/\sqrt{2} - 8/\sqrt{3}] = -2.2e^2/d$.

4.11. Number of atoms in a spherical shell is $4\pi d^2\,\Delta d\rho_N$ for a macroscopic shell.

4.12. Look it up in a textbook on electricity and magnetism. For Gauss A, $\mu_A \cdot \mu_B = \mu_A\mu_B$ and $\mu \cdot r = \mu r$. For Gauss B, $\mu_A \cdot \mu_B = -\mu_A\mu_B$ and $\mu \cdot r = 0$.

4.13. For $dE/dx = 0$, $x = d_0 = (2B/A)^{1/6}$. $E(x) = -\Delta E = -(A^2/4B)$.

4.15. $(d^2E/dx^2)_{d_0} \propto (13A - 7A)$.

4.17. f.c.c.: 12 at $a/\sqrt{2}$, 6 at a, 24 at $(\sqrt{3}/2)a$, etc. b.c.c.: 8 at $(\sqrt{3}/2)a$, 6 at a, etc.

4.18. $m_e v^2/a_0 = e^2/a_0^2$, $\therefore$ $v^2/a = e^2/m_e a_0^2 = 2.6 \times 10^{24}$ cm s^{-2} $(a_0 = 0.53$ Å$) \approx 3 \times 10^{21}$ g.

4.19. Show that $(d^2E/dr^2)_{r=a_0} > 0$.

4.21. $\Delta x\, \Delta p \geq \hbar$, $E = p^2/2m_e > (1/2m_e)\hbar^2/\Delta x^2 \approx (1/2m_e)\hbar^2/r_0^2 \approx 0.03$ erg $\approx 2 \times 10^{10}$ ev = 20 Gev. Nuclear binding energies are of order 10^7 to 10^8 ev.

4.22. $(d^2E/dx^2)_{d_0} = 72\, \Delta E d_0^{-2} \sim 10^3$ erg cm^{-2}. $(d^2E/dx^3)_{d_0} = -1492\, \Delta E d_0^{-3} \sim -5 \times 10^{11}$ erg cm^{-3}. The values used in Table 4.2 were 4×10^3 erg cm^{-2} and -1.4×10^{11} erg cm^{-3} respectively.

4.23. σ is the distance of closest approach of two atoms which are initially at rest at a large distance.

CHAPTER 5

5.1. $F \propto \eta^r a^s v^t$ $\therefore$ MLT$^{-2} = (MT^{-1}L^{-1})^r L^s (LT^{-1})^t$ $\therefore$ $r = 1$, $s + t - r = 1$, and $-(r + t) = -2$, that is $r = s = t = 1$. More generally, $F \propto \eta^r a^s v^t \rho^u$ so that $F \propto (av\rho/\eta)^t (\eta^2/\rho)$. $t = 1$ gives Stokes' law as above, $t = 2$ gives a second result. In the latter case, the force is independent of η but depends on ρ; the energy is therefore dissipated in kinetic energy and could therefore be turbulent flow.

5.2. $I = \sum m_i r_i^2$, $I_{cm} = \sum m_i (\mathbf{r}_i - \mathbf{R})^2$, $M = \sum m_i$, $\mathbf{R} = \sum m_i \mathbf{r}_i/M$.

$$\therefore\quad I_{cm} = \sum m_i r_i^2 - 2(\sum m_i \mathbf{r}_i)\cdot \mathbf{R} + \sum m_i R^2 = I - 2(M\mathbf{R})\cdot \mathbf{R} + MR^2 = I - MR^2.$$

$$\therefore\quad I = I_{cm} + MR^2.$$

5.4. $M_E = gR_E^2/G \approx 6.0 \times 10^{27}$ g; $M_E/(\frac{4}{3}\pi R_E^3) = 5.5$ g cm^{-3}.

5.5. $M_M R_{EM} \omega^2 = GM_M M_E/R_{EM}^2$, $2R_M/R_{EM} = \frac{1}{2}°$, $\therefore$ $R_M = 1.7 \times 10^8$ cm.

5.6. At these points, $dA/dt = \frac{1}{2}v_1 r_1 = \frac{1}{2}v_2 r_2$.

5.7. $x = r\cos\theta$ $\therefore$ $\Delta x = -r\sin\theta\, \Delta\theta + \cos\theta\, \Delta r$; similarly for y. $\therefore$ $F_x\, \Delta x + F_y\, \Delta y = (xF_y - yF_x)\Delta\theta + (xF_x + yF_y)(\Delta r/r)$ and $\Delta r = 0$.

5.8. K.E. $= \frac{1}{2}mv^2 = \frac{1}{2}m(v^2\cos^2\theta + v^2\sin^2\theta) = \frac{1}{2}m\dot{r}^2 + \frac{1}{2}mv^2\sin^2\theta$. $I = mr^2$, $J = |\mathbf{r} \times \mathbf{p}| = |\mathbf{r} \times m\mathbf{v}| = mrv\sin\theta$, $\therefore$ $\frac{1}{2}J^2/I = \frac{1}{2}mv^2\sin^2\theta$.

5.9. $N(t) = N(0)\exp(-t/t_d)$. $\therefore$ $t = (1/t_{d_1} - 1/t_{d_2})^1 \ln\{[N_1(0)/N_2(0)][N_2(t)/N_1(t)]\}$, but $N_1(0)/N_2(0) = 1$, $N_2(t)/N_1(t) = 138$, and $t_d = t_{1/2}/\ln 2$, $\therefore$ $t = 6.2 \times 10^9$ years.

5.10. $mv^2/R = GmM/R^2$ $\therefore$ $v = (GM/R)^{1/2}$. Angular momentum of space craft $= mvR$. Change in angular momentum of Earth $= -I\, \Delta\omega$ and $\Delta\omega = -2\pi T^{-2}\, \Delta T$, $\therefore$ $\Delta T = 5mT^2 G^{1/2}/4\pi M^{1/2}R^{3/2} \approx 10^{-13}$s.

5.11. Gravitational potential due to ring at (R, θ)

$$= G(2\pi R\sin\theta R\, \Delta R\, d\theta\rho)S^{-1} = 2\pi G\rho R^2\, \Delta R\, d(-\cos\theta)S^{-1} = 2\pi G\rho L^{-1}R\, \Delta R\, dS,$$

since $S^2 = L^2 + R^2 - 2RL\cos\theta$. $\therefore$ Gravitational potential of spherical shell at point outside shell,

$$V(L) = (2\pi G\rho R\, \Delta R/L)\int_{L-R}^{L+R} dS = \frac{4\pi R^2\, \Delta R\rho G}{L} = (\text{mass of shell}) \times (G/L).$$

If inside we have

$$\int_{R-L}^{R+L} dS \rightarrow \text{(mass of shell)}(G/R) = \text{const.}$$

From outside, the radial variation in density has no effect on the L^{-2} dependence of g.

5.12. $g(L)$ is often given as $\propto L^{-2}$ for $L > R_E$ and $\propto L$ for $L < R_E$ as for a sphere of uniform density. If the density is greater at the centre, dg/dL just below the surface is smaller. For the Earth it is negative (see the table). For a core of radius R_1, density ρ_1 and a mantle of density ρ_2 and the radius of the Earth R_2 then for L infinitesimally less than R_2, $dg/dL = (d^2V/dL^2) = \frac{4}{3}\pi G[\rho_2 - (R_1^3/R_2^3)(\rho_1 - \rho_2)]$, hence, since $(dg/dL)_{R_2}$ is negative for the Earth, $\rho_1/\rho_2 - 1 > \frac{1}{2}(R_2/R_1)^3$ and this inequality is a possible one since $\rho_1 > \rho_2$ and $R_2 > R_1$.

5.13. $g_{rot} = \omega^2 R = (2\pi/T)^2 R$, $\therefore R = (T/2\pi)^2 g_{rot}$. $T = 1$ day and $g_{rot} = 5$ cm s^{-2}. $\therefore R \approx 10 \times 10^8$ cm. Correct radius is 6.4×10^8 cm. N pole.

5.14. $i = (e/c)v$ e.m.u., $\mu = iA = (e/c)v \times \pi a^2$; $I_0 = m_e a^2$. $I_0(2\pi v) = \frac{1}{2}(h/2\pi)$. $\therefore v = h/8\pi^2 m_e a^2$ $\therefore \mu = eh/8\pi mc$ e.m.u., but e in e.s.u. Probability of mass or charge at r is $p(r)$, $\therefore \rho_q(r) = ep(r)$ and $\rho_m(r) = m_e p(r)$. Consider a ring of volume dV and radius x. $dI_0 = dV(m_e p(r))x^2$, $\therefore dJ = dVm_e p(r)x^2 2\pi v$ $\therefore J = \frac{1}{2}(h/2\pi) = m_e 2\pi v \int p(r)x^2\, dV$. Again, $d\mu = dV(ep(r))(v/c)\pi x^2$, $\therefore \mu = e(\pi v/c) \int p(r)x^2\, dV$. $\therefore \mu/\frac{1}{2}(h/2\pi) = (e\pi v/c) \times (1/m_e 2\pi v)$; $\therefore \mu = eh/8\pi m_e c$ independent of $p(r)$.

5.15. In the expansion in a power series in x, every term must have the same dimensions.

5.16. From Problem 5.11, V at the surface is $-GM/R$, i.e. P.E. of mass m is $-mGM/R$ and this must equal $\frac{1}{2}mv^2$. 2.4 km s^{-1}.

5.18. Rates of rotation of each must be equal; $\therefore 2\pi r_1 v_1 = 2\pi r_2 v_2$. Centrifugal forces of each are equal since each is equal to gravitational force. $\therefore m_1 v_1^2/r_1 = m_2 v_2^2/r_2$. $\therefore m_1/m_2 = (r_1/r_2)^3 = R^3$.

5.19. Velocities after collision are v_1 and v_2. Conservation of momentum and energy and elimination of the initial velocity of projectile particle gives $v_1/v_2 = \frac{1}{2}(1 - m_2/m_1)$. If $|v_2| > (<) |v_1|$, we must have $m_2/m_1 < (>) 3$.

5.20. $mv^2/R = GmM_E/R^2$ and $vT = 2\pi R$, $\therefore R = (GMT^2/4\pi^2)^{1/3}$. $T = 24$ h. $\therefore R - R_E = 22{,}000$ miles.

5.23. $\partial F_x/\partial y = (\partial/\partial y)(-\partial V/\partial x) = -\partial^2 V/\partial y\, \partial x$ and $\partial F_y/\partial_x = -\partial^2 V/\partial x\, \partial y$. $\therefore \partial F_x/\partial y = \partial F_y/\partial x$, etc.

5.24. Evaluate $\partial F_x/\partial y - \partial F_y/\partial x$, etc. (a) No, (b) Yes.

5.25. $R_{CG,S} = (R_{ES}/R_S)(M_S/M_E + 1)^{-1} \approx 1/2000$.

5.28. Velocities before and after are $\mathbf{v}_1$, $\mathbf{v}_2$, $\mathbf{v}_1'$ and $\mathbf{v}_2'$. $\mathbf{v}_{cm} = (m_1\mathbf{v}_1 + m_2\mathbf{v}_2)/(m_1 + m_2) = (m_1\mathbf{v}_1' + m_2\mathbf{v}_2')/(m_1 + m_2)$. Consider $(\mathbf{v}_1 - \mathbf{v}_{cm}) + (\mathbf{v}_1' - \mathbf{v}_{cm}) = m_2/(m_1 + m_2)\{(\mathbf{v}_1 + \mathbf{v}_1') - (\mathbf{v}_2 + \mathbf{v}_2')\}$. Conservation of energy gives

$$m_1(\mathbf{v}_1 - \mathbf{v}_1')(\mathbf{v}_1 + \mathbf{v}_1') = m_2(\mathbf{v}_2' - \mathbf{v}_2)(\mathbf{v}_2' + \mathbf{v}_2)$$

and of momentum

$$m_1(\mathbf{v}_1 - \mathbf{v}_1') = m_2(\mathbf{v}_2' - \mathbf{v}_2). \qquad \therefore \quad \mathbf{v}_1 + \mathbf{v}_1' = \mathbf{v}_2 + \mathbf{v}_2'.$$
$$\therefore \quad (\mathbf{v}_1 - \mathbf{v}_{cm}) = -(\mathbf{v}_1' - \mathbf{v}_{cm}).$$

5.29. $W_{OBC} = \displaystyle\int_0^B F_x \, dx + \int_B^C F_y \, dy$ and $W_{OAC} = \displaystyle\int_0^A F_y \, dy + \int_A^C F_x \, dx,$

$$W_{OBC} = W_{OAC} = \tfrac{1}{2}a\beta^2 + b\alpha^2\beta.$$

5.31. $14°$.

5.35. $I_{H_2} = \tfrac{1}{2}m_p d_m^2 = 0.47 \times 10^{-40}$, $I_{HD} = \tfrac{2}{3}m_p d_m^2 = 0.63 \times 10^{-40}$ g cm².

5.36. No.

5.38. $V = \tfrac{1}{2}Kx^2$.

5.39. $I = mr^2$ and $\omega = -y_0 px/r^2$, ∴ $I(d\omega/dt) + \omega(dI/dt) = 0$.

5.40. $g = GM_E/R_E^2 = 981$ cm s⁻².

5.41. $GM_E/(R_E + h)^2 \approx (GM_E/R_E^2)(1 - 2h/R_E)$.

CHAPTER 6

6.1.

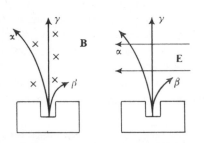

6.2. Chemical oxygen weighs $16 \times 0.99759 + 17 \times 0.00037 + 18 \times 0.00204 = 16.004453$. ∴ Factor is $16.004453/16 = 1.000278$. The currently favoured scale is based on ¹²C, and ¹⁶O scale $= 1.0003179$ ¹²C scale (see Problem 6.5).

6.3. 5.6% and 4.5%. The "C_6H_{12}" molecules at 85 are $^{12}C_5^{13}CH_{12} \to 6 \times 1.1\%$ and $^{12}C_6H_{11}D \to 12 \times 0.016\%$, i.e. 6.7%.

6.4. The masses on the ¹²C scale are 27.99488, 28.00608, 28.01868, and 28.03128 which differ by 1 in 3000 or more.

6.5. $16/15.99488 = 1.00032$.

6.6.

$d' = d \cos \alpha \approx d(1 - \tfrac{1}{2}\alpha^2)$, ∴ $(d - d')/d = \tfrac{1}{2}\alpha^2$.

6.7. $mv^2/R = q(V/d)$.

6.8. $s = s_m \cos \theta$, $p_\theta \, d\theta = p_s \, ds$ and $p_\theta = 1/2\pi$, ∴ $p_s = (1/2\pi)(d\theta/ds) = (1/2\pi)(s_m^2 - s^2)^{-1/2}$

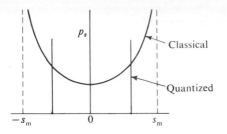

6.9. $(^{12}C)^+$ at 12 to $(^{13}C^{18}O_2)^+$ at 49. $(^{12}C^{16}O_2)^+$ at 44.

6.11. $x = (q/m)dDE/v^2$ and $y = (q/m)dDB/cv$.

6.12. $r(t) = r(0)t + \frac{1}{2}(F/m)t^2$ and $F = qE$.

6.13. $eB/2\pi m_e$.

CHAPTER 7

7.1. $l = 1/\mathscr{A}N$, $\mathscr{A} = \pi[(d_1 + d_2)/2]^2 = \pi(d^2/4) = \pi r^2$.

7.2. $\frac{1}{2}\kappa\overline{x^2} = \frac{1}{2}kT$, $\therefore \overline{x^2} = kT/\kappa$, from Section 4.2, $\kappa \sim 10^4$, $\therefore \overline{x^2} \approx 5 \times 10^{-18}$ cm^2, $l \sim 1/\pi\overline{x^2}N$.

7.3. For example, KAYE and LABY give for Ar, 2.7 and 1.4, and for H_2, 0.5 and 1.2 for $10^3 a$ and $10^3 b$, for 0°C and 1 atm. For Ar,

$$(a/Rb) = \frac{PV^2 \times 2.7}{R \times V \times 1.4} = \frac{PV}{R} \times \frac{2.7}{1.4} = 273 \times \frac{2.7}{1.4} = 530°\text{K}.$$

H_2 gives 112°K.

7.4. $Mvb = Mr^2\dot\varphi$ (1), $2Mv \sin \theta/2 = \int_0^\infty F \cos \varphi \, dt$ (2), where $F = ZZ_n e^2/r^2$ (3). Use (1) and (3) in (2).

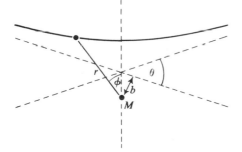

7.5. Conservation of momentum, $2v = v_1 + 3v_2$. Conservation of energy, $\frac{1}{2}(2m)v^2 = \frac{1}{2}mv_1^2 + \frac{1}{2}(3m)v_2^2 - Q$ ($Q = 3.3$ Mev, $\frac{1}{2}(2m)v^2 = 0.1$ Mev). Eliminate v^2 and get

$$\tfrac{1}{2}mv_1^2 - \tfrac{1}{2}[\tfrac{1}{2}(2m)v^2] \pm (1/\sqrt{2})[\tfrac{1}{2}(2m)v^2]^{1/2}[\tfrac{1}{2}mv_1^2]^{1/2} - \tfrac{3}{4}Q = 0.$$

$\therefore \frac{1}{2}mv_1^2 = 2.85$ for v_1 positive or 2.15 for v_1 negative.

7.6. $mv = mv_1 + mv_2$, $\therefore$ $v^2 = v_1^2 + v_2^2 + 2\mathbf{v}_1 \cdot \mathbf{v}_2$, but $\frac{1}{2}mv^2 = \frac{1}{2}mv_1^2 + \frac{1}{2}mv_2^2$, $\therefore$ $\mathbf{v}_1 \cdot \mathbf{v}_2 = 0$. Hence $\mathbf{v}_1$ and $\mathbf{v}_2$ are at right angles (for head on $\mathbf{v}_1 = 0$).

7.7. Elastic head-on collision of m (initial v, final $-v_1$), with Am (initial 0, final v_2). $A = 2$ for deuterium and 12 for carbon. $mv = -mv_1 + Amv_2$, $\therefore$ $v_2 = (v + v_1)/A$. $\frac{1}{2}mv^2 = \frac{1}{2}mv_1^2 + \frac{1}{2}Amv_2^2$, $\therefore$ $v^2 = v_1^2 + Av_2^2$.

$$\text{Fractional loss of energy} = 1 - (\tfrac{1}{2}mv_1^2)/(\tfrac{1}{2}mv^2) = 1 - (v_1/v)^2.$$

Eliminate v_2 and so fractional loss $= 4A/(A + 1)^2$, i.e. $\frac{8}{9} = 89\%$ for ^{2}D and $\frac{48}{169} = 28\%$ for ^{12}C.

7.8. Initial D with v gives DH with v_2 and H with v_1. $2mv = 3mv_2 + mv_1$,

$$\therefore \quad v_1/v = 2 - 3(v_2/v).$$

$$\tfrac{1}{2}(2mv^2) = \tfrac{1}{2}(3mv_2^2) + \tfrac{1}{2}mv_1^2, \qquad \therefore \quad 3(v_2/v)^2 = 2 - (v_1/v)^2.$$

Substitute for v_1/v,

$$\therefore \quad 6(v_2/v)^2 - 6(v_2/v) + 1 = 0, \qquad \therefore \quad (v_2/v) = \tfrac{1}{2}(1 \pm 1/\sqrt{3}),$$

but must have $v_1 > v_2$,

$$\therefore \quad (v_2/v) = \tfrac{1}{2}(1 - 1/\sqrt{3}) = 0.21.$$

7.9. Volume per unit area $= dx$, number of particles $= N\,dx$, area of particles $= N\mathscr{A}\,dx$. $\therefore$ Proportion of light scattered $= N\mathscr{A}\,dx$ in the distance dx. $\therefore$ $dI/I = -N\mathscr{A}\,dx$. $\therefore$ $I = I_0 \exp(-N\mathscr{A}x)$.

7.10. Blue light is appreciably scattered but red is not, in the depth of the atmosphere. $\therefore$ $N\mathscr{A}x \approx 1$ for blue light where x is h, the depth of the atmosphere (if this is true for blue, we have $N\mathscr{A}x \ll 1$ for red because of λ^{-4}) $\therefore$ $(2/3\pi)[(n - 1)^2/N](2\pi/\lambda)^4 \times h \ll 1$, that is $N \sim (2/3\pi)(n - 1)^2(2\pi/\lambda)^4 h$. Put $n - 1 \approx 3 \times 10^{-4}$, $\lambda \approx 4{,}000$ Å $= 4 \times 10^{-5}$ cm, and $h \approx 10$ km $= 10^6$ cm. $\therefore$ $N \sim 4 \times 10^{19}$ cm^{-3} and $N_0 \approx N \times 22.41 \sim 8 \times 10^{23}$.

7.11. v is initial velocity of α. At closest approach, α and p are at same velocity v_1. Conservation of momentum gives $v_1 = \frac{4}{5}v$. Conservation of energy gives

$$\tfrac{1}{2}(4m_p)v^2 = \tfrac{1}{2}(5m_p)v_1^2 + 2e^2/d, \qquad \therefore \quad d = 2e^2 \times \tfrac{5}{8} \text{ Mev} \approx 1.8 \times 10^{-13} \text{ cm}.$$

7.12. Number/cosec$^4\frac{1}{2}\theta \sim 0.03$, independent of θ.

7.13. The orbits are a pair of hyperbolae with the fixed particle at the "focus" of the attractive orbit.

7.14. Particle m_1; initial $\mathbf{v}$ and final $\mathbf{v}_1$. m_2; initial 0, final $\mathbf{v}_2$. $m_1\mathbf{v} = m_1\mathbf{v}_1 + m_2\mathbf{v}_2$ and $\frac{1}{2}m_1v^2 = \frac{1}{2}m_1v_1^2 + \frac{1}{2}m_2v_2^2$.

$$\therefore \quad \left(\frac{m_1 - m_2}{m_1}\right)v_2^2 = 2(\mathbf{v}_1 \cdot \mathbf{v}_2), \qquad \therefore \quad \cos\theta = \frac{\mathbf{v}_1 \cdot \mathbf{v}_2}{v_1 v_2} = \frac{1}{2}\left(\frac{m_1 - m_2}{m_1}\right)\left(\frac{v_2}{v_1}\right).$$

For (a) $m_1 > m_2$, $\therefore$ $\cos\theta > 0$, $\therefore$ $\theta < 90°$; (b) $m_1 = m_2$, $\theta = 90°$; (c) $m_1 < m_2$, $\theta > 90°$.

7.15. Use notation of Problem 7.14. Maximal velocity is for head on. $v/v_2 = \frac{1}{2}(1 + m_2/m_1)$ and $v/v_3 = \frac{1}{2}(1 + m_3/m_1)$, $\therefore$ $v_2/v_3 = (1 + m_3/m_1)/(1 + m_2/m_1)$. $v_2/v_3 = 7.5$ and $m_3/m_2 = 14$. $\therefore$ $m_2/m_1 \approx 1$.

7.16. In solution of Problem 7.8, assume an internal energy E. In order to get a physically possible, result $E \leq \frac{1}{2}mv^2$ and so $0.21 \leq v_2/v \leq 0.5$.

7.17. In the centre of mass system, we have initial velocities $\mathbf{v}$ and $-\mathbf{v}$ and final velocities $\mathbf{v}'$ and $-\mathbf{v}'$, from conservation of momentum. From conservation of energy $|\mathbf{v}'| = |\mathbf{v}|$. Increase in energy of particle 1 is $m(\mathbf{v} \cdot \mathbf{v}_{cm} - \mathbf{v}' \cdot \mathbf{v}_{cm}) = mvv_{cm}(\cos \theta' - \cos \theta)$ say. If $|\mathbf{v}'| > |\mathbf{v}_2|$, $\cos \theta > 0$, $\therefore$ need $\cos \theta' > \cos \theta > 0$, $\therefore |\theta| < \pi/2$ which is the first condition, and $\theta' < \theta$ which is the second.

7.19. Put $x/d_0 = y$ and $E(x)/kT = (\Delta E/kT)F(y)$ in formula for B_2.

7.20. Transport of momentum per second per unit area is

$$S = \int_0^\pi m\left(u + l\cos\theta\,\frac{du}{dz}\right)\tfrac{1}{2}n\bar{v}\cos\theta\sin\theta\,d\theta = \tfrac{1}{3}nm\bar{v}l\,\frac{du}{dz}.$$

But $\eta = $ shear stress/velocity gradient $= S(du/dz)$.

$$J_z = \int_0^\pi \left(1 + l\cos\theta\,\frac{1}{n}\frac{dn}{dz}\right)\tfrac{1}{2}n\bar{v}\cos\theta\sin\theta\,d\theta = \tfrac{1}{3}l\bar{v}\,\frac{dn}{dz}.$$

7.22. Probability of getting to x is $P(x)$. Probability of *not* colliding in x to $x + \Delta x$ is $[1 - (\Delta x/l)]$, $\therefore P(x + \Delta x) = P(x)[1 - (\Delta x/l)]$.

CHAPTER 8

8.1. $m_e v^2/r = e^2/r$ and $m_e vr = \hbar$.

8.2. $\frac{1}{2}m_e v^2 - eV_a$ $\therefore$ $v/c = (2eV_a/m_e c^2)^{1/2} = (2eV_a/0.5\text{ Mev})^{1/2} = (V_a/250\text{ kv})^{1/2} = (1/50)^{1/2}$.

8.4. 11 μs. 65 Gev, $130{,}000 m_e$.

8.5. Yes. If we assume non-relativistic velocities, we get $v_f/c \approx 8$.

8.6. Expand $(m - m_0)/c^2 - \frac{1}{2}mv^2$ in powers of (v/c).

8.7. $mvr = nh$, $mv^2/r = e^2/r^2$; therefore λ, which equals $h/mv = 2\pi nh^2/me^2$.

8.8. Force on photon is $G(hv/c^2)M_s/R^2$, transverse force $f = G(hv)c^{-2}M_s R_s R^{-3}$.

$$\text{Transverse momentum} = \int f\,dt = G(hv)c^{-2}M_s R_s \int_{-\infty}^\infty R^{-3}\,ds.$$

$$\alpha = \Delta p/p = (GM_s R_s/c^2)\int_{-\infty}^\infty R^{-3}\,ds = 2GM_s/R_s c^2.$$

8.9. Electron binding energies are tens of electronvolts (ev). X-ray energies are tens of kiloelectronvolts (kev).

8.10. $\lambda = 5000$ Å say; $E_{ph} = hv = hc/\lambda$.

$$n = 10^{-17}\,\text{w}/E_{ph} = \frac{(10^{-17} \times 10^7)(5 \times 10^{-5})}{(6.6 \times 10^{-27})(3 \times 10^{10})} \approx 25 \text{ photons per second.}$$

8.11. $hc/\lambda = 25$ kev.

8.12. $v^2/c^2 = (\frac{1}{2}mv^2)/(\frac{1}{2}mc^2) = [(\frac{1}{2}mv^2)/(\frac{1}{2}m_ec^2)](m_e/m) \approx [(\frac{1}{2}mv^2)/(\frac{1}{2}\text{ Mev})](1/1800A)$ where $A = 2$ or 1. Hence, when $(\frac{1}{2}mv^2) = 0.1$, 2.85, or 2.15 Mev, we have $v \ll c$.

8.13. Need $\lambda = h/p \lesssim 1$ fermi $= 10^{-13}$ cm $\therefore p > 10^{13}h$. For this relativistic electron, $E = pc$, $\therefore$ need $E > 10^{13}ch \sim 1000$ Mev.

8.14. Photon energy $= h\nu = hc/\lambda$. If $hc/\lambda \sim 3$ ev, $\lambda \sim hc/3$ ev ~ 4000 Å.

8.18. $T = m_0c^2(1 - v^2/c^2)^{-1/2} - m_0c^2$.

8.20. The α particle is very stable.

8.21. $x = \int_0^t v(t')\, dt'$; substitute for t' and transform to an integral of v.

8.22. N.B. $E = T + m_0c^2$.

8.23. See Problem 8.22 to obtain p.

8.24. hc/λ in ev is 2.11.

8.25. $C_v \approx 12$, $C_s \approx -1$, and $C_c \approx -1$ Mev.

CHAPTER 9

9.3. $x' = x \cos \theta + ict \sin \theta$, which must be the same as $x' = (x - ut)/(1 - u^2/c^2)^{1/2}$.

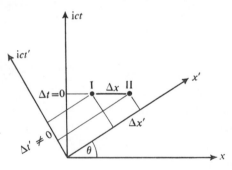

9.4.

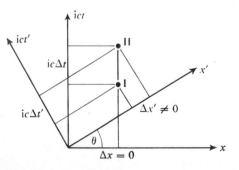

9.5. $u/c \approx 10^{-4}$. Δt in text is $2Lu^2/c^3$ for $u^2/c^2 \ll 1$. $\therefore$ number $= 2Lu^2/\lambda c^2 \approx 0.12$.

9.6. Shift in mean is $\delta\lambda = \lambda_0(1 - v^2/c^2)^{1/2} - \lambda_0 \approx \lambda_0 \frac{1}{2}v^2/c^2$. Doppler shift is $\Delta\lambda = \pm(v/c)\lambda_0$, neglecting relativistic correction. $\therefore$ $\delta\lambda = \frac{1}{2}(\Delta\lambda)^2/\lambda_0$ $\therefore$ $\delta\lambda$ versus $\Delta\lambda$ is parabolic and the curve fits for $\lambda_0 \approx 4800$ Å.

9.9. Transform $\partial^2/\partial x^2 + \partial^2/\partial y^2 + \partial^2/\partial z^2 - (1/c^2)(\partial^2/\partial t^2)$ using the relations given in Section 9.5 remembering that

$$\frac{\partial\varphi}{\partial x'} = \frac{\partial\varphi}{\partial x}\frac{\partial x}{\partial x'} + \frac{\partial\varphi}{\partial y}\frac{\partial y}{\partial x'} + \frac{\partial\varphi}{\partial z}\frac{\partial z}{\partial x'} + \frac{\partial\varphi}{\partial t}\frac{\partial t}{\partial x'}, \text{etc.}$$

CHAPTER 10

10.1. By equipartition, $\frac{1}{2}m_e\bar{v}_e^2 = \frac{1}{2}m_p\bar{v}_p^2$, $\therefore$ $(\bar{v}_e^2)^{1/2}/(\bar{v}_p^2)^{1/2} = (m_p/m_e)^{1/2} \approx (1800)^{1/2} \approx 40$.

10.2. The deuteron kinetic energy in the plasma should be about 0.1 Mev, that is $\frac{3}{2}kT \approx$ 0.1 Mev, $\therefore$ $T \sim 0.1 \times 10^6 \times 1.6 \times 10^{-12} \times \frac{2}{3}/(1.38 \times 10^{-16}) \approx 10^{9\circ}$K.

10.3. Fitting the maximum to $(b/s)^5 \exp[-(a/s)^2]$ gives $b = 4.4$ and $a = 2.7$. This then fits the experimental curve moderately well.

10.4. Number emitted per sec per unit area is proportional to

$$\int_{v_{x_0}}^{\infty} v_x p(v_x)\, dv_x,$$

$p(v_x) = (m/2\pi kT)^{1/2} \exp(-\frac{1}{2}mv_x^2/kT)$, $\frac{1}{2}mv_{x_0}^2 = e\varphi$, gives $T^{1/2} \exp(-e\varphi/kT)$. Image force is $e^2/(2r)^2$, $\therefore$ energy to remove from r_0 to ∞ is $e^2/4r_0 = e\varphi$, $\therefore$ $\phi = e/4r_0 = 4.8 \times 10^{-10}/(4 \times 10^{-8})$ e.s.u. $\approx 10^{-2}$ e.s.u. ≈ 3 v that is $e\varphi \approx 3$ev.

10.5. Calculate as for pressure. Energy for x direction is $(\frac{1}{2}nv_x)(\frac{1}{2}mv_x^2)/(\frac{1}{2}nv_x)$ where the average refers to the range 0 to ∞ for v_x. Use the Maxwell–Boltzmann distribution to show that this is kT.

10.6. $\frac{1}{2}m\bar{v}^2 = \frac{3}{2}kT$, $(\bar{v}^2)^{1/2} = (3kT/m)^{1/2} = (3kT/m_p)^{1/2}M^{-1/2} = 2.7M^{-1/2}$ km s^{-1}. 1.9 for H_2, 1.35 for He, 0.51 for N_2, and 0.47 for O_2. This is partly the reason why there is almost no H_2 and He in the atmosphere.

10.7. $\exp[-32(m/N - \frac{1}{2})^2]$.

10.8. Higher up, the slow ones from below do not arrive and the fast ones from below have been slowed down by the hill.

10.9. $p_v(v) = 4\pi(m/2\pi kT)^{3/2}v^2 \exp[-(m/2kT)v^2]$.

$$p_{|v_x|}(|v_x|) = 2(m/2\pi kT)^{1/2} \exp[-(m/2kT)v_x^2]$$

since we now consider v_x values for one direction).

$$\therefore \quad \bar{v}/|\bar{v}_x| = \int_0^{\infty} v p_v(v)\, dv \bigg/ \int_0^{\infty} v_x p_{v_x}(v_x)\, dv_x = 2.$$

(HINT: Integrate numerator by parts and cancel denominator.)

10.10. Probability of a molecule passing through A depends on the solid angle subtended by A at the point of origin, that is $(1/4\pi)(\Delta A \cos\theta/r^2)$. For time Δt and molecules with velocity v, $r = v\Delta t$, and the number of molecules passing with speed v to $v + \Delta v$ in

Δt through A is

$$\int_0^{v\Delta t} r^2 \, dr \int_0^{\pi/2} \sin\theta \, d\theta \int_0^{2\pi} d\varphi n(v) \, dv \left(\frac{1}{4\pi} \frac{\Delta A \cos\theta}{r^2}\right) = \tfrac{1}{4} n(v) v \, dv \, \Delta A \, \Delta t.$$

Hence efflux is $\tfrac{1}{4} \int vn(v) \, dv = \tfrac{1}{4} n\bar{v}$.

10.12. $\Delta V \sim V_v$ and $P_v V_v = N_0 kT$, $\therefore$ $dP_v/dT = LP_v/N_0 kT^2$, $\therefore$ $\ln P_v = L/N_0 kT +$ constant.

CHAPTER 11

11.1. The coins should represent quanta of energy which are not distinguishable and so the coins must not be. The complexions then have equal probability.

11.2. $N = 6$ $U = \epsilon$, $\mathcal{N} = 6$, $P(0) = 0.83$, $P(\epsilon) = 0.17$.

$\qquad\qquad U = 2\epsilon$, $\mathcal{N} = 21$, $P(0) = 0.72$, $P(\epsilon) = 0.24$, $P(2\epsilon) = 0.05$.

$\qquad\qquad U = 3\epsilon$, $\mathcal{N} = 56$, $P(0) = 0.62$, $P(\epsilon) = 0.27$, $P(2\epsilon) = 0.09$, $P(3\epsilon) = 0.02$.

$U = 3\epsilon$, $A = 0.67$ and $a = 1.1$. $P^*(0) = 0.67, P^*(\epsilon) = 0.17, P^*(2\epsilon) = 0.17, P^*(3\epsilon) = 0.00$.

The distribution function $P(\mathcal{E})$ is well approximated by the Boltzmann distribution and varies in the correct way with U. There is a most probable distribution. The most probable distribution is a good approximation to the actual distribution. $\mathcal{N}$ increases rapidly with U.

11.3. (a) Relative error in $\ln \mathcal{N}$ is $\ln \mathcal{N} f/\ln \mathcal{N} = 1 + \ln f/\ln \mathcal{N}$, e.g. if $f = 2$ we have $\ln f = 0.7$ and

$\mathcal{N}$	2	10	100	10^4
$\ln \mathcal{N}$	0.7	2.3	4.6	9.2
$\ln f/\ln \mathcal{N}$	1	0.3	0.15	0.07

(b) Number of ways of arranging N is $N!$ Number of ways of arranging n_1 of the N is $n_1!$ If this latter is irrelevant, number of distinguishable ways is $N!/n_1!$ and so on.

(c) A simple proof is

$$\ln N! = \ln N + \ln(N-1) + \cdots + \ln 2 + \ln 1$$

$$\approx \int_1^N \ln x \, dx = [x \ln x]_1^N - \int_1^N x \times \frac{1}{x} \, dx = N \ln N - N.$$

The reader should appreciate how very large $N!$ is for quite moderate N and the general significance of this.

11.4. $P(\varepsilon_1) = C \exp(-\varepsilon_1/kT)$, $P(\varepsilon_2) = C \exp(-\varepsilon_2/kT)$; $\therefore$ $P(\varepsilon_2)/P(\varepsilon_1) = \exp[(\varepsilon_1 - \varepsilon_2)/kT]$.

11.5. $P(\varepsilon) = \exp(-\varepsilon/kT)/\sum \exp(-\varepsilon/kT)$. Change zero level by putting $\varepsilon = \varepsilon_0 + \varepsilon'$.

$\therefore$ $P(\varepsilon') = \exp[-(\varepsilon_0 + \varepsilon')/kT]/\sum \exp[-(\varepsilon_0 + \varepsilon')/kT]$

$$= \frac{\exp(-\varepsilon_0/kT) \exp(-\varepsilon'/kT)}{\exp(-\varepsilon_0/kT) \sum \exp(-\varepsilon'/kT)} = \exp(-\varepsilon'/kT)/\sum \exp(-\varepsilon'/kT)$$

i.e. independent of ε_0.

11.6. Regard the degenerate system of g_s levels as g_s separate levels very close together which are coincident in the limit. The usual Boltzmann distribution, $\exp(-\varepsilon/kT)$, then goes over to $g_s \exp(-\varepsilon_s/kT)$ when the terms corresponding to degenerate levels are grouped together.

11.7. Every squared term in the energy yields $\frac{1}{2}kT$ to the mean energy.

(a) Kinetic energy only $\to \frac{1}{2}mv^2 = \frac{1}{2}m(v_x^2 + v_y^2 + v_z^2) \to 3 \times \frac{1}{2}kT.$

(b) Rotation about two axes $\frac{1}{2}I(\omega_1^2 + \omega_2^2)$ gives an extra $2 \times \frac{1}{2}kT$, $\therefore \frac{5}{2}kT.$

(c) Additional internal vibration, one harmonic oscillator $\to kT$, $\therefore$ total is $\frac{3}{2}kT + \frac{2}{2}kT + kT = \frac{7}{2}kT.$

No contribution from rotation about figure axis for linear molecules or about any axis for atoms since $\Delta E \gg kT$ and so this rotation is not excited. If $\bar{\varepsilon} = \frac{3}{2}kT$, for N_0 particles $U = \frac{3}{2}N_0 kT$, $C_v = (\partial U/\partial T)_V = \frac{3}{2}N_0 k = \frac{3}{2}R \approx 3$ cal deg^{-1}.

11.8. Try $\eta = A \exp(\Delta E/RT)$. $\therefore$ Plot $\ln \eta$ against $10^3/T$ and slope gives $\Delta E = 6$ kcal mol^{-1}. N.B. The table entry for $10°$c seems to be in error; it should be 39. The argument is that the Boltzmann distribution gives the probability of jumping over a barrier ΔE.

11.9. An energy barrier ΔE to reaction leads to $\mathscr{R}$ (for rate) $= C \exp(-\Delta E/RT)$,

$$\therefore \quad \frac{\mathscr{R}(T + \Delta T)}{\mathscr{R}(T)} = \exp\left(\frac{\Delta E}{R} \frac{\Delta T}{T^2}\right).$$

11.10. $\therefore \Delta E = (RT^2/\Delta T) \ln[\mathscr{R}(T + \Delta T)/\mathscr{R}(T)] = [1.98 \times (300)^2/10] \ln 10 \approx 40 \times 10^3$, that is $\Delta E \approx 40$ kcal mol^{-1}.

Number of complexions is $N!/n_1! \ldots n_{i-1}! n_i! n_{i+1}! \ldots$. After moving the particles, this becomes $N!/n_1! \ldots (n_{i-1} + 1)!(n_i - 2)!(n_{i+1} + 1)! \ldots$. Hence number of complexions is changed by factor $n_i(n_i - 1)/(n_{i-1} + 1)(n_{i+1} + 1)$ which is less than $n_i^2/(n_{i-1} n_{i+1})$. For a Boltzmann distribution, $n_i \propto \exp(-i\varepsilon/kT)$ and so $n_i^2/(n_{i-1} n_{i+1}) = 1$ and so factor is less than 1, i.e. number of complexions is a maximum.

11.11. Probability is

$$\sum_{S' = \Delta E/\epsilon}^{\infty} \exp(-\epsilon_s/kT) \Bigg/ \sum_0^{\infty} \exp(-\epsilon_s/kT).$$

If $\epsilon_s = s\epsilon$, this is

$$\frac{\exp(-s'\epsilon/kT) + \exp[-(s' + 1)\epsilon/kT] + \cdots}{\exp(-0) + \exp(-\epsilon/kT) + \cdots}$$

$$= \frac{\exp\{-s'\epsilon/kT[\exp(-0)\exp(-\epsilon/kT) + \cdots]\}}{\exp(-0) + \exp(-\epsilon/kT) + \cdots}$$

$= \exp(-s\epsilon'/kT) \approx \exp - \Delta E/kT$($s'$ is the integer nearest and above $\Delta E/\epsilon$). In general the result is

$$\exp(-\epsilon_{s'}/kT)\left[\frac{\exp(-0) + \exp[-(\epsilon_{s'+1} - \epsilon_{s'})/kT] + \exp[-(\epsilon_{s'+2} - \epsilon_{s'+1})/kT] + \cdots}{\exp(-s_0/kT) + \exp(-s_1/kT) + \exp(-s_2/kT) + \cdots}\right]$$

The factor $[\ ] \neq 1$ and depends on s' and T. Even so, main variation is often in $\exp(-\epsilon_{s'}/kT)$, i.e. probability $\propto \exp(-\Delta E/kT)$.

11.16. $\overline{\cos\theta} = \cos 0° \, P(0°) + \cos 180° \, P(180°) = P(0°) - P(180°)$. $P(0°) \propto \exp(+\mu B/kT)$, $P(180°) \propto \exp(-\mu B/kT)$.

CHAPTER 12

12.1. $S = k \ln \mathcal{N}$ $\Delta S = k \ln \mathcal{N}_2/\mathcal{N}_1$ and $\Delta S = \text{K.E.}/T$.

12.2. 1.74 and 0.78. Doubled; $1/\sqrt{2}$ times.

12.3. $\frac{1}{2}\kappa\theta^2 = \frac{1}{2}kT$ $\therefore \theta_{\text{rms}} = (kT/\kappa)^{1/2}$. $\kappa \sim 10^{-6}$ dyn cm rad^{-1}. $T = 300°$K, $\therefore \theta_{\text{rms}} \approx 10^{-4}$ rad $\approx \frac{1}{10}$ mm at 1 m.

12.4. Photons.

12.5. $U_A + U_B = U$ and $\bar{U}_A + \bar{U}_B = U$. Eliminate U_A and $\bar{U}_A$ from $(\overline{U_A - \bar{U}_A})^2$.

12.6. $\mathcal{N} = 2^N$ and $S = Nk \ln 2$.

12.7. $S = k \ln \mathcal{N} = \frac{1}{2}fNk \ln U +$ constant; use $1/T = \partial S/\partial U$ to find U/N.

12.8. Density of states $\propto [J^2 - (J-1)^2]/(2J+1) = (2J-1)/(2J+1) \approx 1$.

12.9. P_{AB} versus U_A is obviously always symmetrical, as in Table 12.1.

12.10. For $U = 2\epsilon, 4\epsilon$, or 6ϵ, $(P_{AB})_{\text{max}}/(P_{AB})_{\text{min}}$ is $25/15 = 1.7, 225/70 = 3.2$, or $1225/210 = 5.8$. NOTE: Use entries in column 3 of Table 12.1.

CHAPTER 13

13.1. $2N_{AB} + N_A + N_B =$ constant. Use $S = U/T + Nk \ln Z/N$ and $S = S_{AB} + S_A + S_B$ is stationary, that is $\Delta S = 0$. Then use $\Delta N_A = \Delta N_B = -\Delta N_{AB}$ which gives

$$-\ln Z_{AB}/N_{AB} + \ln Z_A/N_A + \ln Z_B/N_B - 1 = 0.$$

13.2. $Z = \sum \exp\left[-(n + \frac{1}{2})h\nu/kT\right]$
$= \exp(-\frac{1}{2}h\nu/kT)[1 + \exp(-h\nu/kT) + \exp(-2h\nu/kT) + \cdots]$
$= \exp(-\frac{1}{2}h\nu/kT)[1 - \exp(-h\nu/kT)]^{-1}$
  $\therefore$ $U = Nh\nu\{\frac{1}{2} + \exp(-h\nu/kT)/[1 - \exp(-h\nu/kT)]\}$.

$T \to 0$, $h\nu/kT \gg 1$ $U \to N \times \frac{1}{2}h\nu$; all oscillators in lowest level. $T \to \infty$, $h\nu/kT \ll 1$ $U \to NkT = RT$;   classical   equipartition,   that   is $N \times 2 \times \frac{1}{2}kT$.   If $h\nu \approx kT$, $U \approx Hh\nu$; region in which C_v depends most on T. For $\nu \sim 10^{14}$ and $T \sim 300$,

$$h\nu/kT \sim \frac{6.6 \times 10^{-27} \times 10^{14}}{1.4 \times 10^{-16} \times 300} \sim 10.$$

$\therefore$ U is independent of T $\therefore$ $C_v \approx 0$.

13.3. $F = U - TS, G = U - TS + PV$. Differentiate and use $T \, dS = dU + P \, dV$.

13.6. $n_s/N = \exp(-\epsilon_s/kT)/Z$; if $\epsilon_s = 0$, $n_0/N = 1/Z$.

13.7. $Z = 1 + \exp(-\epsilon_1/kT) + \exp(-\epsilon_2/kT) + \cdots$.

13.8. If $\Delta\epsilon \ll kT$ many terms in Z are almost unity.

13.9. If $\epsilon_s < kT$, $\exp(-\epsilon_s/kT) \sim 1$ and if $\epsilon_s > kT$, $\exp(-\epsilon_s/kT) \sim 0$.

13.10. $\mathscr{A} \sim \pi(2 \times 2 \text{ Å})$, $m \sim 2 \times 10^{-24}$, $n \sim 3 \times 10^{19}$.

CHAPTER 14

14.1. Total number of particles $N \propto \sum_s \{\exp[-\alpha(T) + \epsilon_s/kT] \mp 1\}^{-1}$ and sum must remain finite for any set of ϵ_s. The higher T, the more levels this must be true for and so we must have $[-\alpha(T) + \epsilon_s/kT] \gg 1$ for more and more levels as T increases. Hence for high T we must effectively have $[\ ] \gg 1$ for all levels and so this gives a Boltzmann distribution.

14.2. E_F is the value of $\mathcal{E}$ for which $\exp[-\alpha(T) + \mathcal{E}/kT]$ changes from a small number to a large number compared with unity and this is smaller if T is low enough. The condition is therefore $[-\alpha(T) + \mathcal{E}/kT] \approx 0$ or $\mathcal{E} \approx \alpha kT$.

14.3. Number of excited particles at $T \propto kT$ and each has a mean energy of order kT, $\therefore\ U(T) \propto T^2$, that is $C_v = \partial U/\partial T \propto T$.

14.4. 0.012 Å, 1.86 Gev.

14.5. For $U/\epsilon = 1, 3, 5, 7$, and 9, $(\mathcal{N}_B/\mathcal{N}_{B-E})/N! = 0.04, 0.10, 0.15, 0.21$, and 0.26.

Index

Page numbers in italic indicate the pages giving a definition or most important use. § preceding a (decimal) number indicates a whole section, and P indicates a problem.